COMPUTER GLOSSARY
FOR
ENGINEERS AND
SCIENTISTS

by
Wen M. Chow, Ph.D.
Charles J. Sippl

Funk & Wagnalls

New York

ACKNOWLEDGMENT: Reference source for the terms and definitions in this glossary is "Computer Dictionary and Handbook" published by Howard W. Sams & Co., Inc., 4300 West 62nd Street, Indianapolis, Indiana 46268. It is available through book stores, electronic parts distributors, or directly from the publisher.

Dr. Wen M. Chow is current Professor of Quantitative Methods at the California State University, Fullerton, teaching computer science, statistics and operations research. For the past ten years he has served as computer systems manager in the Plastics Division of Union Carbide Corporation (1958-1968).

Charles J. Sippl has taught a variety of Computer, Management, and Mathematics courses at several California colleges and universities. His Bachelor of Science Degree in Finance is from the University of Wisconsin, Master of Arts in Economics from the University of Miami. He has written extensively in the computer field over the past ten years and has lectured nationwide on computer industry structure and financial topics.

LIBRARY OF COMPUTER SCIENCE

Computer Glossary for Students and Teachers
Beginning Computer Glossary for Businessmen
Computer Glossary for Accountants and Bankers
Computer Glossary for Engineers and Scientists
Computer Glossary for Medical and Health Sciences
Computer Glossary for Production Automation

PREFACE

During the past decade, the computer has developed from an item of curiosity into an integral part of the tools-of-the-trade for the majority of engineers and scientists. Although the bulk of computer usage is in the commercial electronic data processing (EDP) field, there can be no denial that many of the major breakthroughs advancing the frontiers of knowledge and promoting the welfare of society have been accomplished through the use of computers in the many natural science and engineering disciplines.

The trend and use of new computer applications has been accelerating, with no tapering off in sight, simply because computers have become more powerful, less expensive, easier to use, and easier to access. Meanwhile, the population of trained personnel is steadily increasing.

The proliferation of the computer has been accompanied by an intolerable verbal communications problem. A whole new vocabulary of computer terminology has developed, along with literally hundreds of computer languages and dialects. This is further compounded by the dynamic advancement of computer technology and the lack of effective standardization. Even the most knowledgeable engineers and scientists are constantly confronted with new computer terminology; and, in many cases, the precise definitions of these terms are unavailable.

The previously stated problems clearly illustrate a compelling need for a computer glossary specifically designed for engineers and scientists. With this glossary, we have attempted to produce the most up-to-date, pertinent, and useful tool to assist engineers and scientists in breaking down the communications barrier. Obviously, in order to offer a concise, low-priced glossary such as this, many exotic or less-frequently used terms had to be omitted. The reader should find, however, that most of the important terminology has been covered quite comprehensively.

Several useful appendices have been added, including a survey of recent computer articles relating to applications in the various disciplines of engineering and science. The goal of this appendix is to inform the reader of the current literature and activities involving computers in his own field of endeavor and also to display the amazingly diversified applications of this versitile machine — today's modern computer.

Wen M. Chow, Ph.D.

TABLE OF CONTENTS

Page

Preface v
Terms and Definitions 1
Appendix A 167
   IMPACT OF THE COMPUTER ON SCIENCE AND ENGINEERING
Appendix B 175
   CLASSIFICATION INDEX OF COMPUTER APPLICATIONS
   IN SCIENCE AND ENGINEERING
Appendix C 199
   BASIC PRINCIPLES OF COMPUTER SYSTEMS
Appendix D 213
   SUMMARY OF MODERN COMPUTER LANGUAGES
Appendix E 233
   FLOWCHARTING — ABBREVIATIONS, SYMBOLS
   AND PROCEDURES

HOW TO USE THIS BOOK

In the dictionary section of this book all terms of more than one word are treated as one word, regardless of spaces or punctuation. For example, "check indicator" appears between "check digits" and "checking program"; and "characters, alphameric" appears between "character recognition" and "character set." Abbreviations are also treated alphabetically; the letters "I/O" follow "inverter" rather than appearing at the beginning of the I's.

If you do not find a compound term under the first word, try the second word of the term. For example, "parallel access" may be found under "access, parallel."

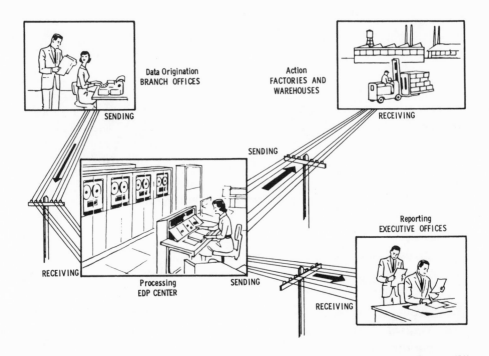

Person-to-machine-to-person communications.

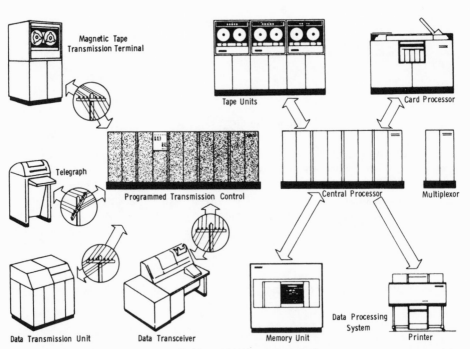

Machine-to-machine communications.

TERMS & DEFINITIONS

absolute coding—Refers to coding designed so that instructions are written in the basic machine language; i.e., coding using absolute operators and addresses. Coding that does not require processing before it can be understood by the computer.

abstracting, automatic—A process of searching for the criteria by which human beings judge what should be abstracted from a document, as programmed.

access—The process of obtaining data from or placing data in storage.

access arm—Relates to a mechanical device or unit which positions another device or portion of itself in proper alignment or position relative to operations as designed, i.e., a reading head when positioned properly to read or record information.

access-coding, minimal—A type of reference for programming which is completed in order to locate the data in such a manner as to reduce the access time and minimize the amount of time required to transfer words from auxiliary storage to main memory.

access, direct—Refers to a memory device or process designed to contain the address which allows the particular address to be accessed in a manner independent of the location of that address; thus, the items stored in the memory can be addressed or accessed in the same amount for each location. Thus, access by a program is not dependent upon the previously accessed position.

access, random—1. Concerns the process or procedure of obtaining information from or placing information in storage, where the time required for such access is independent of the location of the information most recently obtained or placed in storage. 2. Pertaining to a device in which random access, as defined in definition 1, can be achieved without effective penalty in time.

access, serial—Concerns the procedure or process of obtaining information from or placing information in storage, where the time required for such access is dependent on the necessity for waiting while nondesired storage locations are processed in turn.

access, simultaneous—The process or procedure of developing or obtaining information from storage or placing information in storage, where the time required for such access is dependent on the simultaneous transfer of all elements of a word from a given storage location.

access time—1. Time interval between the instant at which information is called for storage and the instant at which delivery is completed, i.e., the read time. 2. Time interval between the instant at which data are ready for storage and the instant at which storage is completed, i.e., the write time.

accumulator—1. A part of the logical-arithmetic unit of a computer. It is used for intermediate storage, to form algebraic sums, or for other intermediate operations. 2. The zero-access register (and associated equipment) in the arithmetic unit in which are formed

1

sums and other arithmetical and logical results; a unit in a digital computer where numbers are totaled, i.e., accumulated. Often the accumulator stores one quantity and upon receipt of any second quantity, it forms and stores the sum of the first and second quantities. See: register.

accumulator shift instruction—A specific computer instruction designed to cause the contents of a register to be displaced some specific number of bit positions left or right.

A-conversion—A Fortran instruction designed to transmit alphanumeric data to and from variables in storage.

acronym—The word formed from the first letter or letters of the words in a name, term, or phrase; e.g., SAGE from Semi-Automatic Ground Environment, and ALGOL from ALGOrithmic Language.

active element—Refers to those circuits or devices that receive energy from a source other than the main input signal.

activity ratio—A measurement developed when a file is processed, i.e., the ratio of the number of records that have activity to the total number of records in that file.

adapter (CLAT), communication line—In some systems the communication-line adapter (CLAT) for teletype is a semi-automatic device used to link buffer units with the remote teletype units. The CLAT is usually incorporated within the buffer cabinet, which is often located with the processor at the central site. The purpose of the CLAT is to receive data in serial bit form from the remote inquiry station and convert the data to parallel bit form for use in the inquiry buffer unit.

Similarly, data transmitted from the buffer to a remote inquiry station is converted by the CLAT from parallel to serial bit form.

adapters, dataphone—Various types of transceivers, transmitters, and receivers are dataphone adapters or components of digital-plotting communication systems. They are designed to enable high-speed digital incremental plotting of digital computer outputs at remote locations—either nearby or thousands of miles from the data source. The dataphone adapter drives the plotter over regular telephone lines using standard telephone company dataphone terminals. For the nominal service charge of a regular telephone call, the computer may "talk" directly to a remote plotter or, on a conference hookup, to many remote plotters simultaneously, at any place where there is a standard telephone. Dataphone-adapter installation options can provide two-way communications between stations.

adapter, transmission—In some systems the transmission adapter (XA) provides for the connection of remote and local devices to the data adapter as well as the necessary controls to move data to or from the processing unit via the TIC (Transmission Interface Converter). A number of data adapters are available to allow attachment of various remote devices through their communication facility as well as the attachment of various local devices.

add, Boolean—Same as OR in set theory and the same as OR Gate, positive.

adder, half—Refers to specific logic elements that have two input channels to which signals may be applied and which represent two input digits, the

2

addend and the augend. The two output-channels from which the signals may-emerge are those which represent the sum and carry digits.

address—1. A label, name, or number identifying a register, location, or unit where information is stored. 2. The operand portion of an instruction. 3. In communications, the coded representation of the destination of a message. 4. To call a specific piece of information from the memory or to put it in the memory. Types: absolute, effective, immediate, indirect, direct, level, instruction, machine, multiple, symbolic, and third-level address.

address, absolute—Relates to an address designed to indicate the exact storage location where the referenced operand is to be found or stored in the actual machine-code address numbering system. (Synonymous with specific address, and related to absolute code.)

address, base—1. Refers to a number that is designed as an address in a computer instruction, but which serves as the base, index, initial or starting point for subsequent addresses to be modified. (Synonymous with presumptive address and reference address.) 2. A number used in symbolic coding in conjunction with a relative address.

address, calculated—An address designed to be generated or developed by machine instructions contained in the program which uses the address. This address may be determined as a result of some program or process and it may depend upon some set of criteria or condition.

address, direct—An address designed to indicate the location where the referenced operand is to be found or stored with no reference to an index register or B-box. (Synonymous with first-level address.)

address, effective—1. A specific modified address. 2. The address actually designed to be used in a particular execution of a computer instruction. 3. An address obtained by the combination of the contents of a specific index register with the address of an instruction. 4. The address designed to be used for the execution of an instruction. This may differ from that of the instruction in storage.

address, indirect—1. A basic address type designed to specify a storage location whose content is either a direct address or another indirect address. 2. A single instruction address that is immediately the address of another address. The second address is the specific address of the data to be processed. This is classified as single-level indirect addressing. But, the second address could also be indirect, which is then second-level indirect addressing. This same process could develop third, fourth, fifth, and other levels of indirect addressing.

addressing, virtual—A specific design or system used to specify the locations of operands and instructions in the same storage location, i.e., at the same address. This is contrasted with normal addressing in which the instruction word is stored at one address or location and contains the addresses of other locations in which the operands are stored.

address, instruction—The basic address of the storage location where the instruction word is located. The next instruction to be performed is determined by the control program of the instruction addresses, and the machine control automatically refers to these addresses sequentially unless otherwise directed to skip or branch or directed by other schemes.

address, machine—Refers to an absolute, direct, unindexed address expressed as such, or one which results after indexing and other processing has been completed.

address modification—1. The process of changing the address part of a machine instruction by means of coded instruction. 2. A change in the address portion of an instruction or command which, if the routine containing the instruction or command is repeated, the computer will go to a new address or location for data or instructions. 3. A process used to obtain the address of the effective memory location, starting from a given reference address value in an instruction word. Related to address computation.

address, Nth-level—Refers to an indirect address designed to be second level, third level addresses, etc., that specify addresses of desired operands.

address-two—A specific instruction that is designed to include an operation and specifies the location of an operand and the result of the operation.

address, zero-level—A particular instruction address designed so that the address part of the instruction is the operand.

ADI—American Documentation Institute but now, American Society for Information Science (ASIS).

ADP (Automatic Data Processing)—1. This acronym pertains to equipment such as EAM (Electronic Accounting Machines) and EDP (Electronic Data Processing) equipment units, or systems. 2. Data processing performed by a system of electronic or electrical machines so interconnected and interacting as to reduce to a minimum the necessity for human assistance or intervention.

AED—Automated Engineering Design System, an MIT-designed extension of ALGOL.

AFIPS—Abbreviation for American Federation of Information Processing Societies. An association of American data processing groups formerly called AFIP.

agenda—The set of control-language statements used to prescribe a solution path or run procedure; an ordered list of the major operations constituting a procedure for a solution or computer run (this usage corresponds roughly to the ordinary "agenda" for a meeting).

alarm, audible—Refers to an audio signal designed to indicate that a predetermined condition has been met or detected, that a malfunction has occurred in the equipment, or that a program error or a problem condition exists.

alarm display—Refers to various visual display signals, usually on a CRT or radar screen, which would alert the operator to conditions which require attention.

ALGOL—1. ALGOrithmic Language. A data processing language used to express problem-solving formulas for machine solution. 2. ALGebraic Oriented Language (some authors). The international procedural language. 3. An arithmetic language by which numerical procedures may be precisely presented to a computer in a standard form. This language is intended not only as a means of directly presenting any numerical procedure to any suitable computer for which a compiler exists, but also as a means of communicating numerical procedures among individuals. The language itself is a result of international cooperation to obtain a standardized algorithmic language. The International Algebraic Language is the forerunner of ALGOL.

algorithm—1. A fixed step-by-step procedure to accomplish a given result; usually a simplified procedure for solving a complex problem, also a full statement of a finite number of steps. 2. A defined process or set of rules that leads and assures development of a desired output from a given input. A sequence of formulas and/or algebraic/logical steps to calculate or determine a given task; processing rules.

algorithm, scheduling—Refers to a specific set of rules developed to be included in the scheduling routine of the executive program. The scheduling algorithm determines the length of a user's quantum and the frequency with which this quantum is repeated.

allocate—The assignment of storage locations to the main routines and subroutines, thereby fixing the absolute values of any symbolic address.

allocation, dynamic-storage—Whenever a subroutine is called using this feature, the unique storage area for that subroutine is assigned to the first storage available. Thus, all subroutines called on the same level will share the same storage area. This procedure develops a significant storage saving in many cases. In addition, a recursive subroutine call is possible because a new storage area is assigned each time a subroutine is entered. This feature, together with in-line symbolic coding, provides real-time capability.

alphabetic-numeric—The characters that include letters of the alphabet, numerals and other symbols, such as punctuation or mathematical symbols.

ALTRAN—A language for symbolic algebraic manipulation in FORTRAN, by Bell Laboratories.

ALU (Arithmetic and Logical Unit)—The specific modem or unit of the hardware of a computer in which arithmetic and logical operations are performed. The arithmetic unit generally consists of an accumulator, some special registers for the storage of operands and results, supplemented by shifting and sequencing circuitry for implementing multiplication, division, and other desired operations.

AMBIT—An acronym for a programming language for algebraic symbol manipulation.

American Standards Association—The former name for present USASI; United States of America Standards Institute.

amplifier, computing—Refers to a specific amplifier designed to combine functions of amplification and performance of operations. Computing amplifiers are often summing amplifiers, analog adders, or sign reversing amplifiers; most are used in analog computing systems.

amplifier, differential—This very basic amplifier has two signal-input channels and one signal output channel, which have characteristics such as instantaneous output signals which are directly proportional to the difference between the instantaneous values of the input signals.

amplifier, inverting—Refers specifically to an analog computer amplifier designed so that its output voltage is

5

equal in magnitude to the input voltage but opposite in sign.

AMTRAN–Abbreviation for Automatic Mathematical TRANslation.

analog adder–Most frequently known as a summer in analog representation; it is a unit with two or more input variables and one output variable which is equal to the sum, or a specific weighted sum, of the input variables.

analog comparator–A unit which performs range checking on digital values developed by the ADC (analog-to-digital converter). The high and low limits are selectively obtained from the processor-controller (P-C) for those values to be checked. When values are determined to be out-of-limit, then an interrupt informs the P-C. Only one P-C cycle is required for each value to be limit checked. (IBM)

analog computer–A computer that represents variables by physical analogies. Thus, any computer that solves problems by translating physical conditions such as flow, temperature, pressure, angular position, or voltage into related mechanical or electrical quantities and uses mechanical or electrical-equivalent circuits as an analog for the physical phenomenon being investigated. Generally, it is a computer that uses an analog for each variable and produces analogs as output. Thus, an analog computer measures continuously, whereas a digital computer counts discretely.

analog-digital-analog converter system–A specific system which is designed to perform fast, real-time data conversion between digital and analog computers. Maximum sample rate for D/A conversion is 200kc; for A/D and interlaced conversions, 100kc. Digital word length is 10 bits. Actual conversion times are 5 microseconds for A/D and 2 micro-

seconds for D/A. Semiautomatic features enable the converter system to perform many of the functions that a computer normally performs for other converter interfaces (some computers).

analog multiplier–The analog device which develops the analog product from two or more analog input signals, i.e., the output variable is proportional to the product of the input variables.

analysis, numerical–Refers to the study system, or methods designed to obtain useful quantitative solutions to mathematical problems, regardless of whether an analytic solution exists or not, and the study of the errors and bounds on errors in obtaining such solutions.

analytical engine–Store by pioneer Charles Babbage, the analytical engine was the first general-purpose automatic digital computer. It embodied all the fundamental principles of the modern digital computer. It was theoretically capable of executing any mathematical operation; it stored sequences of instructions in memory, and it was to use punched cards modeled after those used in the Jacquard loom as mass memory for storage of mathematical tables. Babbage's concept of the analytical engine is one of the truly great intellectual achievements of all time.

analyzer, differential–Refers to an analog computer designed and used primarily for solving many types of differential equations.

AND–1. The most basic Boolean operator that gives a truth table value of true only when both of the variables connected by the logical operator are true. 2. A logical operator that has the property that if P is a statement and Q is a statement, then P AND Q are true if both statements are true, false if either is false or both are false. Truth is normally expressed by the value 1, falsity by 0. The AND operator is often represented by a centered dot (P·Q), by no sign (PQ), by an inverted "u" or logical product symbol (P∩Q), or by the letter "X" or multiplication symbol (P✕Q). Note that the letters AND are capitalized to differentiate between the logical operator and the word "and" in common usage. 3. The logical operation which makes use of the AND operator or logical product.

AND gate—Refers to a specific signal circuit with two or more input wires in which the output wire gives a signal, if and only if, all input wires receive coincident signals. (Synonymous with AND circuit.)

applications programs—Most often these are mathematical routines, including sine, cosine, tangent, arc sine, square root, natural logarithms, and exponential functions. Recently thousands of business, scientific and accounting programs have been developed as standards.

area, user—Relates to a specific area on a magnetic disk where semipermanent data is stored. This area is often used to store programs, subprograms and subroutines. This area is contrasted with reserved areas that contain compilers, track and sector information, etc., which may not be written into.

area, working—Same as working storage.

argument—1. The known reference factor necessary to locate the desired item (function) in a table. 2. A variable upon whose value the value of a function depends. The arguments of a function are listed in parentheses after the function name, whenever that function is used. The computations specified by the function definition occur using the variables specified as arguments.

arithmetic, fixed-point—1. Refers to a procedure or method designed for calculation in which operators take place in an invariant manner, and in which the computer does not consider the location of the radix point. This is illustrated by desk calculators or slide rules, with which the operator must keep track of the decimal point. Similarly with many automatic computers, in which the location of the radix point is the programmer's responsibility. (Contrasted with floating point arithmetic.) 2. A type of arithmetic in which the operands and results of all arithmetic operations must be properly scaled so as to have a magnitude between certain fixed values.

arithmetic, floating-decimal—Refers to a procedure or method designed for calculation which automatically accounts for the location of the radix point. This is usually accomplished by handling the number as a signed mantissa times the radix raised to an integral exponent; e.g., the decimal number +88.3 might be written as $+.883 \times 10^2$; the binary number $-.0011$ as $-.11 \times 2^{-2}$. (Contrasted with fixed-point arithmetic, definition 1.)

arithmetic, multiprecision—A basic design or form of arithmetic similar to double precision arithmetic except that two or more words may be used to represent each number.

arithmetic, parallel—A process designed so that simultaneous operations are performed on all digits of a number and in which partial sums and numbers are formed or shifted.

arithmetic, serial—Refers to specific operations designed so that each number is divided into digits to be operated upon singly usually in the adder-subtracter or a comparator. The same number of addition operations are required as there are binary digits in the operands; a simpler and slower operation than parallel arithmetic.

arithmetic shift–1. Refers to a specific shift of bits to the left or right within a fixed framework in order to multiply or divide by a power of the given number base equivalent to the number of positions shifted. 2. A procedure designed to multiply or divide a quantity by a power of the number base; e.g., if binary 1101, which represents decimal 13, is arithmetically shifted twice to the left, the result is 110100, which represents 52, which is also obtained by multiplying 13 by 2 twice; on the other hand, if the decimal 13 were to be shifted to the left twice, the result would be the same as multiplying by 10 twice, or 1300. (Related to shift, and cyclic shift.)

arithmetic, signed-magnitude–Refers to some systems designed to use signed-magnitude computers; that is, all the arithmetic operations are accomplished by the process of addition and subtraction of magnitudes. Since multiplication and division can be broken down into a series of additions and subtractions, respectively, the computer will perform these operations as well. Operations with signed-magnitude numbers are identical with algebraic addition using a pencil and paper.

arithmetic statement–One of several types of FORTRAN statements that specify a numerical computation.

arm, access–See access arm.

array–1. A series of items arranged in a meaningful pattern. 2. Usually the arrangement or positioning of the elements of an array in columns and rows provides for ease of computation in matrix algebra or using other manipulative rules fixed to yield values as when arrays are used as operands, a new array is the result of executed operations.

artificial intelligence–1. Research and study in methods for the development of a machine that can improve its own operations. The development or capability of a machine that can proceed or perform functions which are normally concerned with human intelligence as learning, adapting, reasoning, self-correction, automatic improvement. 2. The study of computer and related techniques to supplement the intellectual capabilities of man. As man has invented and used tools to increase his physical powers, he now is beginning to use artificial intelligence to increase his mental powers. In a more restricted sense, the study of techniques for more effective use of digital computers by improved programming techniques.

ASA, American Standards Association–Now changed to United States of America Standards Institute (USASI). This is an association which developed American Standards for optical character recognition, coded character sets, data transmission, programming languages, computer definitions, magnetic ink character recognition, and others.

ASA code–An information-interchange seven-level code recently adopted as a standard code by the American Standards Association (now USASI for United States of America Standards Institute).

ASCII–American Standard Code for Information Interchange, i.e., specific bit patterns are assigned for various signs, symbols, numbers, letters and operations in a specific set.

ASR–An acronym for Automatic Send-Receive set. A basic unit which is a combination teletypewriter, transmitter, and receiver with transmission capability from either keyboard or paper tape. Most often used in half-duplex circuit.

assembler—A computer program that operates on symbolic input data and produces machine instructions from such data by carrying out such functions as: translation of symbolic-operation codes into computer-operating instructions, assigning locations in storage for successive instructions, or computation of absolute addresses from symbolic addresses. An assembler generally translates input symbolic codes into machine instructions, item for item, and produces as an output the same number of instructions or constants that were defined in the input symbolic codes.

assembler, macro facilities—In many systems an assembler is available for use in the operating system designed to assemble object programs from source programs written in a flexible but easy-to-use symbolic language. The assembler language is a versatile machine-oriented language that can be used for a variety of applications, both commercial and scientific. A number of facilities for assisting the programmer are provided by the assembler. These include macro facilities as well as facilities for defining constants, for defining data-storage areas, for referring to files and storage locations symbolically, and for using literals.

assembler, symbolic—The symbolic assembler is designed to permit the programmer code instructions in a symbolic language. The assembler allows mnemonic symbols to be used for instruction codes and addresses. Constant and variable storage registers can be automatically assigned. The assembler produces a binary object tape and lists a symbol with memory allocations and useful diagnostic messages.

assembly line balancing—Refers to a specialized program designed to allow production control management to plan most efficient and profitable man-work element relationship in an assembly line operation.

assembly system—1. Refers to the basic automatic system (softwear) that includes a language and machine-language programs. Such supplementary programs perform various programming functions as checkout, updating, and others. 2. An assembly system comprises two elements, a symbolic language and an assembly program, that translate source programs written in the symbolic language into machine language.

association indexing—A specific procedure which usually follows two approaches — the automatic generation of word association maps based on lists of words from the text, and representations based on the number of times words appear in the text.

associative memories—Associative-memory capability, is developed by high-speed memory searches within computers and is based on content or subject matter rather than being limited to locating data through specified "addresses."

associative storage—A storage system or device wherein storage locations are identified by their contents. Such systems are often considered synonymous with parallel search and content-addressed storage.

assumed decimal point—The point within a numeric item at which the decimal point is assumed to be located. When a numeric item is to be used within a computer, the location of the assumed decimal point is considered to be at the right, unless otherwise specified in the appropriate record description entry. It does not occupy an actual space in storage, but it will be used by the computer to align the value properly for calculation.

asynchronous—1. Pertaining to a lack of time coincidence in a set of repeated events where this term is applied to a computer to indicate that the execution of one operation is dependent on the signal that the previous operation is completed. 2. A mode of computer operation in which performance of the next command is started by a signal that the previous command has been completed. Contrast synchronous, characterized by a fixed time cycle for the execution of operations.

atom—1. A term used in compiling techniques, denoting either an operator or an operand. 2. Smallest unit of a chemical element.

attenuate—A procedure designed to reduce the amplitude of an action or signal.

attribute—An inherent characteristic that sets something apart from other things that do not have the specific characteristic. For data items, attributes could include the location, length, and type of data.

audio response—A form of output designed to use verbal replies to inquiries. Various types of computers can be programmed to seek answers to inquiries made on a time-shared on-line system and then to utilize a special audio response unit which elicits the appropriate pre-recorded response to the inquiry. Of course, inquiries must be of the nature for which the audio response has been prepared.

audit trail—1. The retraceable trail or path of a transaction when it is processed. The trail begins with the original documents, transactions entries, posting of records and is completed with the report. Validity tests of records are achieved by this method. 2. An audit trail must be incorporated into every procedure; provision for it should be made early so that it becomes an integral part. In creating an audit trail it is necessary to provide: (A) Transaction documentation which is detailed enough to permit the association of any one record with its original source document. (B) A system of accounting controls which provides that all transactions have been processed and that accounting records are in balance. (C) Documentation from which any transaction can be recreated and its processing continued, should that transaction be misplaced or destroyed at some point in the procedure.

autoabstract—1. Refers to collections of words selected from a document, arranged in a meaningful order, commonly by an automatic or machine method. 2. Preparation of abstracts from larger bodies of information are often completed by the use of programs which select key words as key word in context (KWIC) indexes which are then printed out with titles of the articles or reports.

autobalance—Refers to a device composed of various shafts, discs, wheels, integrating and differential gears so connected as to perform approximate differentiation of one input variable with respect to another input variable.

auto-index—1. The procedure for preparation of an index to a body or corpus of material by means of a data processing procedure. 2. An index prepared by data processing procedures.

automata theory—The development of theory which relates the study of principles of operations and applications of automatic devices to various behaviorist concepts and theories.

Automath—A Honeywell scientific computer program that translates mathematical notation into machine instructions. The Automath 800 will accept FORTRAN II language as will Automath 400 and 1400. Automath 1800 (which will also run on large H-800 systems) will accept FORTRAN IV.

automatically programmed tools (APT)—APT is a system developed and designed for the computer-assisted programming of numerically controlled machine tools, flame cutters, drafting machines, and similar equipment. It is production-oriented, written to simplify the effort, and to reduce time and money needed to take full advantage of numerically controlled techniques in engineering and manufacturing.

automatic control—See control, automatic.

automatic data processing (ADP)—Data processing performed by a system of electronic or electrical machines so interconnected and interacting as to reduce to a minimum the need for human assistance or intervention.

automatic interrupt—Relates to an automatic program-controlled interrupt system that is designed to cause a hardware jump to a predetermined location. There are five types of interrupt: (1) input/output, (2) programmer error, (3) machine error, (4) supervisor call, and (5) external (for example, timer turned to negative value, alert button on console, external lines from another processor). There is further subdivision under the five types. Unwanted interrupts, such as an anticipated overflow, can be "masked out" (some computers).

automatic publishing—Automated writing, printing and publishing capability which will be provided by interactive processing and large, low-cost memory systems. In the future, authors will publish materials as follows: The author will do his writing on the keyboard of a remote terminal. His typed input will be stored in his private files by the computer, which can retrieve it on demand and display it on his CRT device. By retyping or using a light pen the author can correct typing or spelling errors, add or delete sentences, or insert pictorial or reference material. Once satisfied with the rough text, the author requests the computer to prepare final copy, properly formatted, corrected, margin adjusted and with the appropriate page headings. To publish the copy the author notifies the computer of the existence of his document and authorizes its inclusion into the public files, where it becomes readily available to all others.

automatic recovery program—A program enabling a system to remain functioning when a piece of equipment has failed. The automatic recovery program often activates duplex circuitry, a standby computer, or switches to a mode of degraded operation.

automatic teaching—An educational application of the computer which involves an interplay between a student and a programmed set of messages that not only present material to be learned, but also test and assist the student's comprehension and allow him to proceed at his own pace.

automation—The generalized term used to convey the dedicated use or exploitation of automatic machines or devices designed to control various processes, such as: control of machines, machine tools, routine office procedures, accounting, and several thousand other applications.

*_*_*

background—Concerns time-sharing and multiprogramming and relates to the lower-priority work done by the computer when real-time, conversational, high-priority, or quick-response programs are inactive.

background program—A program that is not time-dependent. This program is of a lower priority than the foreground or main program and is at half or standby while the main program runs.

backing storage—Same as storage, auxiliary.

back-mounted—Refers to an electronic connector usually mounted from the panel, box or flanges which are on the inside of the equipment.

backspace—A procedure for moving one unit in the reverse or backward direction as opposed to moving one unit in the forward direction; e.g., to move back one record or file on an I/O device.

Backus normal form (BNF)—Refers to a formal language structure for syntax parsing used in design of ALGOL-60.

band—1. A cylindrical recording area on a magnetic drum. 2. Range of frequency between two defined limits. 3. A set of recording tracks on a magnetic drum or tape.

band, dead—Relates to a specific range of values concerning incoming signal which can be altered, without also changing the outgoing response. (Synonymous with dead space, dead zone, switching blank, and similar to neutral zone.)

bandpass—A measurement of the difference in cycles/sec between the limiting frequencies of a band in which the attenuation of any frequency, with respect to the central frequency, is less than a speci-fied value (usually half power or three db).

bandpass filter—Concerns a specific filter having a single transmission band with either of the cutoff frequencies being zero or infinite.

band, proportional—1. Pertains to the specific range of values of a condition being regulated designed to cause the controller to operate over its full range. Usually expressed by engineers in terms of percentage of instrument full scale range. 2. A particular change in input required to produce a full range change in output, due to proportional control action, i.e., it is reciprocally related to proportional gain.

bandwidth, nominal—Refers to the maximum band of frequencies, inclusive of guard bands, assigned to a channel.

base—1. The number of characters for use in each of the digital positions of a numbering system. In the more common numbering systems the characters are some or all of the Arabic numerals as follows:

System Name	Characters	Radix
binary	(0,1)	2
octal	(0,1,2,3,4,5,6,7)	8
decimal	(0,1,2,3,4,5,6,7,8,9)	10

Unless otherwise indicated, the radix of any number is assumed to be 10. For positive identification of a radix-10 number, the radix is written in parentheses as a subscript to the expressed number, i.e., $125_{(10)}$. The radix of any nondecimal number is expressed in similar fashion, e.g., $11_{(2)}$ and $5_{(8)}$ (synonymous with base number and radix number). 2. A quantity used to define a system of representing numbers by positional notation.

base address—1. A fundamental number that appears as an address in a computer instruction, but which also serves as the base, index, initial or starting point for subsequent addresses to be modified. (Synonymous with presumptive address and reference address.) 2. Refers to a number used in symbolic coding in conjunction with a relative address.

BASIC—Beginner's All-Purpose Symbolic Instruction Code. A procedure-level computer language that is well suited for time-sharing. BASIC, developed at Dartmouth College, is probably one of the easiest computer programming languages to learn and master. These are attributes which have allowed BASIC to become instrumental in the spread of time-sharing to businesses that are not within the computer industry.

batch processing—1. Relates to a fundamental technique designed so that items to be processed must be coded and collected into groups prior to processing. 2. A systems approach to processing where a number of similar input items are grouped for processing during the same machine run.

batch, remote—The procedure of entering jobs for the computer to perform through the use of a remote terminal as opposed to normal batch processing, where inputting the job must take place in the computer center.

baud—1. A unit of signalling speed equal to the number of code elements per second. 2. The unit of signalling speed equal to twice the number of Morse code dots continuously sent per second.

Baudot code—The standard five-channel teletypewriter code consisting of a start impulse and five character impulses, all of equal length, and a stop impulse whose length is 1.42 times all of the start impulse. Also known as the 1.42 unit code. The Baudot code has been used by the telegraph industry for about 100 years.

beam storage—Refers to storage units designed to use one or more beams of electrons or light to gain access to individual storage cells for operation, most often cathode ray tube storage.

BEMA (Business Equipment Manufacturers Association)—The acronym and organization name for a large respected trade association of business equipment, data processing equipment, office supplies and furniture manufacturers, and a sponsor, Standards Institute Sectional Committee X3 on information processing.

benchmark—A point of reference from which measurements are based, timed, or judged as a type of standard and from which other moving points may be made.

biased exponent—Refers to floating point number systems, and those systems which bias the exponent by a constant so that all exponents become positive, e.g., 10^{-50} becomes 10^{0} and 10^{+50} becomes 10^{100}.

binary—1. Numbering system based on 2's rather than 10's which uses only the digits 0 and 1 when written. 2. A characteristic, property, or condition in which there are but two possible alternatives; e.g., the binary number system using 2 as its base and using only the digits zero (0) and one (1) (related to binary-coded decimal, and clarified by number systems).

binary cell—1. The basic cell which has one binary digit capacity. 2. A one-bit register or bit position.

binary code—1. A system designed so the encoding of any data is done through the use of bits; i.e., 0 or 1. 2. A code for the ten decimal digits, 0, 1, . . . , 9 in which each is represented by its binary, radix 2, equivalent; i.e., straight binary.

binary-coded decimal (BCD)—1. This pertains to a decimal notation in which the individual decimal digits are each represented by a binary code group; i.e., in the 8-4-2-1 coded decimal notation, the number twenty-three is represented as 0010 0011. In pure binary, notation twenty-three is represented by 10111. 2. Describing a decimal notation in which the individual decimal digits are represented by a pattern of ones and zeros; e.g., in the 8-4-2-1 coded decimal notation, the number twelve is represented as 0001 0010 for 1 and 2, respectively, whereas in pure or straight binary notation it is represented as 1100.

binary column—Usually relates to binary representation of data on punched cards such that adjacent positions in a column correspond to adjacent bits of the data. Example: each column in a 12-row card may be used to represent 12 consecutive bits of a 36-bit word.

binary deck—Refers to a deck of punched cards containing data, information and instructions in binary codes.

binary digit (bit)—1. A numeral presentation in the binary scale of notation. This digit may be zero (0), or one (1). It may be developed by and equivalent to an "on" or "off" condition, a yes, or a no. Often abbreviated to (bit). 2. The kind of number that computers use internally. There are only two binary digits, 1 and 0, otherwise known as "on" and "off." Follow the table below by progressing geometrically per column right to left, and add the column values where one appears, i.e.; 7 is 1, 2, 4, 0, right to left.

COLUMN VALUES

```
      8 4 2 1
0 is  0 0 0 0
1 is  0 0 0 1
2 is  0 0 1 0
3 is  0 0 1 1
4 is  0 1 0 0
5 is  0 1 0 1
6 is  0 1 1 0
7 is  0 1 1 1
8 is  1 0 0 0
9 is  1 0 0 1
```

binary point—That point in a binary number separating the integral from the fractional part. It is analogous to the decimal point for a decimal number.

binary search—The procedure for finding an element of an order table by successively halving a search interval to then evaluate the remaining half where the element is known to exist.

binary-to-decimal conversion—Refers to the process of converting of a binary number to the equivalent decimal number; i.e., a base two number to a base ten number.

binary variable—A specific variable which is designed or selected to assume values in a set containing exactly two elements, often symbolized as 0 and 1. This is often confused with double-value variable; e.g., $y = \pm\sqrt{x}$. (Synonymous with two-state variable.)

bionics—A system of applying the knowledge gained from the analysis of living systems to the creation of hardware that will perform functions in a manner analogous to the more sophisticated functions of the living system.

biosensor—A particular mechanism designed to detect and transmit biological data from an organism in a way which permits display or storage of results.

BISEC—A General Electric Co. process control language.

bistable—1. Capability of assuming either of two stable states, hence of storing one bit of information. 2. Pertaining to devices capable of assuming either one or two stable states.

bit—1. Abbreviation of binary digit. 2. A single character in a binary number. 3. A single pulse in a group of pulses. 4. The smallest element of binary machine language represented by a magnetized spot on a recording surface or a magnetized element of a storage device. Whether the bit represents a 0 or a 1 is determined by ascertaining whether the magnetism was created by a positive or negative electrical charge.

bit check—A binary check digit; often a parity bit (related to parity check and self-checking number).

bit density—A measure of the number of bits recorded per unit of length or of area.

bit (information theory)—Refers to a specific measure or unit of Information Content equal to the Information Content of a Message the probability of which is one-half. Note: If, in the definition of Information Content the logarithm is taken to the base two, the result will be expressed in bits.

bit, parity—A designation of the fundamental check bit designed to indicate whether the total number of binary "1" digits in a character or word (excluding the parity bit) is odd or even. If a "1" parity bit indicates an odd number of "1" digits, then a "0" bit indicates an even number of them. If the total number of "1" bits, including the parity bit, is always even, the system is called an even-parity system. In an odd-parity system, the total number of "1" bits, including the parity bit, is always odd.

bit, sign—A binary digit used as a value sign.

bits, service—Refers to specific overhead type bits which are not check bits. For example, request for repetition, numbering sequence, others.

bit stream transmission—A specific method designed to transmit characters at fixed time intervals. No stop and start elements are used and the bits making up the characters follow each other without pause.

bit string—Refers to a one-dimensional array of bits designed and ordered by reference to the relations between adjacent numbers.

bit, zone—1. A fundamental concept which refers to one of the two left-most bits in a commonly used system in which six bits are used for each character. Related to over-punch. 2. Any bit in a group of bit positions that are used to indicate a specific class of items; e.g., numbers, letters, special signs, and commands.

black box—1. A generic or slang term frequently used to describe an unspecified device which performs a special function or in which known inputs produce known outputs in a fixed relationship (computer). 2. A generic term for any integral unit or device, but most often used to refer to electronic devices; i.e., a kludge (slang) (computer).

block—1. A group of consecutive machine words or characters considered or transferred as a unit, particularly with reference to input and output (contrast with record). 2. In real-time systems, blocks are used to describe input/output or working storage areas in main storage. A file storage block is often called a "physical record." 3. The set of locations or tape positions in which a block of words, as defined above, is stored or recorded. 4. A circuit assemblage which functions as a unit; e.g., a circuit building block of standard design, and the logic block in a sequential circuit.

block chaining—A procedure designed to associate a block of data in core with another block, in order to allow an item or queue of items to occupy more than one block. The blocks may be linked by programming, but some machines do it automatically.

block diagram—1. A planning or design chart aligns the particular sequence of operations to be performed for handling a particular application. Used as a tool in programming. 2. A sequential, graphic representation of operations of the various computer machines through the use of symbols which represent functional steps rather than the physical structural details. The block diagram is usually the gross or macro diagram for the entire integrated system or large application areas. Flow charts then provide the specific detail of various operations. 3. The graphic representation of the logic of a sequence of methodological or procedural steps; a data-processing chart. 4. A graphical representation of the hardware in a computer system. The primary purpose of a block diagram is to indicate the paths, along with information and/or control flows, between the various parts of a computer system. It should not be confused with the term flow chart. 5. A coarser and less symbolic representation than a flow chart.

block sort—1. Sorting of one or more of the most significant characters of a key to serve as a means of making workable sized groups from a large volume of records to be sorted. 2. Sorting by separation of the entire field on the highest order portion of the key, usually implying separate ordering of these segments and then adjoining the entire file.

block, table—A distinct group or subset of a specific table of data or instructions, usually specifically identified for more convenient access.

board, plotting—Usually refers to the specific flat surface part of an automatic plotter; that part of a plotting machine or unit of which plots, curves or displays of lines, diagrams, symbols, etc., are transferred or transformed. The plotting board is the output section of the total plotter machine displaying the results of the plotters manipulation of analog or digital data, usually for human use.

book—For computer usage this refers to a particular large segment of memory most often used in virtual memory addressing.

bookkeeping operation—1. A computer operation that does not directly contribute to the solution; i.e., arithmetical, logical, and transfer operations used in modifying the address section of other instructions, in the counting cycles, and in the rearrangement data. 2. Those internal operations that are necessary to process the data, but do not contribute to any final solution.

Boolean algebra—1. An algebra named for George Boole. This algebra is similar in form to ordinary algebra, but with classes, propositions, on-off-circuit elements, etc., for variables rather than data values. It includes the operators AND, OR, NOT, EXCEPT, IF, THEN, etc. 2. The logic and functions constructed from two-valued variables: truth/falsity; go/no go; zero/one; yes/no. Set algebra, class algebra, and propositional calculus are similar math systems used in computer switching theory and computer design.

Boolean calculus—Relates to a type of Boolean algebra modified to include time. Thus, such additional operators as after, while, happen, delay, before, etc., are provided. It is concerned with binary-state changes with time (triggers, delay lines).

Boolean complement—Same as gate, NOT.

Boolean connective—A specific design to fit between two operands or before the operands. Such symbols are for exclusive, conjunction, nonequivalence, disjunction, etc.

Boolean operation, dyadic—A specific operation in Boolean algebra designed to be performed on or with two operands and in which the result is dependent upon both of them. Operations on or with two operands are usually represented with connective symbols written between them . . . . as "union" or other Boolean connectives. Such connective operands or operations are most often related to 16 Boolean truth tables.

Boolean operation, monadic—A fundamental operation performed on one operand.

Boolean variable—The use of two-valued Boolean algebra to assume either one of the only two values possible. Examples: true or false; on or off; open or closed. Basically, all digital computers use the two-state or two-variable Boolean algebra in construction and operation.

bootstrap loader—A subroutine which is usually automatic and built into the hardware of the computer, which is capable of initiating the reading of another subroutine whose first instructions are designed to bring in the rest of the subroutine and thus initiate the total program schedule.

borrow—An arithmetically negative carry. It occurs in direct subtraction by raising the low order digit of the minuend by one unit of the next higher order digit; e.g., when subtracting 67 from 92, a tens digit is borrowed from the 9, to raise the 2 to a factor of 12; the 7 of 67 is then subtracted from the 12 to yield 5 as the units digit of the difference; the 6 is then subtracted from 8, or 9-1, yielding 2 as the tens digit of the difference.

bottom-up method—A compiling technique which identifies the statement type by examination of the syntactical relationship of each atom with its neighbor. Reverse of top-down method.

boundary, page—The address of the first word or byte within a page of memory, i.e., a memory address expressed as a number having 9 to 12 low-order zeros, the exact number of trailing zeros is related to the size of the page used by a specific computer. All programs in a paged-memory system should begin on a page-boundary address.

boundary register—A special register used in a multi-programmed system to designate the upper and lower addresses of each user's program block in the core memory.

box, stunt—A device used in teleprinters to perform nonreadout functions such as carriage return, line feed, ring signal bell, answer cdc's and tsc's, etc.

BPS—Abbreviation for basic programming support. BPS card and BPS tape systems are the two simplest and smallest operating systems available for main-line IBM System 360 computers.

branch—1. Departure from the normal sequence of executing instructions in a computer (synonymous with jump). 2. A machine instruction that can cause a departure as in definition 1 (synonymous with transfer). 3. A sequence of instructions that is executed as a result of a decision instruction.

branch, conditional—1. An instruction which is interpreted as an unconditional transfer if a specified condition or set of conditions is satisfied. If the condition is not satisfied, the instruction causes the computer to proceed in its normal sequence of control. A conditional transfer also includes the testing of the condition. 2. A specific instruction will depend upon the result of some arithmetical or logical operation or the state of some switch or indicator as to whether or not that instruction will cause a jump or skip to another preset instruction.

branch instruction—An instruction to a computer which enables the programmer to instruct the computer to choose between alternative subprograms, depending upon the conditions determined by the computer during the execution of the program (synonymous with transfer instruction).

branchpoint—A point in a routine where one of two or more choices is selected under control of the routine.

branch, unconditional—An instruction which switches the sequence of control to some specified location. (Synonymous with unconditional jump, and unconditional transfer of control.)

breakpoint—1. A point in a program as specified by an instruction, instruction digit, or other condition, where the program may be interrupted by external intervention or by a monitor routine. 2. A point in a computer program at which conditional interruption, to permit visual check, printing out, or other analyzing, may occur. Breakpoints are usually used in debugging operations.

B-register—Same as register, index.

BRIDGE—A Honeywell (Liberator) program which performs direct translation from the machine language of competitive systems to the machine language of the Honeywell 200 Computer.

broadband—As applied to data transmis-

sion, it is used to denote transmission facilities capable of handling frequencies greater than those required for high-grade voice communications; i.e., higher than 3 to 4 kc.

broadcast—Some control stations have the ability to broadcast messages simultaneously to all stations on a circuit. This is accomplished by using a call which is common to all stations.

BSI (British Standards Institution)—A British institution corresponding somewhat to the USA Standards Institute. It publishes various standards including a glossary of terms used in electronic data processing.

bubble sort—A sorting method which exchanges a pair of numbers if they are out of order at a particular time.

buffer—1. A word often implying buffer storage. 2. An isolating circuit used to avoid any reaction of a driven circuit upon the corresponding driving circuit. 3. The auxiliary data-storage device which holds data temporarily and which may also perform other functions in conjunction with various input/output machines. 4. A storage device used to compensate for a difference in rate of flow of data, or time of occurrence of events when transmitting data from one device to another. 5. An extremely temporary storage device of relatively small capacity capable of receiving and transmitting data at different rates of speed. Used as an equalizer when positioned between any set of components that operates at different speeds than the computer itself, such as a card reader and a card punch. 6. A logical OR circuit. 7. An isolating component designed to eliminate the reaction of a driven circuit on the circuits driving it; e.g., a buffer amplifier. 8. A diode.

buffered computer—A computing system with a storage device permitting input and output data to be stored temporarily in order to match the slow speed of input/output devices with the higher speeds of the computer. Thus, simultaneous input/output computer operations are possible. A data transmission trap is essential for effective use of buffering, since it obviates frequent testing for the availability of a data channel.

buffered input/output—Magnetic-core buffers outside the main processor memory compensate for speed differences between slower electromechanical input/output devices and processor speeds. Operations are overlapped, with all units operating simultaneously at rated speeds. Buffering eliminates the need for more expensive, multiple I/O channels—and eliminates complex I/O timing considerations from the programming job.

buffer storage locations—A set of locations used to compensate for a difference in rate of flow of data, or time of occurrence of events, when transmitting data from one device to another.

bug—1. Any mechanical, electrical or electronic defect which interferes with, or "bugs up" the operation of the computer. It can also be a defect in the coding of the program. 2. A mistake in the design of a routine or a computer, or a malfunction. 3. A high speed telegraph key.

building block principle—A system which permits the addition of other equipment units to form a larger system. Also called modularity.

built-in check—A provision constructed in hardware for verifying the accuracy of information transmitted, manipulated, or stored by any unit or device in a computer.

bulk storage—Storage of large volume capacity used to supplement the high speed storage which can be made addressable, such as disks, drums, or remain nonaddressable with magnetic tapes. Other names for this type of storage are external or secondary storage.

burst mode—A mode of communications between the processor and I/O devices. When a signal from an I/O device operating through the multiplexer channel indicates burst mode, the receiving unit continues to fetch bits until the specified data transfer is finished.

bus, check—Relates to a set or group of parallel lines for transmission of data to a particular checking device or unit such as a check register, a parity checker, or a comparator.

byte—1. Generic term indicating a measurable portion of consecutive binary digits; e.g., an 8-bit or 6-bit byte. 2. A sequence of adjacent binary digits operated upon as a unit and usually shorter than a word.

* – * – *

cable—Refers to an assembly or wrapping of one or more conductors within an enveloping protection sheath so constructed as to permit the use of conductors separately or in groups.

calling sequence—1. A basic set of instructions designed to be used to begin or initialize or to transfer control to a subroutine, but usually to complete the return of control after the execution of a subroutine is finished. 2. The fundamental instructions used for linking a closed routine with the main routine; i.e., basic linkage and a list of the parameters.

CAM—Content Addressed Memory. Associative memory capability; high-speed memory searches within computers

19

are based on content or subject matter rather than being limited to locating data through specified "addresses."

Cambridge Polish—A special type or modification used in the LISP language, the Polish operators = and X are allowed to have more than two operands.

card code—Refers to the specific combinations of punched holes designed to represent characters (letters, digits, etc.) in a punched card.

card column—1. Refers to one of the vertical lines of punching positions on a Hollerith card. 2. One of twenty to ninety single-digit columns in a tabulating card. Usually when punched, a column contains only one digit, one letter, or one special code.

card, header—A Hollerith card designed to contain information necessary for the processing of the data on cards to follow.

card, Hollerith—A common name for the standard punched card, 3-1/4 by 7-3/8 inches, usually divided into 80 columns of 1 punch hole sites, i.e., a combination of punches in a column (zone and field) can represent letters, digits, or symbols. The card was named in honor of Dr. Herman Hollerith who invented it in 1889.

card image—1. A representation in storage of the holes punched in a card, by which the holes are represented by one binary digit and the unpunched spaces are represented by the other binary digit. 2. In machine language, a duplication of the data contained in a punch card.

card leading edge—Pertains to that specific edge of a Hollerith card which is most forward as regards the direction of motion of the card during processing. Any of the edges may be used to enter the machine first depending on the machine requirements.

card, magnetic—A card, usually designed with a rectangular flat surface, of special materials coated with various types of magnetic substances on which data is recorded, such that it can be read by an automatic device.

card punch—The item of peripheral equipment for punching holes (data) into cards, such as hand punches, keyboard print punches, high speed punches, paper tape-to-card punches, magnetic tape-to-card conversion units.

card reader—This peripheral unit converts holes punched in cards into electrical impulses, and transmits the data to the memory of the computer for processing.

card receiver—1. Refers to the receptacle on many types of equipment that accumulates cards after they have passed through a machine. 2. A hopper.

card row— Pertains to one of the horizontal lines of punching positions on a Hollerith card.

card verifying—This is a means of checking the accuracy of key punching and is a duplication check. A second operator verifies the original punching by depressing the keys of a verifier while reading the same source data. The machine compares the key depressed with the hole already punched in the card.

carriage control tape—This tape contains the control codes related to the movement of the carriage of the printer and thus controls the vertical and horizontal positioning of the carriage as well as the paper feed unit.

carry—1. A signal, or expression, produced as a result of an arithmetic operation on one digit place of two or more numbers expressed in positional notation and transferred to the next higher place for processing there. 2. A signal or expression, as defined in (1) above, which arises in adding, when the sum of two digits in the same digit place equals or exceeds the base of the number system in use. If a carry into a digit place will result in a carry out of the same digit place, and the normal adding circuit is bypassed when generating this new carry, it is called a high-speed carry, or standing-on-nines carry. If the normal adding circuit is used in such a case, the carry is called a cascaded carry. 3. A signal or expression in direct subtraction, as defined in (1) above, which arises when the difference between the digits is less than zero. Such a carry is frequently called a borrow (related to borrow). 4. The action of forwarding a carry. 5. The command directing a carry to be forwarded.

carry, end-around—1. A specific type of carry from the most significant digit place to the least significant place. 2. A carry designed to be sent directly from the high-order position to the least significant place; e.g., using 9's complement addition to subtract numbers. 3. Same as carry, definition 2.

cascaded carry—1. A specific carry designed to use the normal adding circuit rather than any special or high-speed circuit. 2. Concerning parallel addition, a carry process in which the addition of two numerals results in a sum numeral and a carry numeral which are in turn added together, this process being repeated until no new carries are generated. 3. Same as carry, definition 2. (Contrast with high-speed carry.)

cathode-ray tube (CRT)—1. An electronic vacuum tube containing a screen on which information may be stored by means of a multigrid modulated beam of electrons from the thermionic emitter storage effected by means of charged or uncharged spots. 2. Abbreviated as CRT.

A vacuum tube in which a beam of electrons can be focused to a small point on a luminescent screen and can be varied in position and intensity to form a pattern. 3. A storage tube. 4. An oscilloscope tube. 5. A picture tube.

central processing unit (CPU)—1. The unit of a computing system which contains the circuits which control and perform the execution of instructions. 2. The central processor of the computer system. It contains the main storage, arithmetic unit, and special register groups.

chain code—An arrangement or design in a cyclic sequence of some or all of the possible different N-bit words, designed so that adjacent words are linked by the relationship that each word is derived from its neighbor by displacing the bits one digit position to the left or right, dropping the leading bit, and inserting a bit at the end. The value of the inserted bit needs only to meet the requirement that a word must not recur before the cycle is complete; e.g., 000 001 010 011 111 100 000 . . . .

chained file—See file, chained.

chaining—1. A fundamental system, procedure, or design for storing records in which each record belongs to a list or group of records, and has a linking field for tracing the chain. 2. Refers to the capability of an object program to call another object program for execution after its own execution has been performed.

chain search—A search key is used to search through chained data.

channel—1. A path along which signals can be sent; e.g., data channel, output channel. 2. The portion of a storage medium which is accessible to a given reading station, e.g., track, band. 3. A unit which controls the operation of one or more

21

I/O units. 4. One or more parallel tracks treated as a unit. 5. In a circulating storage, a channel is one recirculating path containing a fixed number of words stored serially by word (synonymous with band). 6. A path for electrical communication.

channel adapter—A specific modem designed to permit the connection between data channels of differing equipment. The device allows data transfer at the rate of the slower channel.

channel capacity—1. Refers to a measurement of the maximum number of binary digits or elementary digits to other bases which can be handled in a particular channel per unit time. 2. The maximum possible information-transmission rate through a channel at a specified error rate. The channel capacity may be measured in bits per second or bauds.

channel, duplex—A channel designed to provide simultaneous transmission in both directions.

channel, half-duplex—A channel designed to transmit and receive signals, but in only one direction at a time.

channel, multiplex—A data channel which can operate either in burst or multiplexor mode. In the latter mode, several slow I/O devices can be served simultaneously by time-slicing.

channel, selector—A high speed data channel dedicated to one I/O device at a time, operating in burst mode.

channel, simplex—A channel designed to permit transmission in one direction only.

channel status routine (BSY)—BSY (busy) is a unique routine and is called by drivers to determine the status of a channel. A driver usually (unless overlapped) cannot use a channel until the channel is free. When BSY is called, it retains control until the channel is free. The status of each channel available to the system is contained in the channel status table (CST). This table contains one entry for each channel. Each time a driver is called, it waits for the necessary channel to be free. When an input/output operation is initiated, the driver sets the channel status at busy. Upon completion of the interrupt, the channel status is set at not busy.

channel, voice-grade service—A specific term which originally referred to a service provided by the common carriers that included a circuit capable of carrying a voice transmission. Now, when used in reference to the transmission of data, it also refers to a circuit of sufficient bandwidth to permit a data-transfer rate up to 2400 bits per second. Primarily the term distinguishes this service from teleprinter grade service in reference to regulatory agencies' tariffs.

character, binary-coded—An element of notation designed to represent alphanumeric characters as decimal digits, letters, and symbols by a set configuration of consecutive binary digits.

character, coded—A character represented by a specific code.

character, command—Characters, when used as code elements, can initiate, modify, or stop a control operation. Characters may be used, for example, to control the carriage return, etc. on various devices or complete devices or peripheral units themselves.

character design—Refers to a geometric shape distinguishable from another character, i.e., style, shape.

character edge—An optical character recognition term, which refers to an imaginary edge which runs along the optical discontinuity between the printed area and the unprinted area of a printed symbol or character. The optical discontinuity is observed by a change in the reflectivity along this imaginary line which is transverse to the character edge.

character, end-of-message—A term used by some programmers to designate specific characters or groups of characters such as: OUT, ROGER, EOM to indicate the end of a message.

character, erase—A character designed to represent a character to be ignored or to signify that the preceding or following item is to be ignored as prescribed by some fixed convention of the machine or as programmed. It may signify that some particular action is to be prevented, or it may signify an erase or destroy action on a tape or disc.

character, functional—See character, command.

characteristic—Refers to the integral part of a logarithm; the exponent of a normalized number.

character set—An agreed set of representations, called characters, are made to denote and distinguish data. Each character differs from all others, and the total number of characters in a given set is fixed; e.g., a set may include the numerals 0 to 9, the letters A to Z, punctuation marks and a blank or space (related to alphabet).

character set, alphanumeric—A special character set of letters, digits and other special characters and specifically including punctuation marks.

character, special—Usually refers to special characters which are neither numerals nor letters but may be symbols, such as /,*,&,$,=,or ?.

character subset—Relates to smaller sets of certain characters developed from a larger or universal set, all with specified common features. If all men is one set, white men would be a subset; both sets being men and the subset a smaller group with the common characteristic, men.

character, transmission control—Refers to those characters which may be interspersed with regular data characters, but in effect are so designed or coded to control an operation such as recording, interpreting, transferring, or some type of processing. A character controlling transmission is one of these types.

check bit—A fundamental binary check digit; often a parity bit. (Related to parity check, and self-checking number.)

check digit, sum—A specific check digit produced by a sum check.

check, echo—Refers to a specific check for accuracy of transmission in which the information which was transmitted to an output device is returned to the information source and compared with the original information, to ensure accuracy of output.

check indicator, overflow—A device or modem designed to be turned on by incorrect or unplanned for operations in the execution of an arithmetic instruction, particularly when an arithmetic operation produces a number too large for the system to handle.

check indicator, read-write—See indicator, read-write check.

checking code, error—A code designed to be either detecting or correcting errors in the information as represented and used particularly in transmission or storage of data in computers. Various types of check bits are the main components of such codes.

checking features—Some computers have various built-in capabilities to automatically check their own performance. This is a feature of the particular machine, a check feature.

check, longitudinal—Refers to an odd or even parity check developed at fixed intervals during data transmission.

checkpoint and restart procedures—Checkpoint and restart procedures, are techniques associated with computers, designed to make it possible, in the event of an error or interruption, to continue processing from the last checkpoint rather than from the beginning of the run. These techniques are included in applications which require many hours of processing time, since heavy machine scheduling and deadlines generally do not permit a complete rerun. To establish checkpoints, processing intervals are determined, each being based upon a certain number of items, transactions, or records processed. At each interval or checkpoint, the stored program identifies input and output records and then records them along with the contents of important storage areas such as counters and registers; at the same time, accuracy of processing up to that point is established. Restart procedures are the means by which processing is continued after an error or interruption. Each set of restart procedures includes the necessary operator and stored-program instructions for (1) locating the last checkpoint, (2) reading the machine for reprocessing, and (3) entering the main routine at that point.

check, validity—A specific check developed and based upon known limits or upon given information or computer results; e.g., a calendar month will not be numbered greater than 12, and a week does not have more than 168 hours.

Chomsky Type II—Similar to Backus normal form, a meta-language.

chopper-stabilized amplifier—A specific modulator, called a chopper, which is most often designed to be a vibrating contact or a solid state electronic switch is the basic part of a drift-corrector amplifier for the reduction of drift in a high-gain amplifier.

circuit, interlock—The specific signal on this circuit most often originates in the signal converter and shall be in the "on" condition only when all the following conditions are met: (a) That its internal switching circuits are arranged for signaling on a communication facility; (b) That it is not in any abnormal or test condition which disables or impairs any normal function associated with the class of service being used.

circuit, monolithic integrated—Refers to one of several logic circuits, gates, flip flops which are etched on single crystals, ceramics or other semiconductor materials and designed to use geometric etching and conductive ink deposition techniques all within a hermetically sealed chip. Some chips with many resistors and transistors are extremely tiny, others are in effect "sandwiches" of individual chips.

citation index—A specific index or reference list of documents that are displayed or mentioned in a specific document or document set. The references are mentioned or quoted in the text. The citation index lists these references.

clear—To erase or return all registers and accumulators to zero in preparation for new entries, problems, input data, etc.

clock—A timekeeping, pulse-counting, frequency-measuring or synchronizing device within a computer system. Such clocks are of various types as: real-time clock, which measures the past or used time in the same analogous scale as external events it will be used to describe; a master clock, which is the source of pulses required for computer operation; programmable clock, whose time values are transmitted into a clock register and which may be accessed as determined by clock instructions in the program.

closed loop—1. A group of instructions which are repeated indefinitely. 2. Pertaining to a system with feedback type of control, so the output is used to modify the input.

closed subroutine—1. A specific type of subroutine that is not stored in the main path of the routine. Such a subroutine is entered by a jump operation and provision is made to return control to the main routine at the end of the operation. The instructions related to the entry and re-entry function constitute a linkage. (Synonymous with linked subroutine.) 2. A frequently used subroutine which can be stored in one place and then connected to a routine using various linkages or calling sequences or commands, at one or more locations, i.e., when it is stored separately from the main routine, jump instructions from program control will fetch or call the beginning of this subroutine, and at its end, another transfer instruction will return it.

COBOL—1. COmmon Business Oriented Language. This is a common procedural language designed for commercial data processing as developed and defined by a national committee of computer manufacturers and users. 2. A specific language by which business data processing procedure may be precisely described in a standard form. The language is intended not only as a means for directly presenting any business program to any suitable computer for which a compiler exists, but also as a means of communication concerning such procedures among individuals.

CODASYL—Refers to the Conference On DAta SYstems Languages. Organized by the Department of Defense, computer users, and manufacturers.

code—1. A system of symbols for meaningful communication (related to instruction). 2. A system of symbols for representing data or instructions in a computer or a tabulating machine. 3. The translating and writing of information in the form of abbreviations and specific notation to develop machine instructions or symbolic instructions from the statement of a problem. 4. To express a program in a code that a specific computer was built or programmed to interpret and execute.

code, ASA—Refers to a basic information interchange seven-level code recently adopted as a standard code by the American Standards Association.

code, Baudot—The standard five-channel teletypewriter code which consists of a start impulse and five character impulses, all of equal length, and a stop impulse whose length is 1.42 times the start impulse. Also known as the 1.42 unit code. The Baudot code has been used by the telegraph industry for about 100 years.

code, binary—1. The basic coding system designed so that the encoding of any data is done through the use of bits; i.e., 0 or 1. 2. A code for the ten decimal digits, 0 through 9, in which each is represented by its binary, radix 2, equivalent, i.e., straight binary.

code, biquinary—A two-part code in which each decimal digit is represented by the sum of the two parts, one of which has the value of decimal zero or five, and the each decimal digit separately is expressed in some other number system; e.g., in the other the values zero through four. The abacus and soroban both use biquinary codes. An example follows.

Decimal	Biquinary	Interpretation
0	0 000	0+0
1	0 001	0+1
2	0 010	0+2
3	0 011	0+3
4	0 100	0+4
5	1 000	5+0
6	1 001	5+1
7	1 010	5+2
8	1 011	5+3
9	1 100	5+4

code, check—To isolate and remove mistakes from a routine.

code, column-binary—A specific code designed to be used with punch cards in which successive bits are represented by the presence or absence of punches on contiguous positions in successive columns as opposed to rows. Column-binary code is widely used in connection with 36-bit word computers where each group of 3 columns is used to represent a single word.

code, cyclic—A specific binary code designed so that sequential numbers are represented by expressions which are the same, except in one place, and in that place differ by one unit; e.g.,

Decimal	Binary	Cyclic
0	000	000
1	001	001
2	010	011
3	011	010
4	100	110
5	101	111

thus, in going from one decimal digit to the next sequential digit, only one binary digit changes its value. (Synonymous with gray code.)

coded decimal—A specific code used for describing a form of notation by which

8-4-2-1 coded decimal notation, the number twelve is represented as 0001 0010, for 1 and 2; whereas in pure or straight binary notation it is represented as 1100. Other coded decimal notations used are the 5-4-2-1, the excess three, and the 2-3-2-1 codes.

code, error-correcting—1. A specific code designed so that each data signal conforms to rules of construction, so that departures from this construction in the received signals can be automatically detected, and which permits the automatic correction, at the receive terminal, of some or all of the errors. Such codes require more signal elements than are necessary to convey the basic information. 2. An error-detecting code in which the forbidden-pulse combination produced by gain or loss of a bit indicates which bit is wrong.

code, error-detecting—A specific code designed so that errors produce forbidden combinations. A single error-detecting code produces a forbidden combination if a digit gains or loses a single bit. A double error-detecting code produces a forbidden combination if a digit gains or loses either one or two bits and so forth. (Synonymous with self-checking code, and related to self-checking number.)

code, excess-three—A specific binary-coded decimal code designed so that each digit is represented by the binary equivalent of that number plus three, for example:

Decimal Digit	XS 3 Code	Binary Value
0	0011	3
1	0100	4
2	0101	5
3	0110	6
4	0111	7

Decimal Digit	XS 3 Code	Binary Value
5	1000	8
6	1001	9
7	1010	10
8	1011	11
9	1100	12

code, Gray—1. Positional binary notation for numbers in which any two sequential numbers whose difference is 1 are represented by expressions that are the same except in one place or column, and in that place or column differ by only one unit. 2. A type of cycle unit-distance binary code.

code, Hamming—One of the fundamental error-correction code systems in use today, named after the inventor.

code, input instruction—A code designed for the convenience of programmers which has mnemonic symbols or groupings which appear somewhat like the actual operations to be performed, i.e., MPY for multiply, etc. The computer then translates these into actual machine instructions for execution.

code, MICR—In magnetic ink character recognition, the special code has been designed to consist of a set of 10 numeric symbols and four special symbols standardized as Font E-13B developed for the American Bankers Association. The characters are visually readable through the use of magnetic sensing heads in various types of magnetic ink recognition equipment. The special symbols mentioned above are: amount, dash, transit number, and on us.

code, micro-—1. Refers to instructions written by a programmer or systems analyst in a source program developed to specify and execute a routine to be extracted from the computer library to

give the processor program information and instructions required to regularize the routine to fit into the specific object program. 2. A system of coding making use of sub-operations not ordinarily accessible in programming; e.g., coding that makes use of parts of multiplication or division operations. 3. A list of small program steps. Combinations of these steps, performed automatically in a prescribed sequence to form a macro-operation like multiply, divide, and square root.

code, mnemonic—A very common instruction code designed to use conventional abbreviations instead of numeric codes in order to facilitate easy recognition. Examples: MLT for multiply, SUB for subtract.

code, object—The basic code produced by any of hundreds of compilers or special assemblers which can be executed on the target computer.

code, pseudo-—1. A specific code designed to express programs in source language; i.e., by referring to storage locations and machine operations by symbolic names and addresses which are independent of their hardware-determined names and addresses. (Contrasted with machine-language code.) 2. An arbitrary code, independent of the hardware of a computer and designed for convenience in programming, that must be translated into computer code if it is to direct the computer.

code, self-checking—A specific code designed so that errors produce forbidden combinations. A single-error detecting code produces a forbidden combination if a digit gains or loses a single bit. A double-error detecting code produces a forbidden combination if a digit gains or loses either one or two bits and so forth.

(Related to self-checking number.)

code, symbolic—A specific code designed to express programs in source language; i.e., by referring to storage locations and machine operations by symbolic names and addresses which are independent of their hardware-determined names and addresses.

code, two-out-of-five—A system of encoding designed with the decimal digits 0, 1,... 9, where each digit is represented by binary digits of which 2 are zeros and 3 are ones or vice versa.

coding, absolute, relative or symbolic—Coding designed to use absolute, relative, or symbolic addresses, respectively; coding in which all addresses refer to an arbitrarily selected position, or in which all addresses are represented symbolically.

coding sheet—A form or document upon which computer instructions are written prior to being punched into cards.

COGENT—Argonne National Laboratory List Processor.

cognition, artificial—Refers to optical sensing of a displayed character designed so that the machine or equipment selects from memory the shape of the character that is closest to the character being displayed.

COGO (COordinated GeOmetry)—1. Coordinated geometry program. 2. A higher-level language originated by Prof. C. L. Miller and his staff at MIT in association with the staff of the Puerto Rico Dept. of Public Works, Bureau of Highways. The COGO system is designed to be used for civil engineering applications.

collate—1. To merge two or more ordered sets of data, or cards, in order to produce one or more ordered sets which still reflect the original ordering relations. The collation process is the merging of two sequences of cards, each ordered on some mutual key, into a single sequence ordered on the mutual key. 2. To produce a single sequence of items, ordered according to some rule (i.e., arranged in some orderly sequence), from two or more ordered sequences. The final sequence need not contain all of the data available in the original sets. If, for example, two sets of items are being matched, items that do not match may be discarded.

collating sequence—Refers to a specific sequence of characters designed and arranged in the order of their relative precedence. The collating sequence of a particular computer is determined as part of its design; each character acceptable to the computer has a preassigned place in this sequence. A collating sequence is used primarily in comparing operations.

COMIT—A string manipulation and pattern matching language by MIT, Massachusetts Institute of Technology.

common area—FORTRAN programs and other programs may specify that data storage is to occupy a common area. This allows programs to share temporary storage, and FORTRAN-coded programs to communicate with assembly-coded routines by using a common data storage. The system loader automatically allocates common area when it is loading programs. Common storage occupies the same memory space during execution as the system loader does when loading programs. This allows effective utilization of memory storage, since the space taken up by the loader can be used by the programs during execution.

common carrier (communication)—Refers to those companies recognized as appropriate regulatory agencies having vested interest in carrying or furnishing communication service.

common language (OCR)—One universally acceptable for optical character readers (OCR) adopted by most manufacturers and which usually includes commonly accepted character shapes.

communication channel—Voice, mail, messenger, telephone, telegraph, microwave, teletype, and other media are available for transmitting business data over short or very great distances, i.e., a Telpak or microwave channel is a communication channel with data transmission rates up to 100,000 characters per second.

communication-interface modules—These modules are furnished to interface CLT's (Communication Line Terminals) with currently available modems in addition to telegraph facilities for which no modem is necessary. Where required, interface modules conform to EIA specifications. The modular concept of the standard communication subsystem permits the addition of new interface modules as new offerings are made available by the common carriers. Jacks are provided on each telegraph interface module which permit a teletypewriter to monitor all data passing through the interface. (Interface means synchronize or mesh with other modules or units.)

communication line adapter— The reference to Teletype (CLAT), this is a semi-automatic device used to link the buffer units with the remote teletype units. The CLAT is incorporated within the buffer cabinet, which is located with the processor at the central site. The purpose of the CLAT is to receive data in serial bit form from the remote inquiry station and convert the data to parallel bit form for use in the inquiry buffer unit. Similarly, data transmitted from buffer to remote inquiry station is converted by the CLAT from parallel to serial bit form.

communication line terminals (CLT)— These fit into three basic kinds of input and output CLT's: low speed (up to 300 bps), medium speed (up to 1600 bps) and high speed (2000-4800 bps). Each is easily adjusted to the speed and other characteristics of the line with which it is to operate. Each CLT requires one position, either input or output, of the communication multiplexer. The CLT-Dialing is an output CLT which is employed to enable the central processor automatically to establish communications with remote points via the common carrier's switching network. Each CLT-Dialing requires one output position of a communication multiplexer. Since CLT-Dialing does not transmit data, it is always used in conjunction with an output CLT, and input CLT, or, for two-way communications. (UNIVAC)

communication multiplexer—This performs as the link between the processor and the CLT's and is available in modules to handle 4, 8, 16, 32, or, 64 CLT's. In each of these modules, an equal number of input and output CLT positions are provided. For example, a 64-position communication multiplexer can accommodate up to 32 input and up to 32 output CLT's.

communication, real-time processing—In order to close the gap in time between the actual transaction and its recognition by the processing system, a new concept has been devised—real-time processing. A real time system is a combined data processing and communications system which involves the direct communication of transaction data between remote locations and a central computer, via communication lines, and allows the data to be processed while the business transaction is actually taking place. A real-time system may be thought of as a communications-oriented data-processing system which is capable of performing batch-processing functions while concurrently processing inquiries or messages, and generating responses in a time interval directly related to the operational requirements of the system.

communications, audio-response unit—An audio-response unit (ARU) is used to furnish recorded voice response to inquiries made from telephone-type terminals and similar terminals such as the data-transmission terminal. The ARU attaches to the system via the multiplexor channel; it connects the computer to the telephone network.

The audio response is composed from a vocabulary prerecorded in male or female voice (optional) on a magnetic drum. An inquiry consists of a series of digits from a terminal (usually a telephone).

communications buffer—In reference to a computer communications network, a buffer is a storage device used to compensate for a difference in the flow rate of data received and transmitted along the numerous communication lines converging on the data processing center. The communications buffer orders information from many operators and controls the information so it can be processed by the computer without confusion. The buffer has memory and control circuitry of its own for storing incoming messages that the computer is not ready to process and storing outgoing messages which have to be delayed because of busy lines.

compaction of file records—To decrease the space required for records by compressing or compacting the records by means of specialized coding and for-matting under a programmed routine. A balance, though, must be maintained in a system between processing time and core storage, and the reduction of file size and channel utilization.

comparand—A word or number utilized in the comparison of another word or number.

comparator—1. Device used to compare two different transcriptions of the same information to verify the accuracy of transcription, storage, arithmetic operation or other processes, in which a signal is given dependent on some relation between two items; i.e., one item is larger than, smaller than, or equal to the other. 2. A form of verifier. 3. A circuit that compares two signals and indicates agreement or disagreement; a signal may be given indicating whether they are equal or unequal.

comparator (analog)—1. A specific hardware unit used for the comparison of two signals and giving an output dependent on some relation between them, usually of numerical quantities, i.e., whether one is larger than, equal to, or less than the other. 2. Performs range checking on digital values developed by the ADC (analog-to-digital converter). The high and low limits are selectively obtained from the processor-controller (P-C) for those values to be checked. When values are determined to be out-of-limit, then an interrupt informs the P-C. Only one P-C cycle is required for each value to be limit checked. (IBM)

compatibility—The characteristic of an instruction to be translatable or executable on more than one class of computer.

compiler—1. A routine used to produce a specific program for a particular problem by determining the intended meaning of an element of information expressed in pseudocode, selecting or generating the required subroutine, transforming the subroutine into specific coding for the specific problem, assigning specific storage registers, etc., and entering it as an element of the problem program, maintaining a record of the subroutines used and their position in the problem program and continuing to the next element of information in pseudocode. 2. A computer program more powerful than an assembler. In addition to its translating function which is generally the same process as that used in an assembler, it is able to replace certain items of input with series of instructions, usually called subroutines. Thus, where an assembler translates item for item and produces as output the same number of instructions or constants which were put into it, a compiler will do more than this. The program which results from compiling is a translated and expanded version of the original. (Synonymous with compiling routine, and related to assembler.)

compiler-compiler—A machine-independent language used to generate compilers for any specific machine.

compiler, syntax-directed—A compiler structured on the syntactic relationships of the character string.

complement—1. A number expressed to the base N, which is formed from a given number by a particular rule; frequently used to represent the negative of the given quantity. 2. A complement on N, obtained by subtracting each digit of the given quantity from N−I, adding unity to the least significant digit, and performing all resulting carrys; e.g., and two's complement of binary 11010 is 00110; the tens complement of decimal 456 is 544.

3. A complement on N−1, obtained by subtracting each digit of the given quantity from N−1; e.g., the ones complement of binary 11010 is 00101; the nines complement of decimal 456 is 543. (Synonymous with radix-minus-1 complement, and radix complement.)

complement, ones—A binary number obtained from another binary number when it is the result of a change in the sense of every digit, i.e., the sum of a number and its ones complement is a number of all 1-bits. A number 110, 101, 100, 011 when added to its ones complement, 001, 010, 011, 100 has a sum of 111, 111, 111, 111.

complement, tens—The radix complement of a numeral whose radix is ten. The tens complement is derived by subtracting each digit of the number from 9, and adding 1 to the least significant of the resultant number. For example, the tens complement of 2456 is 7544.

computation, address—A computation used to produce or modify the address portion of an instruction.

computational stability—That distinct tolerance level to which a computational process remains valid and reliable when subjected to various conditions which tend to produce errors, mistakes, or malfunctions.

computer—A device capable of accepting information, applying prescribed processes to information, and supplying the results of these processes. It usually consists of input and output devices, arithmetic, storage, communications units and a control unit. Types: absolute, value, all-purpose, analog, buffered, general-purpose, hybrid, incremental, parallel, second generation, serial, slave, target, and third generation computers.

computer-aided design (CAD)—The capability of adapting the computer for automated industrial, biological, statistical, (etc.) design through visual devices.

computer-aided instruction (CAI)—An educational technique which puts the student in a conversational mode with a computer which has a preprogrammed study plan. The programmed course selects the next topic or phase of study according to previous responses from the student, allowing each student to progress at a pace directly related to his learning capability.

computer, analog—1. A computer representing variables by physical analogies. Thus, any computer that solves problems by translating physical conditions such as flow, temperature, pressure, angular position, or voltage into related mechanical or electrical quantities, and uses mechanical or electrical equivalent circuits as an analog for the physical phenomenon being investigated. In general, it is a computer which uses an analog for each variable and produces analogs as output. Thus, an analog computer measures continuously, whereas a digital computer counts discretely. (Related to data-processing machine.) 2. A computer which calculates by using physical analogs of the variables. Usually a one-to-one correspondence exists between each numerical variable occurring in the problem and a varying physical measurement in the analog computer. The physical quantities in an analog computer are varied continuously instead of in discrete steps as in the digital computer; for example, as in the speedometer on a car.

computer, concurrent—A type of or a specifically designed computer which executes two or more instructions simultaneously, for example, read, search, compute. Such action is program controlled in some cases, but is built in or automatic depending upon the specific purpose for which the mainframe was designed.

computer configuration—The particular set of equipment so connected to form a single computer center or system for various computer runs. Such configurations run as wild as almost any system man's imagination: mainframes of various sizes, speeds, and architecture, store units of a hundred varieties, peripheral equipment in almost endless variety.

computer, digital—1. Fundamentally, a computer operating by the use of numbers to express all quantities and variables of a problem. In most digital computer systems, the numbers, in turn, are expressed by electrical inpulses. 2. A computer which processes information represented by combinations of discrete or discontinuous data as compared with an analog computer for continuous data. More specifically, it is a device for operations, not only on data but also on its own program. 3. It is a stored program digital computer capable of performing sequences of internally stored instructions as contrasted to non-programmed calculators.

computer efficiency—Determined by the ratio of the number of hours of correct machine operation to the total hours of scheduled operation; e.g., on a 168-hour week scheduled operation, if 12 hours of preventive maintenance are required and 4.8 hours of unscheduled down time occurs, then the operation ratio is (168-16.8)/168, which is equivalent to a 90% operation ratio.

computer, general-purpose—A computer devised to solve a large variety of problems; e.g., a stored-program computer which may be adapted to any of a very large class of applications.

computer, hybrid—A computer devised for performing both analog and digital computing for distinct or special purposes. Many are used in automated production.

computer-independent language—A programming language which is not categorized as a computer language, but one which requires translation or compiling to any one of a variety of computer languages. The language which is not a particular language of that machine but one which has compilers for translating to its own machine language.

computer, master/slave—See master/slave system.

Computer Optimization Package (COP)—COP is made up of a group of routines which are used to efficiently automate program testing, operating, and maintenance. COP includes monitoring and scheduling routines to facilitate parallel processing, program test systems, thoroughly tested library routines, sort routines, tape handling, maintenance routines, and simulator routines. (Honeywell)

computer-output microfilm (COM)—A microfilm printer which accepts output directly from the computer, thus substituting for line printer or tape output.

computer, parallel—In this computer digits or data lines are used concurrently by separate units of the computer. The units may be interconnected in different ways, as determined by the computation, to operate in parallel or serially. Mixed serial and parallel machines are frequently called serial or parallel according to the way arithmetic processes are performed. An example of a parallel computer is one which handles decimal digits in parallel although it might handle the bits which comprise a digit either serially or in parallel. (Contrasted with serial computer.)

computer, sequential—A computer used to execute instructions individually and sequentially without any concurrent activities such as simultaneous reading, writing, and computing.

computer, signed-magnitude—In this computer the arithmetic actions are performed by the process of addition and subtraction of magnitudes. Since multiplication and division can be broken down into a series of addition and subtraction, respectively, the computer will perform these operations as well. Operations with signed-magnitude numbers are identical with algebraic addition using a pencil and paper.

computer, source—The computer that is utilized to prepare problems as input for other computer operations.

computer, special-purpose—A computer developed to solve a specific class or narrow range of problems.

computer word—A series, set, or group of 1's and 0's grouped into units, intelligible to the computer, and representing alphabetic, numeric, and special characters. Many computer systems, at the programmer's discretion, can act on part of a word while leaving the rest of the word intact for future use.

computing message switching—A computer designed to perform communication control functions such as reception of messages, message validation, message storage, and logging of messages.

concatenate—To unite to form a series; to link together; to chain.

concordance—An alphabetic list of words and phrases that appear in a document, with an indication of the place where those words and phrases appear.

concurrent processing—1. The ability to work on more than one program at a time. This is a valuable feature of the new large-scale computer systems. The result is a better utilization of time by taking full advantage of the high speed of the central processor. 2. Concerns the processing of more than one independent task simultaneously by a single computing system involving interlaced time-sharing of at least one section of hardware, which is generally the control unit and memory-address register or the multiplexing unit, for selecting individual control units and memory-address registers for each task.

concurrent real-time processing—To eliminate the gap in time between the actual transaction and its recognition by the processing system, a new concept has been devised, real-time processing. A real-time system is a combined data-processing and communications system which involves the direct communication of transaction data between remote locations and a central computer, via communication lines, and allows the data to be processed while the business transaction is actually taking place. A real-time system may be thought of as a communications-oriented data-processing system which is capable of performing batch processing functions while concurrently processing inquiries or messages, and generating responses in a time interval directly related to the operational requirements of the system.

conditional branch—An instruction which is interpreted as an unconditional transfer if a specified condition or set of conditions is satisfied. If the condition or conditions are not satisfied, the instruction causes the computer to proceed in its normal sequence of control. A conditional transfer also includes the testing of the condition (synonymous with conditional jump, and related to branch).

conditioning, signal—The processing of the mode of a signal so as to make it intelligible to, or compatible with, a given device, including such manipulation as pulse shaping, pulse clipping, digitizing, and linearizing.

connect time—The quantity of time that passes while the user of a remote terminal is connected to a time-shared system. Connect time is usually measured by the duration between sign-on and sign-off.

console—1. The "operator" unit of a computer containing the control keys and certain special devices. This unit may contain the start key, stop key, power key, sense switches, etc., as well as lights which display the information located in certain registers. 2. A portion of the computer which may be used to control the machine manually, correct errors, determine the status of machine circuits, registers, and counters, determine the contents of storage, and manually revise the contents of storage.

console debugging—The programmer may debug at the machine console or at a remote console by slowly "stepping" the machine through each instruction and observing the contents of appropriate registers and memory locations.

console display—1. A visual display unit which provides a "window into the computer." It can display a message of thousands of characters of information, or tables, charts, graphs and the lines and curves of drawings as a series of points. A "light pen" (stylus), available with the display, can detect information that has been displayed on the screen and enable the operator to change information under program control. 2. There are binary displays on many computer operator's consoles. One display bit indicates the memory word parity; other display bits may indicate:

1. The next instruction.
2. The contents of any memory location.
3. The contents of the accumulator.
4. The contents of index registers.
5. The status of the traps.

When the computer halts, the display register will indicate the next instruction word, while a register will contain the address of the halt instruction that stopped the computer. To display anything else, the appropriate push-button display switch must be pressed.

console keyboard, display—1. Designed to make possible interpretive operations. Its function for a particular job is assigned by the computer program and the keys for that job are identified by removable illuminated overlays. 2. An operator control panel for those processors where the display is used in place of the typewriter control console. (IBM)

console, operator's—This provides capability of manual intervention and monitoring of computer operation.

console typewriter (monitor)—The console typewriter is a standard feature of the computer. The primary function of the typewriter is to monitor system and program operations. Such system conditions as Add Overflow, Exponent Overflow, etc. and program conditions as Syntax Error, Symbol Length, Integer Size, etc. are brought to the operator's attention via the typewriter. The typewriter may also be programmed to request information from the operator. The typewriter may also be used to enter programs and data into the central processor and to type out the results in lieu of other peripheral equipment specifically designed for these functions.

content-addressed memory—A particular memory designed so the storage locations are identified by their contents rather than their addresses. Enables faster interrogation to retrieve a particular element.

contention—1. A special condition found on a multipoint communication channel when two or more locations try to transmit at the same time. 2. A real-time method of terminal transmission control. If the channel is not free, the requesting terminal will have to queue. The queue of contention is solved either on a first come first served basis or by a prearranged sequence.

continuation column—A column (usually 6) reserved for a non-zero numerical punch which indicates that the card is a continuation of a statement from a previous card, especially in FORTRAN programming.

control, automatic—This is achieved by electronic devices receiving signals of measurements of particular variables involved in the process or program. The devices automatically regulate or control processes or perform calculations with the variables to direct or correct actions of a process which is programmed for control under constraints or guides.

control, cascade—An automatic-control system where various control devices are linked in sequence, each control unit regulating the operation of the next control unit in line.

control computer—A computer which, by means of inputs from and outputs to a process, directly controls the operation of elements in that process.

control, ESI—A feature providing communications control for many systems is ESI (externally specified index). ESI makes it possible to handle a substantial number of computer channels, using buffers in memory. This buffer control permits other transactions to run without interruption. Communications instructions that involve other memory areas interrupt other programs for a minimum period of time, measured in microseconds, because subsequent instructions are in a "ready" position at all times. Real-time circuitry provides tight, accurate operations in rapid succession, handling a vast number of instructions in real-time, communications, and batch-processing modes simultaneously, or with logical priorities.

control instruction register—A distinct register in which the content is the address of the next instruction.

control module, input-output (IOC)—A program-controlled macro processor used for servicing peripherals. It has up to four parts for connections to memory modules. The I/O commands are stored in memory and the I/O is activated by master-mode processor commands to the IOC through the system controller. The IOC proceeds independently until the I/O process terminates, then communicates this status back to the processor through the system controller. The I/O control module provides control signals, parity checks, time interface, and data transformations for I/O devices. It consists of an instruction register and associated decoding circuitry, a data register, and a manipulation register with associated timing circuits. Each control module is capable of controlling any standard device of the I/O complement. There can be as many simultaneous I/O

operations as there are I/O control modules. The I/O exchange automatically connects control modules with any of the I/O devices or command from processor modules. The I/O control modules also provide interface with associate data-processing systems.

control, proportional—A technique of control used so the intensity of action varies linearly as the condition being regulated deviates from the prescribed condition.

convergence, algorithm—This occurs when it is certain to yield its solution in a finite number of steps. It is a much stronger requirement than the mathematical convergence of the sequence of obtained function values.

conversational mode—1. A mode of operation meaning real-time man-machine communications are maintained. In this mode the system is used exclusively for servicing remote terminals. 2. The term given to the man-machine communicating technique which is the great dream of the future. This permits the user to "talk" to the machine locally instead of operating with the present restriction of having to tell the machine precisely what it is to do.

conversion—1. The process of changing information from one form of representation to another; such as, from the language of one type of machine to that of another, or from magnetic tape to the printed page (synonymous with data conversion). 2. The process of changing from one type of equipment to another, or from one data-processing method to another, i.e., conversion from punch-card equipment to magnetic-tape equipment.

converter, analog-digital-analog—Accomplishes fast, real-time data conversion between digital and analog computers. Maximum sample rate for D/A conversion is 200kc; for A/D and interlaced conversion, 100kc. Digital word length is 10 bits. Actual conversion times are 5 microseconds for A/D and 2 microseconds for D/A. Semiautomatic features enable the converter system to perform many of the functions that a computer normally performs for other converter interfaces. (DEC)

CORAL—Abbreviation for graphical communications and control language.

core dump—A listing of the selected parts or contents of a storage device (synonymous with memory dump and memory printout).

core image—Relates to the images of ones and zeros as represented by polarized magnetic cores as formed or stored in other media. Each binary digit is represented as on or off in some media or by direction in magnetic tape devices, or by magnetized spots on the surface of a magnetic storage drum.

core, magnetic—1. A magnetic material pulsed or polarized by electric currents carried in a wire or wires wound around it. This device is capable of assuming and remaining at one of two conditions of magnetization, thus providing storage, gating, or switching functions. See core memory. 2. A small doughnut-shaped ferrite designed and constructed for on or off magnetization and used to store information in the computer. 3. A miniaturized ring of ferromagnetic substance that may be instantaneously magnetized to a negative or positive flux and remains so until changed by further computer operations.

core memory, thin-film—This is used to provide high-speed internal storage. By using this thin-film storage area as an auxiliary, temporary storage medium, faster computation can be obtained. Any one of the addresses in control store can be accessed as quickly as 167 nanoseconds, and have a complete cycle time of 667 nanoseconds. Because of this high speed, thin-film is the most frequently used portion of the computer's internal-storage area; it may be referenced three times in the same time that it takes to make one reference to the core-storage area. The high access and internal switching times of thin-film store make it ideal for use as temporary storage of operands while the actual computation of data is taking place. Special address assignments for arithmetic registers, index registers, and other purposes are provided. These special addresses have dual accessibility in most instructions; that is, they can be referenced directly by the base operand (U), address of an instruction word, or by a special (A) designator within the word. (UNIVAC)

counter, instruction—Concerns a specific hardware register which is used by the computer to remember the location of the next instruction to be processed in the normal sequence, but subject to branching, execute instructions and interrupts.

coupled computers—Refers to computers that are joined to carry out special applications such as two computers operating in parallel and used as a check on one another, or coupled or joined so that the off-line computer is programmed to watch the on-line computer and, if needed, switch operation to itself.

cps—Abbreviation for both "characters per second" and "cycles per second."

CPU—1. Central Processing Unit. The central processor of the computer system. This unit contains the main storage, arithmetic unit, and special register groups. 2. The principal unit of the computer which controls the processing routines, performs the arithmetic functions, and maintains a quickly accessible memory. It also contains the console in some computers.

CPU time—The actual computational time needed to perform a set of instructions in the arithmetic and logic units of the computer.

critical path—The longest time path in a project. Because the overall time required to complete the project cannot be less than that required along the critical path, it requires the most careful monitoring. Any delay along this path causes the project to be delayed, while minor delays along noncritical paths do not.

cross talk—Cross talk happens when signals on one particular circuit emerge on another circuit as interference. The circuit which is the source of the signals is known as the disturbing circuit, and that on which the signals are heard is the disturbed circuit.

CRT—See definition for cathode-ray tube (CRT).

cryogenic storage—One which depends for its operation on the properties of specific materials, which can become superconductive when their temperatures and the magnetic fields in which they are situated fall below certain very low temperatures. Since superconductors have zero resistance, they have the ability to maintain or store a current permanently.

Culler-Fried—An on-line symbol manipulation system developed by Fried, of TRW, Inc.

curve follower—A peripheral unit used to read data that is represented on graphs.

cybernetics—The field of technology involved in comparative study of the control and intracommunication of information handling machines and nervous systems of animals and man in order to understand and improve communication.

cycle, memory—1. The process used to read and restore information in magnetic-core memory. 2. The time required to complete this process.

cycle stealing, data channels—Data channels are used to give the processor-controller (P-C) the ability to delay the execution of a program for communication of an I/O device with core storage. For example, if an input unit requires a memory cycle to store data that it has collected, the data channel with its "cycle stealing" capability makes it possible to delay the program during execution of an instruction and store the data word without changing the logical condition of the P-C. After the data is stored, the program continues as though nothing had occurred. This capability should not be confused with interrupt which changes the contents of the instruction register. Cycle stealing by the data channels can occur at the end of any memory cycle. Maximum delay before cycle stealing can occur is one memory cycle time.

cylinder concept—The concept which makes data available on all tracks above and below the one currently being used by merely switching read/write heads. Allows access to large amounts of information with no extra movement of the access device.

* – * – *

DAS—Abbreviation for digital-analog simulator.

data acquisition and control system (DAC)—The system is designed to handle a wide variety of real-time applications, process control, and high speed data acquisition. Each system is individually tailored with modular building blocks which are easily integrated to meet specific system requirements. A large family of real-time process input/output (I/O) devices is included, such as analog input, analog output, contact sense, and contact operate, as well as data processing I/O units, such as magnetic tape, disk storage, line printer, graph plotter, card and paper tape input and output. Data are received and transmitted on either a high speed cycle-steal basis or under program control, depending on the intrinsic data rate of the I/O device.

data acquisition system—A system used to gather data from multiple remote locations at a certain computing facility.

data, analog—The physical depiction of information so that the representation bears an exact association to the original information. The electrical signals on a telephone channel are an analog-data representation of the original voice.

data base—The set of data or information used to base operations and conclusions. This is the set of data that is internally accessible to the computer and on which the computer performs.

data channel—The bidirectional data path between the I/O devices and the main memory in a digital computer which permits one or more I/O operations to happen concurrently with computation.

data channel multiplexer—Used for enlarging the data-break facilities of the computer to allow large numbers of input/output devices to transfer data directly with the core memory, via the memory buffer register. Simultaneous data-break requests are serviced by the multiplexer according to prewired priority.

data net—A General Electric model which can be used for production control. A message exchange which receives and transmits automatically. Another use is a data collection system for the purpose of transmitting data from a remote station to a central unit. Still another use permits an operator to dial and send perforated-tape data over a phone line.

dataphone—1. A word used by A.T.&T. to denote any of a family of devices used in permitting data communications over telephone channels. 2. A generic term to describe a family of devices available to facilitate data communication.

dataset—A circuit termination device which is used to provide interface between a circuit and terminal input/output equipment.

DDG—Abbreviation for digital display generator.

dead band—A distinct range of values in which the incoming signal can be changed, without also changing the outgoing response. (Synonymous with dead space, dead zone, switching blank, and similar to neutral zone.)

debug—1. To locate and correct any errors in a computer program. 2. To detect and correct malfunctions in the computer itself (related to diagnostic routine). 3. To test a program on a computer to discover if it works properly. If mistakes are revealed, they must be traced to their source and corrected.

decibel—A particular unit measurement of transmission loss, gain, or relative level. The formal definition is 1 db = $10 \log_{10} P_1/P_2$; P_1 and P_2 are expressed in watts. It is also a convenient general practice to speak of voltage or current gains in "db."

decimal, binary-coded—See binary coded decimal.

decimal point, assumed—Concerns the specific point within a numeric item at which the decimal point is inferred to be located. When a numeric item is to be used within a computer, the location of the assumed decimal point is considered to be at the right unless otherwise specified in the appropriate record-description entry. It will not occupy an actual space in storage, but it will be used by the computer to align the value properly for calculation.

decimal-to-binary conversion—The procedure of converting a number written to the base of ten, or decimal, into the equivalent number written to the base of two, or binary.

decision rules—The programmed criteria which an on-line, real-time system uses to make operating decisions. It is dangerous to neglect to periodically review the decision rules which are being used by a system because the nature of the problems to be solved changes over time and because new situations may have arisen which were not at first anticipated.

decision table—1. Specifically developed and organized tabular representations of relationships between variables and parameters; sets of conditions, and ordering of actions or related sequences which make up sets of rules. 2. A tabulation or array of possible courses of action, selections, or alternatives which can be possible and thus considered in the analysis of various problems, i.e., a graphic aid to problem description, flow, and potential results, such as the purpose of a flow chart.

decode—1. To apply a code so as to reverse some previous encoding. 2. To determine the meaning of individual characters or groups of characters in a message. 3. To determine the meaning of an instruction from the set of pulses describing the instruction, command, or operation to be performed. 4. To translate coded characters to a more understandable form.

decoder—1. A device that ascertains the meaning of a set of signals and initiates a computer operation based thereon. 2. A matrix of switching elements that selects one or more output channels according to the combination of input signals present. (Contrasted with encoder, and clarified by matrix.) 3. A specific device capable of ascertaining the significance or meaning of a group of signals and initiating a computer event based on these signals.

decrement—1. The quantity by which a variable is decreased. 2. A specific part of an instruction word in some binary computers; i.e., a set of digits.

dedicated storage—The allocated, reserved or obligated, set aside, earmarked or assigned areas of storage which are committed to some specific purpose, user, or problem, i.e., exclusively reserved space on a disc storage unit for an accounting procedure, problem or data set.

delay element—The circuitry or electronic mechanism accepting data temporarily, and emits the same data after a specific interval.

delay-line storage—A storage method in which data is stored by permitting it to travel through some medium such as mercury.

delimiter—A character that restricts a string of characters, and therefore cannot be a member of the string.

demodulation—1. The procedure of recovering an original signal from a modulated carrier wave. 2. A procedure for retrieving original signals from modulated carrier waves. Such a technique is utilized to make communication signals compatible with business-machine signals.

density—The compactness of space distribution on a storage medium such as a magnetic drum, magnetic tape, or cathode-ray tube.

derivative control—Control action designed to be the output proportional to the rate of change of the input.

device, analog—A mechanism that denotes numbers by physical quantities; e.g., by lengths, as in a slide rule, or by voltage currents as in a differential analyzer or a computer of the analog type.

device ready/not ready—The capability to notify the central computer that an I/O device is prepared to accept data.

device, remote—An input/output unit, or other piece of equipment, which is outside of the computer center but connected by a communication line. In a typical on-line, real-time communications system, the remote device is usually a teletypewriter, an audio answer back device, or a CRT visual display unit.

device status word (DSW)—The word made up of one bit of information for each indicator within the device. These generally fall into four categories: (1) error or exception interrupt conditions; (2) normal data, or service required interrupts; (3) routine status conditions; (4) process-interrupt indicators. If a device contains interrupt requests which are connected to more than one interrupt level, all of the routine status indicators and the in-

terrupt conditions of the DSW are placed in the accumulator. These indicators are reset (depending upon the device) when sensed. Normally all indicators which place a "1" in the accumulator are considered to be on and would be reset. (IBM)

device, storage—A device used to insert, retain, and retrieve data.

diagram, block—1. A graphical portrayal of the hardware in a computer system. The primary purpose of a block diagram is to indicate the paths along which information and/or control flows between the various parts of a computer system. It should not be confused with the term flow chart. 2. A coarser and less symbolic representation than a flow chart.

diagram, flow—1. A schematic representation of a sequence of subroutines designed to solve a problem. 2. A coarser and less symbolic representation than a flow chart, frequently including descriptions in English words. 3. A schematic or logical drawing of the electrical circuit or logical arrangements within a component.

diagram, Venn—Identifies a diagram in which each point represents an individual. Sets are represented by closed regions including all members of the set and excluding all nonmembers. The diagram is used to facilitate determination whether several sets include or exclude the same individuals.

dial-up—The service whereby a dial telephone can be used to start and effect station-to-station telephone calls.

dictionary, relocation (RLD)—1. The part of an object program used to identify all of the addresses of a program that must be changed when the program is to be relocated. 2. Part of a load module containing directions which enable a fetch program to properly initialize all relocatable address constants within the text section (TXT), by accounting for the actual starting address of the load module in storage and the incremental difference between the desired address and the initial address of the module.

differential analyzer, digital—1. Refers to an incremental differential analyzer, usually electronic. 2. Concerns some incremental computers which compute the changes in variables rather than of variables. The principal type of computing unit is a digital integrator, which is similar in operation to an integrating unit or mechanism, and especially in England, integrators have been called Differential Analyzers which begets the term: Digital Differential Analyzer.

differentiator—A device having an output function proportional to a derivative, i.e., the rate of change, of its input function with respect to one or more variables.

digit—1. One belonging to the set of the n symbols of integral value, ranging from 0 to n-1 inclusive, in a system of numbering with radix n; for example, the ten digits 0, 1, 2, 3, 4, 5, 6, 7, 8, 9 in the decimal system; 0, 1 in the binary system. 2. One of the ideographic characters 0, 1...9...used to designate a quantity smaller than n for the base n number system. 3. A sign or symbol used to convey a specific quantity of information either by itself or with other numbers of its set; e.g., 2, 3, 4, and 5 are digits. The base or radix must be specified and each digit's value assigned.

digital-analog decoder—An analog computer device used to translate digital data into variable electrical flow.

digital system, man-machine—An organization of people, digital computers and equipment to regulate and control events and achieve system objectives.

digit, binary—A whole number contained in the binary scale of notation; this digit may only be 0 (zero) or 1 (one). It may be equivalent to an "on" or "off" condition, a "yes" or a "no," etc. The word "bit" is a contraction of binary digit.

digit, hexadecimal—A digit belonging to the set of sixteen digits: 0 through 9 and then A, B, C, D, E, or F used in a numerical notation system with a radix of 16. Some systems use letters other than A-F for digits 10-15.

digit, high-order—A digit that holds a more significant or highly weighted position in a numeral or positional notation system.

digitize—1. The assigning of digital numbers to characters and words according to fixed rules of ordering. 2. To convert an analog measurement of a physical variable into a numerical value, thereby expressing the quantity in digital form. (Synonymous with quantize.)

digit, least significant (LSD)—The digit adding the smallest quantity to the value of a numeral.

digit, low-order—A digit that holds the low weighted position in a numeral in a positional notation system.

digit, most significant (MSD)—The significant digit contributing the largest quantity to the value of a numeral.

digit, octal—A digit belonging to the 8 digits of the octal system which consists of numerals 0 through 7, in a positional notation system with a radix of 8.

digit, significant—Designed to contribute to the precision of an accurate numeral.

The number of significant digits is counted beginning with the digit contributing the most value, called the most significant digit, and ending with the one contributing the least value, called the least significant digit.

direct access—The ability to read or write information at any location within a storage device in a constant amount of time. Every site available for data storage on a direct access device is identified by its own unique numeric address.

direct address—An address which indicates the location where the referenced operand is to be found or stored, with no reference to an index register or B-box (synonymous with first-level address).

disable—A repression of an interrupt feature.

discrete simulation—The major components of the system are individually identifiable (discrete). Example: queuing networks.

discrimination instruction—A more acceptable term for conditional jump instruction or branch instruction. Also called decision instruction.

disk, magnetic—A storage device used to record information on the magnetized surface of a rotating disk. A magnetic-disk storage system is an array of such devices, with associated reading and writing heads that are mounted on movable arms. (Related to disk storage.)

disk, moving arm—A type of disk containing a movable arm which contains several heads, each of which covers an area of several tracks of digitized information. This is in contrast to a fixed head disk for which the heads are fixed in position, one per track, and the arms are immovable.

disk operating system (DOS)—A more powerful twin of TOS, this is a versatile operating system for IBM System 360 installations having direct-access storage devices. This operating system supports almost every peripheral device available for System 360.

dispatcher—A resident routine that is at the heart of all communication between the computer and its input/output devices. The dispatcher maintains a queue of channel requests for each channel and will honor each in turn as the channel becomes available. In addition, the dispatcher controls the operation of the multiprogrammed symbiont routines, interrupting the user's program temporarily to give control to a symbiont and returning control to the user when the symbiont has released. The dispatcher maintains a pool of buffer areas for the symbionts and a similar pool of drum symbionts are employed. (UNIVAC)

display—Visible representation of data on a console screen in a printed report, graph or drawing which is subject to alteration by a light pen or "stylus."

divide check—An indicator which designates that an invalid division has been attempted or has occurred.

documentation—1. The process of collecting, organizing, storing, citing and dispensing of documents or the information recorded in the documents. 2. The group of techniques necessary for the orderly presentation, organization, and communication of recorded specialized knowledge for maintaining a complete record of reasons for changes in variables. Documentation is necessary not so much to give maximum utility as it is to give an unquestionable historical-reference record.

docuterm—A word or phrase descriptive of the subject matter or concept of an item of information that is considered important for later retrieval of information. (Related to aspect card.)

DO statement range—All FORTRAN statements included in the repetitive execution of a DO loop operation.

DOS (disk operating system)—A more powerful twin of TOS, this is a versatile operating system for IBM System 360 installations having direct-access storage devices. This operating system supports almost every peripheral device available for System 360.

double precision—Refers to a quantity having twice as many digits as are normally carried; e.g., a double-precision number requires two machine words in a fixed-word machine.

drift error—An error in analog computers due to drift or change in component values due to changes in temperature or changes in power supply voltages.

drive, hypertape—A unit which uses magnetic tape packaged in cartridge form, and is capable of transferring data at 340,000 alpha-numeric characters a second or 680,000 digits a second. A cartridge holds more than 65 million digits. Hypertape drives are designed to read or record information at a rate of 340,000 alpha-numeric characters a second or up to 680,000 digits a second. This represents a fast commercially available magnetic-tape system. The drive operates at either of two densities—1,511 or 3,022 bits an inch. Also available is a hypertape drive that operates at 170,000 alpha-numeric characters a second, or up to 340,000 digits a second. (IBM)

drop-in—An accident or unwanted emergence of bits.

drum—A circular cylinder where data is stored on a magnetic surface by selective magnetization of portions of the curved surface.

drum latency time—Occurs while waiting for a given datum to emerge beneath the read-write head and may be minimized by organization procedures, i.e., by programming the next address of the datum to be read or written as a function of the last position of the read-write head, plus the elapsed time for the processing, before the next read-write instruction.

dummy instruction—1. An artificial instruction or address inserted in a list for a purpose other than execution as an instruction. (Related to constant instruction.) 2. A specifically designed artificial instruction to serve a purpose other than its meaningful or purposeful execution, i.e., it is not data. Such an instruction is usually inserted in the sequence for a purpose, but if it is executed no disturbance to the run will occur. It is frequently a no-operation, a do-nothing, or a waste instruction.

dump—1. To accidentally or intentionally withdraw all power from a computer. 2. To record the contents of internal storage at a given instant of time, usually as an aid in detecting program mistakes or errors. 3. To print out or punch out a portion or all of the contents of the computer memory. 4. To transfer all or a part of the contents of one section of computer memory into another section of memory, or to some output device. Types: core, memory, programmed, reserve, and storage.

dump, post-mortem—Refers to a listing of the contents or the full contents of a specific storage device taken after a routine has been run in order that the final condition of sections of storage may be recorded for debugging purposes.

dump, selective—A dump or printout of one or more specified storage locations.

dump, snapshot—Refers to a dynamic, partial (usually very specific) print-out during computing occurring at breakpoints and checkpoints, or at selected items in storage.

duplex—Concerns a combination, a pair, a twin or a two-in-one situation; e.g., a channel providing simultaneous transmission in both directions, or a second set of equipment to be used in event of the failure of the primary.

dynamic allocator—In several large systems the dynamic allocator is responsible for taking runs set up by the coarse scheduler and allotting storage space according to the needs of the individual tasks of a run. Various specific runs may be thought of as being made up of tasks, where a task is defined to be a single operation of a system processor or the execution of a user program. All tasks for a given run will be processed serially; however, tasks of separate runs will be interleaved. When time-sharing of central storage is appropriate, the dynamic allocator is also responsible for initiating "storage swaps," i.e., the writing-out of one program to drum, and replacing it temporarily in central storage with another program. Such action is taken only to provide reasonable response time to remote demand-processing terminals. The CPU dispatching routine is a third level of scheduling which selects among the various tasks currently occupying storage.

dynamic core allocation—Refers to a storage allocation design or procedure used in multiprogramming for the more efficient utilization of core by shifting units of work from location to location within the core.

dynamic dump—Refers to a specific dump that is performed at specific times or periodically during the execution of a program.

dynamic programming (DP)—The essence of dynamic programming is that an optimum decision must be made at every stage of a multistage problem. When considering only a single stage, there may appear to be a number of different decisions of equal merit. Only when the effect of each decision at every stage on the overall goal is determined can the final choice be made. This integrating of the cumulative effect of a path of decisions through each stage of the network is the real essence of DP.

DYNAMO—An acronym. A digital simulation program developed by Jay Forrester at MIT (Massachusetts Institute of Technology).

* — * — *

EBCDIC—An acronym or abbreviation for Expanded Binary Coded Decimal Interchange Code which is an 8-bit code used to represent 256 unique letters, numbers, and special characters.

edit—To rearrange data or information. Editing may involve the deletion of unwanted data, the selection of pertinent data, the application of format techniques, the insertion of symbols such as page numbers and typewriter characters, the application of standard processes such as zero suppression, and the testing of data for reasonableness and proper range. Editing may sometimes be distinguished between input edit (arrangement of source data) and output edit (preparation of table formats).

effective address—1. A modified address. 2. The address actually considered to be used in a particular execution of a computer instruction. 3. An address obtained by the combination of the contents of a specific index register with the address of an instruction. 4. The address used for the execution of an instruction. This may differ from that of the instruction in storage.

effective instruction—To alter a presumptive or unmodified instruction when using a stored program computer, such alteration produces a complete instruction and when it is actually executed it is called an effective instruction or an actual instruction. The modification process uses words or parts of words specifically called modifiers or index words. These are added to or combined with the presumptive or unmodified instruction by means of arithmetical or logical operations.

electromechanical device—Refers to various types of equipment which are partially electronic and partially mechanical in nature. While the central processing unit is a pure electronic device, most random access equipment involves moving parts, and are considered electromechanical devices.

electronic data processing (EDP)—Data processing by way of electronic equipment, such as an internally stored program, electronic digital computer, or an automatic data processing machine.

electronic differential analyzer—Concerns a specific type of analog computer designed to use interconnected electronic integrators to solve differential equations.

electronic stylus—A very popular pen-like device which is on a basic unit commonly used in conjunction with a CRT (cathode-ray tube) which is designed for inputting or changing information under program control. The electronic stylus is often called a light pen, and works by signalling the computer with an electronic pulse. The computer acts on these signals and can change the configuration plotted across the tube face or perform other operations using the inputted data according to previously programmed instructions.

electrostatic printer—A device for printing an optical image on paper, in which dark and light areas of the original are represented by electrostatically charged and uncharged areas on the paper. The paper is dusted with particles of finely powered dry ink and the particles adhere only to the electrically charged areas. The paper with ink particles is then heated, causing the ink to melt and become permanently fixed to the paper.

electrostatic storage—1. Refers to that specific storage of data on a dielectric surface, such as the screen of a cathode ray tube, designed to be in the form of the presence or absence of spots bearing electrostatic charges that can persist for a short time after the electrostatic charging force is removed. 2. A storage device so used. 3. Also refers to a storage device which uses electric charges to represent data.

element, cryogenic—A term which relates to various high speed circuits designed to use the superconductivity characteristics of materials which occur at or near absolute zero temperatures of those materials.

elimination factor—The ratio, in information retrieval, obtained by dividing

46

the number of documents that have not been retrieved by the total number of documents contained in the file.

EL-punch—Refers to a special character which is punched to indicate the end of a line or the end of a paper tape record.

else rule—Refers specifically to a catch-all rule in decision tables designed to handle the conditions not covered by other more exact and explicit rules; it is written by leaving all conditions blank. Action then to be taken may be to halt processing, note the condition, or to correct the situation and continue processing.

emulator—Concerns a specific hardware unit built into a computer which causes the system to accept certain software programs and routines and appear as if it were another system, such as 7094 software running on an IBM 360 computer without translation.

enable—A procedure designed for restoration of a suppressed interrupt feature.

encoded question—Refers to a specific question set up and encoded in a form appropriate for operating, programming or conditioning a searching device.

END—A basic statement designed to indicate the actual or physical end of the source program. This statement is used in both FORTRAN and Assembler language.

end-around shift—A specific shift designed so that the digits dropped off at one end of a word are returned to the other end in a circular fashion. For instance, if the register holds eight digits, 23456789, the result of a cycle shift two columns to the left would be to change the contents of the register to 45678923. (Synonymous with circular shift, logical shift, nonarithmetic shift, and ring shift.)

end mark—1. A specific code or signal designed to indicate the termination of a unit of information. 2. Also an indicator to signal the end of a word or the end of a unit of data.

end-of-file code—This code is a conventional type designed to terminate a set of blocks as indicated by an end-of-file code preceded by 3.75 inches of blank tape. The presence of this code may be tested by appropriate branch instructions. Usually a tape is read in terms of words when a word is a constant number of characters for a fixed-word-length machine.

end-of-job (EOJ) control card—A specific card which returns control to the monitor and abbreviated (EOJ). The monitor automatically processes any jobs remaining in the card reader. Once processing is initiated, intermixed compilations, assemblies, and executions are processed as they are stacked in the card reader. Additionally, a memory dump may be obtained by placing the memory dump program in the job stack. A special termination card terminates the run and places the monitor in an idle state when no more jobs are in the reader.

end-of-message (EOM)—The specific set of characters that indicates the termination of a message.

end-of-record word—The last word of a record on tape. It has a unique bit configuration and may be used to define the end of a record in memory.

end-of-tape marker—Relating to magnetic tapes, several codes, colors, or other miscellaneous markers which are designed to indicate the end of permissable recording areas.

end printing—Concerns the conversion or translation of punched information into bold printing across the end of the card. This is completed simultaneously with gang punching, summary punching, reproducing, or mark-sensed punching. This is similar to interpreting and makes possible a quick reference to the card.

English, ruly—Refers to a unique form of English designed so that every word has one and only one conceptual meaning and each concept has one and only one word to describe it. This is a hypothetical language based on English that complies uniformly to a definite set of rules, without exceptions.

entropy—1. Concerns a measurement of unavailable energy in a system. 2. Also refers to the unavailable information in a set of documents. 3. An inactive or static condition (total entropy).

entry point—1. As relates to programming, most subroutines have particular points or places designed so that control can be transferred and re-entered. The entry point usually corresponds to a new or different function to be performed. 2. Usually the first instruction to be executed in a subroutine or as part of the entry conditions for specific computers or installations. Various subroutines may have a number of different entry points corresponding to different programs, subroutines, or their functions. When an instruction of a subroutine designates a place or point for re-entering, it becomes the re-entry point of the major program.

EOF (end-of-file)—Termination or point of completion of a quantity of data. End-of-file marks are used to indicate this point.

equal-zero indicator—A name for an internal computer-indicator component designed to signal "on" if the result of an arithmetic computation is zero.

equipment, data terminal—Refers to various devices, modems, or units at either end of a data communication channel, line, station, or link.

equipment, off-line—Refers to specific peripheral equipment, modems, or devices which are not in direct communication with the central processing unit of the computer. (Synonymous with auxiliary equipment.)

equipment, on-line—Refers to systems of the peripheral equipment or specific devices in a system in which the operation of such equipment is under control of the central processing unit. Its information reflecting current activity is introduced into the data-processing system as soon as it occurs. Thus, directly in-line with the main flow of transaction processing. (Synonymous with in-line processing, and on-line processing.)

equivalence—A logical operator having the property that if P is a statement, Q is a statement, R is a statement, then the equivalent of P, Q, R, is true if and only if all statements are true or all statements are false, they are otherwise false.

erasable storage—1. Relates to various storage media that can be erased and reused repeatedly, e.g., magnetic-drum storage. 2. Also refers to storage devices whose data can be altered during the course of a computation, e.g., magnetic tapes, drums and cores. 3. An area of storage used for temporary storage.

erase head—A part of a device or unit on a magnetic tape drive whose sole function is to erase previous information prior to writing new information.

error, absolute—Refers to the magnitude of the error but disregarding the algebraic sign, or if a vectorial error, disregarding its direction.

error checking and recovery (parity)—
Parity is computed or checked on all
references to central storage. If a parity
error occurs, the computer will interrupt
to the proper location, an alarm will
sound, and the appropriate fault lights
will be flashed on the operator's
console. For all real-time applications,
the system will attempt to recover. Once
the computer has satisfactorily re-
covered, the system will continue
normal operation.

error-detecting and feedback system—A
system employing an error-detecting
code and so arranged that a signal
detected as being in error automatically
initiates a request for retransmission of
the correct signal.

error diagnostics—Usually refers to a
routine designed so that an erroneous
statement is printed with the erroneous
part of the statement clearly marked.
The entire statement is processed, even
when an error has been detected, whenever possible. Some compilers will
continue to the end of the program.
Thus, complete error diagnostics may be
obtained in one compilation. The errors
are listed on the same device as the
source-language listing.

error, inherent—That specific error in the
initial values, especially the error
inherited or carried over from the
previous steps in the step by step
integration. This error could also be the
error introduced by the inability to
make exact measurements of physical
quantities.

error, machine—Occurs when a deviation
from correctness occurs in data results
from an equipment failure.

error messages—Refers to specific
messages developed and designed by a
program to designate a variety of error
types.

error, parity—A programmed routine used
to indicate if, during the course of the
previous block transfer, a data parity
error was detected or one or more bits
have been picked up or dropped out
from either the timing track or the mark
track.

error, propagated—A specific type of
error which occurs in a previous operation that spreads through and in-
fluences later operations and results.

errors, transmission—Pertains to specific
errors which are safeguarded by a dual
pulse code that effectively transmits the
signals and their complements for a
double check on accuracy of message.

errors, syntactic—Syntactic errors are
considered the responsibility of the
system and are further categorized as
follows:

Composition—Typographical errors,
violations of specific form, of statements and misuse of various names (e.g.,
incorrect punctuation, mixed-mode
expressions, undeclared arrays, etc.).

Consistency—Statements that are
correctly composed but conflict with
other statements (e.g., conflicting
declaratives, illegal statement ending a
DO range, failure to follow each transfer
statement with a numbered statement,
etc.).

Completeness—Programs that are
incomplete (e.g., transfers to non-
existent statement numbers, improper
DO nesting, illegal transfer into the
range of a DO loop, etc.).

error, truncation—1. A specific error
which results from the use of only a
finite number of terms of an infinite
series. 2. The approximation of operations in the infinite-serial calculus by a
calculus of finite differences.

ESI communications—ESI (externally specified index) allows a number of communications networks to operate concurrently on a pair of I/O channels.

evolutionary operations (EVOP)—Relates to a specific statistical technique designed for improving plant operations by slight perturbation of operating conditions repeatedly over a long period of time.

exclusive OR, logical—A specific logical operator or gate designed to produce a "true" result when two logical variables are neither both true nor both false. If "true" is signified by 1, "false" by 0, and logical exclusive OR by (u), then $1(u)0 = 1$ and $0(u)1 = 1$, but $1(u)1 = 0$ and $0(u)0 = 0$.

execution time—1. The sum total of the amount of time required to complete a given command. 2. The portion of an instruction cycle during which the actual work is performed or operation executed; i.e., the time required to decode and perform an instruction (synonymous with instruction time).

executive control logic, multiprogramming—Refers to a specific system in a multiprogram processor. To initiate or preserve a true multiprogramming environment, the executive system must be in complete control of the total system. Therefore, it is necessary that the system contain sufficient control circuitry to effectively and economically maintain this control.

Specific multiprogramming capabilities of the system are based upon guard mode operation, i.e., the setting aside of certain instructions, registers, and storage locations for the exclusive use of the executive system, assuring maximum protection against the interaction of unrelated programs.

executive guard mode—Guard mode prevents programs from executing any of a set of instructions reserved for the executive. It also protects certain locations reserved for executive operations.

executive, real-time—A specific executive system which is designed to interface with programs which have real-time requirements. The standard communication subsystem, together with efficient scheduling and interrupt processing features of the executive system, provides an environment satisfactory for most real-time programs.

executive, resident—Refers to a specific part or section of the supervisory program that is always located in core. The resident executive is a permanent resident of core.

executive routine—1. The coordinating, directing, or modifying routine that controls the operations of other routines or programs. 2. A routine that controls loading and relocation of routines and in some cases makes use of instructions which are unknown to the general programmer. Effectively, an executive routine is part of the machine itself (synonymous with monitor routine, supervisory routine, and supervisory program).

executive supervisor—1. The supervisor is the executive-system component that controls the sequencing, setup, and execution of all runs entering the computer. It is designed to control the execution of an unlimited number of programs in a multiprogramming environment, while allowing each program to be unaffected by the coexistence of other programs. 2. The supervisor contains three levels of scheduling—coarse scheduling, dynamic allocation, and CPU dispatching. Runs entering are sorted into information files and these files are used by the supervisor for run scheduling and processing. Control statements for each run are retrieved and scanned by the control command interpreter to facilitate the selection of runs for setup by the course scheduler.

exception-principle system—Relates to an information system or data-processing system designed to report on situations only when actual results differ from planned results. When results occur within a normal range they are not reported.

exit—1. The time or place at which the control sequence ends or transfers out of a particular program or subroutine. 2. A way of momentarily interrupting or leaving a repeated cycle of operations in a program.

exit macroinstruction—1. Usually refers to a supervisory program macroinstruction designed to be the final instruction in an application program, signifying that processing is complete. The supervisory program takes the needed action such as releasing working storage blocks to return control to other processing. 2. Also concerns the final macroinstruction in an application program that releases memory sections—including the message reference block— and resets associative conditions of the transaction if needed.

exit point—The instruction which transfers control from the main routine to the subroutine.

exjunction gate—Same as gate, exclusive OR.

exponent—That particular number placed at the right and above a symbol in typography to indicate the number of times that symbol is a factor; e.g., 10 to the 4th (10^4) equals 10 X 10 X 10 X 10, or 10,000.

exponential smoothing—This is a statistical technique for predicting future demands based on current and past demands activity without storing and saving masses of past history data.

expression, arithmetic—Pertains to various expressions which contain several types or combinations of data-names, numeric literals, and named constants, joined by one or more arithmetic operators in such a way that the expression as a whole can be reduced to a single numeric value.

extended precision—Refers to a real number which often requires three words of core storage. The maximum precision of the mantissa is 2,147,483,647.

extension register—In many systems this is a 16-bit register treated as an extension of the accumulator register. This register is used to hold the remainder after a division operation and couple to the accumulator to hold the product in a fixed point multiply operation.

external-device interrupts—Refers to various external-device interrupts which may occur for any of several reasons. An external device may interrupt when it has completed an operation if it was told to do so by the program when the operation was initiated. An external device may also interrupt at a different address to indicate that a failure (parity fail, end of tape, etc.) has occurred. Different devices have different failure conditions and different failure interrupt addresses. An external device may be notifying the program that some specific real-time event has occurred.

external device status—Under certain circumstances external devices respond with both their busy status and their interrupt-request status whenever they recognize their own address. They do not clear out an interrupt request until the interrupt succeeds. The processor notifies an external device that its interrupt has been recognized by sending out an interrupt reset signal.

external interrupt status word—Concerns a specific status word accompanied by an external interrupt signal. This signal is designed to inform the computer that the word on the data lines is a status word. The computer, interpreting this signal, automatically loads this word in a reserved address in core memory. If the programmer or operator desires a visual indication of the status word, it must be programmed.

external reference—A distinct reference to a single variable from a range, or an item which is not defined in the particular program, segment or subroutine. A linkage editor or a linking loader usually integrates various independently written routines which are united before execution. The assembler must be informed that an external symbol is being used to avoid an error condition.

extract—1. A procedure designed to copy from a set of items all those items which meet a specified criterion. 2. A process designed to remove a specific given set of digits or characters occupying certain specified locations in a computer word, such as extract the 8, 9, and 10 binary digits of a 44-bit word, as specified by the filter. (Clarified by filter.) 3. A procedure designed to derive a new computer word from part of another word, usually by masking. (Related to unpack.)

* — * — *

facsimile—1. Refers to the exact reproduction of a document which is normally obtained through the use of photocopy equipment. 2. Relates to several types of commercial methods for transmitting images by electrical means developed by American Telephone and Telegraph, Xerox and others. The images may be in the form of letters, pictures, diagrams, and maps.

factor, scaling—Relates to a numerical coefficient which is designed to be used in scaling to multiply one or more quantities occurring in a calculation.

fail safe system—Some real-time computing systems enable process variables to be locked into present values and saves some vital information before termination of operation in case of catastrophic failure, such as power failure.

fail soft, time sharing—Refers to a concept designed for remote computer systems which is being implemented in the principle of "graceful degradation" or "fail-soft". The design concerns a system which can reorganize itself to isolate and cut off the offending equipment while continuing to operate. The capacity and efficiency of the system decreases but service to users is continued in the best manner with the remaining equipment. An example is the Control Data Corp. STAR computer.

fallback—1. The use of the backup module in a redundant system during degraded operation. 2. A condition in processing when special computer or manual functions must be employed as either complete or partial substitutes for malfunctioning systems. Such procedures could be used anywhere between complete system availability and total system failure.

fault—A physical condition that causes a device, a component, or element to fail to perform in a required manner, e.g., a short circuit, a broken wire, an intermittent connection.

fault, sporadic—Usually refers to faults which are failures in performance in the manner required over specified conditions. Sporadic faults are basically intermittent faults.

fax—Abbreviation for facsimile transmission of pictures, maps, diagrams, etc. by radio waves. The image is scanned at the transmitter and reconstructed at the receiving station. (Synonymous with facsimile.)

F-conversion—Specifically concerns one of the three types of FORMAT specifications in FORTRAN. F-conversion is used to convert floating-point data for I/O operations.

feasibility study—1. Usually the initial procedures and criteria for determination of suitability, capability, and compatability of computer systems to various firms or organizations. A preliminary systems analysis of potential costs savings and new higher level of operations and decision-making; problem-solving capacity as a result of computer procurement. 2. A study in which a projection of how a proposed system might operate in a particular organization made to provide the basis for a decision to change the existing system.

feedback—1. The use of parts or all of the output of a machine, process, or system, as input for another phase, as when used for self-correcting purpose. Such feedback systems or programs use the process of continual comparisons of output with input to make necessary corrections. The feedback system is considered self-correcting if it is a closed loop. 2. The feeding back of part of the output of a machine, process, or system to the computer as input for another phase especially for the self-correcting or control purposes.

feedback control—Refers to a specific type of system control designed to be developed when a portion of the output signal is fed back to the input in order to obtain a desired effect.

feedback, degenerative—A technique designed to be used to return part of the output of a machine, system or process and to input it in a way that causes a larger quantity to be deducted from the input with an increase of output results.

feedback impedance—Concerns various operational amplifiers. These consist of input terminals, high gain units, output terminals, and networks for feedback and input impedances. These substantially define the relationships of the input signals to the output signals.

feedback, positive—A technique designed to be used to return part of the output of a machine, system, or process to the input in a way that causes a larger quantity to be added to the input with an increase of output results.

feedforward control action—That control action designed so that information concerning one or more conditions that can disturb the controlled variable is converted into corrective action. This minimizes the deviations of the controlled variable, i.e., feedforward control can be combined with other types of control to anticipate and minimize deviations of the controlled variable.

feed holes—Refers to a specific set or series of small holes in perforated paper or plastic tape designed to convey no intelligence but which are solely for the purpose of engaging the feed pawls or sprockets which transport the tape over the sensing pins of various reading devices.

ferrite core—Concerns various types of magnetic materials, but usually toroidal in shape, which are pulsed or polarized by electric currents carried in a wire or wires wound around it. These devices are capable of assuming and remaining at one of two conditions of magnetization, thus providing storage, gating, or switching functions.

ferro magnetic—Similar to ferro electric; this relates to substances which have properties which retain polarity, i.e., a change in the field of polarity causing an electric force of current.

ferrous oxide spots—Concerns a specific medium by which information is represented on magnetic tape. Specific ferrous oxide spots represent information in binary form which is interpreted by the magnetic tape drive and then stored in computer memory for processing.

fetch—1. A specific action or portion of a computer cycle during which the location of the next instruction is determined, the instruction is taken from memory and modified, if necessary, then entered into the control register. 2. A procedure designed to obtain a quantity of data from a place of storage.

F-format—Concerns a specific fixed-length logical record format. Sizes of logical records for data management are related to the contents. A data set has F-format logical records if nearly all of the logical records are of identical length. In FORTRAN, the F-format is an input-output specification detail. In PL/1 an F-format is also an I/O format specification similar to FORTRAN.

Fibonacci search—A searching technique based on dichotomy. It is developed in such a way that, in each step, the original set or the remaining subset is subdivided in accordance with successive smaller numbers in the specific Fibonacci series. When the number of items in such a set is not equal to a Fibonacci number, the number of items in the set is assumed to equal the next higher Fibonacci number.

field—1. A set of one or more characters (not necessarily all lying on the same word) which is treated as a whole; a set of one or more columns on a punched card consistently used to record similar information. 2. A specified area of a record used for a particular category of data; e.g., a group of card columns used to represent a wage rate, or a set of bit locations in a computer word used to express the address of the operand. 3. The data which is contained in two or more adjacent core positions and which will be treated as a unit. A flag bit is used to designate the high-order position of the field.

file—1. A collection of related records treated as a unit; e.g., in inventory control, one line of an invoice forms an item, a complete invoice forms a record, and the complete set of such records forms a file. 2. The word file is used in the general sense to mean any collection of informational items similar to one another in purpose, form, and content. Thus, a magnetic-tape master file is a file. The term may also be applied to a punched-paper tape of input items, or if convenient, to a set of cards which is equivalent in nature to a magnetic or a paper tape. File may even be applied to an accumulation of information in the processor memory if the need arises to refer in a general way to this collection of data.

file addressing—A procedure designed for those data records which have a particular key or code designed to identify the data. When the program is given this key it can locate and use the data at the particular file address.

file, chained—A procedure designed to conserve searching time and space, some computer files are in chains. Each data item or key in a record in the chain has the address of another record with the same data or key. To retrieve all data which contain the given key, only the first address need be found, since the next address is adjacent to it, and that one is adjacent to the next, etc.

file, dead—A file which is not in current use but which is retained.

file, inverted—A specific file containing item labels designed to be placed in a single record and identified by a label describing the contents of the documents.

file protection—1. A device or method that prevents accidental erasure of operative data on magnetic tape reels. 2. A hardware or software device to protect sections of memory in core or bulk by permitting read only (disable writing).

film, magnetic (thin)—Refers to a process which has a layer of magnetic material frequently used for logic or storage elements. Magnetic thin films are commonly less than a micron in thickness.

film optical-sensing device—A type of peripheral equipment designed to be capable of reading the contents of a film by optical methods; i.e., a system consisting of a light source, sensors, photocells and a film-moving mechanism. The output of the device is digitized and transferred directly to an electronic computer. An example of such a device is the FOSDIC system developed jointly by the Bureau of Census and the National Bureau of Standards.

Filmorex system—A system, devised by Jacques Samain, for the electronic selection of microfilm cards. Each card has a microreproduction of the document or abstract and a field of twenty 5-digit code numbers giving the bibliographic reference and the subjects treated.

film reader—A peripheral unit that is designed to scan patterns of opaque and transparent areas on photographic film and enters the corresponding information into a computer.

film recorder—A type of peripheral equipment which has a mechanism that receives information from a computer and records it in the form of opaque and transparent areas on photographic film.

filter—1. A pattern of characters that is used to control the selection or elimination of portions of another pattern of characters. 2. A device or program that separates data, signal, or material in accordance with special criteria. 3. A machine word that specifies which parts of another machine word are to be operated on. Also called extractor or mask.

firmware—Software that is stored in a fixed (wired-in) or "firm" way, usually in a read-only memory. Changes can often only be made by exchanging the memory for an alternative unit.

first generation computer—Refers to the technological era of development of the computer when the vacuum tube was the main electronic element. First generation equipment was predominantly manufactured in the years 1953-1960 and included the Univac 1, IBM 704, RCA Bizmac, and the Honeywell D-1000. The second generation of computer equipment began in about 1959 and was characterized by the utilization of transistors instead of vacuum tubes. The third generation of computer equipment began in about 1964 and featured microcircuits or miniaturization of components. There is not yet a clear consensus as to the definition of a fourth generation of equipment.

fixed area (FX)—Refers to the specific area on a disk on which data files or core image programs may be stored and protected.

fixed head—A name which relates to the use of stationary, rigidly mounted reading and writing heads on a bulk memory device.

fixed-length word—A fundamental computer word designed to always have a fixed number of characters, i.e., one with 16 alphanumeric characters or 32 binary digits without any variation whatever. Registers, storage locations, gating, etc. are designed to handle a fixed number of digits.

fixed point—1. A notation or system of arithmetic in which all numerical quantities are expressed by a predetermined number of digits, with the point implicitly located at some predetermined position (contrasted with floating point). 2. A type of calculation with integers only and without any decimal point or decimal portions.

fixed storage—Usually relates to storage devices that store data that are not alterable by computer instructions, e.g., magnetic core storage with a lockout feature, and punched paper tape. (Synonymous with permanent storage and nonerasable storage.)

flag—1. A bit of information attached to a character or word to indicate the boundary of a field. 2. An indicator used frequently to tell some later part of a program that some condition occurred earlier. 3. An indicator used to identify the members of several intermixed sets (synonymous with sentinel). 4. Any of various types of indicators used for identification, e.g., a wordmark. 5. A character that signals the occurrence of some condition, such as the end of a word. 6. A request for special handling, such as indirect addressing.

Flexowriter—A proprietary data processing entry unit or data entry processing system marketed by Friden, Inc., a subsidiary of Singer Co. It's unique feature is the punching and reading of paper tape, and limited programming options.

flip-flop—An electronic circuit having two stable states, two input lines, and two corresponding output lines such that a signal exists on either one of the output lines if, and only if, the last pulse received by the flip-flop can store one binary digit (bit) of information.

floating controller—Concerns a special controller designed so that the rate of change of the output develops a continuous function of the actuating error signal, i.e., the output of the controller can remain at any value in its operating range when the actuating error signal is zero and constant and is then said to "float".

floating point—A form of number representation in which quantities are represented by a number multiplied by the number base raised to a power; e.g., the decimal number 397 can be written as 3.97×10^2, or 0.397×10^3.

floating-point arithmetic (operation)—In order to add two floating-point numbers, it is first necessary to equalize the exponents of the numbers. This is accomplished by shifting the mantissa of the smaller expression to the right the number of places that equals the difference of the two exponents. For example, in adding the floating-point decimal numbers 0.3×10^4 and 0.27×10^6, 0.3×10^4 is written as 0.003×10^6 and then the two numbers are added which gives the results of 0.273×10^6.

$$.3 \times 10^4 \qquad\quad .003 \times 10^6$$
$$\underline{+.27 \times 10^6} \quad = \quad \underline{+.27 \times 10^6}$$
$$\qquad\qquad\qquad\qquad .273 \times 10^6$$

The same procedure is required for subtraction except that the subtrahend is subtracted from the minuend in the final step of the operation.

flowchart—1. A system-analysis tool that provides a graphical presentation of a procedure. Includes block diagrams, routine sequence diagrams, general flow symbols, and so forth. 2. A chart to represent, for a problem, the flow of data, procedures, growth, equipment, methods, documents, machine instructions, etc. 3. A graphical representation of a sequence of operations by using symbols to represent the operations such as compute, substitute, compare, jump, copy, read, write, etc.

flow tracing—A type of diagnostics and debugging in which the programmer specifies the start and end of those program segments where he wishes to examine the contents of various registers and accumulators. The program will run at machine speed until it encounters the desired segments, and the printing commences and is terminated when the end of the program segment is encountered. It is also possible to then include "snapshot" traces which indicate the contents not only of the various accumulators and registers but also of specified memory locations.

flutter and wow—Terms used to describe changes in signal output frequency caused by tape speed variations occurring at relatively low and relatively high rates, respectively.

flying spot—Refers to a small, rapidly moving spot of light usually generated by a cathode-ray tube and designed to illuminate successive spots of a surface containing dark and light areas. The varying amount of light reflected is detected by a phototube and used to produce a time succession of electronic signals which effectively describe the surface.

font—A complete typography family or assortment of type characters of a given size and style.

forbidden combination—Refers to a specific code character set or group of individual symbols which appears to be the proper element but really are not true members of the defined alphabet or specific language. If forbidden patterns, characters, of symbols present themselves, they are judged to be mistakes or the results of malfunctions.

foreground—A high priority program, process, or system part utilized immediately or as needed but still allowing less critical or subsidiary programs to be processed as background tasks during the time when the priority programs are not being processed in the foreground. This is the basis of multiprogramming or foreground/background processing. Usually the foreground is a smaller, faster processing program which activates interrupts or suspensions of routines in the background processing to perform its tasks and then release the CPU back to the background processing. It is practical on smaller and medium computers for inquiry processing and also when using slow peripheral equipment.

foreground processing—Top-priority processing most often resulting from real-time entries which usually have precedence, through the use of interrupts, into lower priority or background processing.

format—1. A predetermined arrangement of characters, fields, lines, punctuation, page numbers, etc. 2. A defined arrangement of words, totals, characters, stubs, and headings for a desired clear presentation of data or print-out, such as a profit and loss statement in a record.

format, F—A data set has F-format logical records if nearly all of the logical records are of identical length. In FORTRAN, the F-format is an input--output specification detail. In PL/1 an F-format is also an I/O format specification similar to FORTRAN.

FORTRAN—1. A programming system, including a language and a processor (compiler), allowing programs to be written in a mathematical-type language. These programs are subsequently translated by a computer (under control of the processor) into machine language. 2. FORmula TRANslator. A compiler language developed by the IBM Corporation, originally conceived for use on scientific problems but now widely adapted for most commercial problems as well.

FORTRAN ASA—A standardized FORTRAN set as specified by American Standards Association (formerly USASI).

FORTRAN language—Programs are written directly as algebraic expressions and arithmetic statements. Various symbols are used to signify equality, addition, subtraction, exponentiation, etc. Additional statements are provided to permit control over how the algebraic expres-

sions and arithmetic statements are to be processed. These include transfer, decision, indexing, and input/output statements.

FORTRAN, real constants—A real constant is written with a decimal point, using the decimal digits 0, 1, . . . 9. A preceding + or − sign is optional. An unsigned real constant is assumed to be positive. An integer exponent preceded by an E may follow a real constant. The exponent may have a preceding + or − sign. An unsigned exponent is assumed to be positive.

FORTRAN, real variables—A real variable consists of a series of not more than six alphanumeric characters (except special characters) of which the first is alphabetic but cannot be one of the integer indicators, i.e., I, J, K, L, M, or N.

forward scan—An editing operation which makes an output word conform to the control word by comparing positions from right to left and adding punctuation, such as decimals and dollar signs.

FOSDIC—An acronym for: Film Optical Sensing Device for Input to Computers. Refers to a unit of peripheral equipment capable of reading the contents of a film by optical methods; i.e., a system consisting of a light source, lenses, photocells and a film-moving mechanism. The output of the device is digitized and transferred directly to an electronic computer. An example of such a device is the FOSDIC system developed jointly by the Bureau of Census and the National Bureau of Standards.

frame—Refers to a set or group of bits aligned across a magnetic tape, one per channel, usually making up either one character or two numerals. As referred to paper tape, a frame can be a group of five, six, seven, or eight punches across the tape.

frame, main—The main part of the computer, i.e., the arithmetic or logic unit. The central processing unit (CPU).

frequency modulation—1. A procedure for varying the frequency of a carrier of fixed amplitude above and below the normal carrier frequency in accordance with the amplitude variations of an applied signal voltage. 2. Specifically the rate in hertz or bits per second for a sine wave carrier to be modulated by an intelligence-bearing signal.

frequency spectrum—Refers to the range of frequencies of electromagnetic radiation waves which are divided into LF (low frequency), MF (medium frequency), HF (high frequency), VHF, UHF, VLF, etc. (V = very).

full adder—Relates to a specific half adder circuit arrangement which has an additional input of a carry bit or a no bit from a previous position.

full-duplex operation—Full-duplex or duplex operation refers to simultaneous communication between two points in both directions.

function—1. A special purpose or characteristic action. 2. The relation or association of one item from a set with each item from another set. 3. A means of referring to a type or sequence of calculations within an arithmetic statement.

functional address instruction—Concerns a specific instruction designed to have no particular operation part since the operation is specified by the address parts, i.e., some two addresses which are specified might designate storage locations having contents which are always added.

functional interleaving—The procedure or process designed to have I/O and computing operations proceed independently of one another but interleaved in their sharing of the memory.

functional multiplier—A specific peripheral unit which will take in the changing values of two functions and put out the changing value of their product.

function generator—A computing element designed with an output of a specified nonlinear function of its input or inputs. Normal usage excludes Multipliers and Resolvers.

function generator, analog—A network of biased diodes designed to produce a nonlinear relationship between the input and output voltages of the network. Nonlinear functions can also be generated by means of potentiometers with specially built resistance elements. Other classes of function generators use electromechanical devices which consist of motor-driven pointers that follow arbitrary curves prepared in the form of graphs. A servo motor causes the pointer to move back and forth across the curve in accordance with the value of the independent variable (the "X" coordinate).

* – * – *

gain—The measurement of the ratio between the output signal and the input signal of a device.

game theory models—A popular concept of the theory of games is that it is a branch of mathematics that aims to analyze various problems of conflict by abstracting common strategic features for study in theoretical "models,"—termed "games" because they are patterned on actual games such as bridge and poker. By stressing strategic aspects, that is, aspects controlled by the participants, it goes beyond the classical theory of probability, in which the treatment of games is limited to aspects of pure chance. Zero-sum, two-person games can be solved by linear programming methods.

gang punch—1. A process for duplicating cards and card data, or punching cards in any format. Also called reproduce. 2. To punch all or part of the information from one punched card into succeeding cards.

gap, file—Refers to a specific interval of space or time which is associated with a file and is designed to indicate or signal the end of the file.

gap, record—A specific interval of space or time which is associated with a record and is designed to indicate or signal the end of the record.

garbage—A slang expression suggesting unwanted and meaningless information carried along in storage.

gate—A combination logic element having at least one input channel.

gate, amplitude—A specific transducer which is designed to transmit only portions of an input wave lying between two amplitude boundaries. Note: The term is used especially when the two amplitude boundaries are close to each other as compared with the amplitude range of the input.

gate, coincidence—A specific circuit designed with the capability to produce an output which is dependent upon a specified type of or has the coincident nature of, the input; e.g., an AND gate has an output pulse when there are pulses in time coincidence at all inputs; an OR gate has an output when any one or any combination of input pulses occur in time coincidence. Any gate may contain a number of inhibits in which there is no output under any condition of input, if

there is time coincidence of an inhibit or except signal.

gate, exclusive NOR—A two input (binary) logic circuit designed to perform the logic operation of exclusive-NOR, i.e., if A is and B are input statements, the results is true or 1 when both A and B are true or when both A and B are false. The result is false when A and B are different.

gate, exclusive OR—A binary logic coincidence circuit for completing the logic operation of exclusive OR, i.e., the result is true when A is true and B is false, or when A is false and B is true, and the result is false when A and B are both true or when A and B are both false.

gate generator—1. Refers to a circuit or device that is designed to produce one or more gate pulses. 2. A circuit which produces signals which represent strings of ones in a particular system, i.e., the opposite of gate, null.

gate, NAND—That specific logical operator designed to have the property that if P, Q, and R are all statements, then the NAND of P.Q.R. is true if at least one statement is false and false if all statements are true.

gate, NOR—That specific gate whose output is energized when, and only when, all inputs are absent.

gate, NOT—A logic element or operator designed to have only one binary input signal; the variable represented by the output signal is the negation of the variable represented by the input signal, i.e., an element whose output signal is 1 when its input signal is 0 and vice versa.

gate, NOT-AND—Same as gate, NAND.

gate, OR—A fundamental electrical gate or mechanical unit or device designed to implement the logical OR operator. An output signal occurs whenever there are one or more inputs on a multichannel input. An OR gate performs the function of the logical "inclusive OR operator." (Synonymous with OR circuit.)

gate pulse—A specific pulse with extended duration signals designed to increase the possibility of coincidence with other pulses. Gate pulses present with other pulses cause circuits or devices to perform intended operations.

gate, Sheffer stroke—Same as gate, NAND.

gate, synchronous—A synchronous gate is usually a time gate designed so that the output intervals are synchronized with an incoming signal.

gate, time—Refers to a specific time gate which is a transducer that gives output only during chosen time intervals.

gather-write/scatter-read—Gather-write is the designed capability to place the information from several nonadjacent locations in core storage (for example, several logical records) into a single physical record such as a tape block. Scatter-read is the designed capability to place the information from a physical record into several nonadjacent locations in core storage.

gating—1. Gating is referred to as the process or procedure for selecting those portions of a wave which exist during one or more selected time intervals, or which have magnitudes between selected limits. 2. Transfer of the contents of one register to another.

General Purpose Simulation System (GPSS)—An IBM discrete system simulation language.

generator—1. A basic routine specifically designed to create particular routines from distinct input parameters or conditions and skeletal coding. 2. Concerning

programming it is a program that constructs another program from specifically designed sets of instructions by selecting, adjusting, and arranging them in accordance with given specifications.

generator, analytical function—Refers to either an analog device or a specific program based on some physical law, such as one used with a digital computer to solve a particular differential equation.

generator, clock-pulse—A specifically designed unit which generates pulses for purposes of special timing or gating in a digital computer, i.e., pulses which are used as inputs to gates to aid in pulse-shaping and timing.

generator, empiric function—A computer program or device designed with the capability of generating a mathematical function, curve, or set of values from given values, such as test data or laboratory measurements.

generator, report-program—Report program generators are designed to make report preparation easy by eliminating the tedious coding often associated with report writing. Instead of coding, a programmer fills out the report description form. Some generators use the same input data description as the macro-assembly routine or program, so the file doesn't have to be described again. One can also insert his own coding to tailor the object program to the unique requirements.

generator, sort and merge—Refers to a specific generator designed to use the features of various systems to produce fast efficient object programs with minimum effort. The generators have options for insertion of programmer coding for manipulation of records or files prior to and following the sort.

geodetic system—A computer application

system used to reduce the costs of mining and drilling by performing seismographic studies by a computer. Geodesy is the branch of applied mathematics which determines the curvature, shape and dimensions of the earth. Computers are used for advanced geodetic survey work by mining companies to locate oil and ore deposits.

gigacycle—A measurement which is equal to a kilomegacycle per second (10^9 cycles per second). (Synonynous with kilomegacycle.)

GIGO (garbage in — garbage out)—Unwanted and meaningless information carried along in storage; a result of undesirable input data or information.

GPC—General Purpose Computer.

graphic, data processing—A letter symbol or line which is charted, drawn, or diagrammed (or an omission of such) which can be reproduced or transmitted in some way through an electronic data system, usually by an ordered set of pulses.

graphics—The use of diagrams or other graphical means to obtain operating data and answers. The use of written symbols and visual displays.

graphic solution—Refers to specific solutions which are developed and obtained with graphs or other pictorial devices, as contrasted with solutions obtained by the manipulation of numbers.

grid—An optical character recognition (OCR) device which uses two mutually orthogonal sets of parallel lines designed for specifying or measuring character images.

gross index—Usually designed to be the first of a pair of indexes consulted to locate particular records, etc.; the secondary or supplemental index is the fine index.

guard bit—1. A special bit contained in each word or specific groups of words of memory designed to indicate to computer hardware units or software programs whether or not the content of that memory location may or may not be altered by a program. 2. A bit designed to indicate whether a core or disk memory word or group of words is to be filed — protected.

gulp—A slang-type expression which refers to a small group of bytes, similar to a word or instruction.

gun, holding—A special electron gun designed to produce the holding beam in an electrostatic storage cathode-ray tube.

* _ * _ *

half-adder—A specific circuit designed with two output points, S and C, representing sum and carry, and two input points, A and B, representing addend and augend such that the output is related to the input according to the following table:

INPUT		OUTPUT	
A	B	S	C
0	0	0	0
0	1	1	0
1	0	1	0
1	1	0	1

A and B are arbitrary input pulses, and S and C are sum without carry, and carry, respectively. Two half-adders, properly connected, may be used for performing binary addition and form a full serial adder.

half-adjust—A design or system of rounding in which the value of the least significant digit of a number determines whether or not a one shall be added to the next higher significant digit, or, in which the two least significant digits determine whether or not a one is to be added to the next higher significant digit. If the least significant digits represent less than one-half, nothing is added to the higher significant digit. If the least significant digits represent one-half or more, then a one is added to the next higher significant digit. 2. A procedure for rounding by one-half of the maximum value of the number base of the counter.

half duplex—A communications system designed to permit electrical contacts in only one direction between stations. Technical arrangements may permit operation in either direction, but not simultaneously. This term is therefore qualified by one of the following suffixes: S/O for send only; R/O for receive only; S/R for send or receive.

half-subtracter—1. A specific logic element designed with two inputs, a minuend and a subtrahend, and two outputs, the difference digit and the borrow digit, and used in the digit position of the next higher signifiance. 2. A unit or device designed with the capability for representing the difference between two numbers, usually restricted to permitting the subtrahend to have only one non-zero digit.

half-word—1. A group of characters designed to represent half of a computer word for addressing purposes, as a unit in storage. 2. A fixed group of bits designed to be handled as a unit by the equipment and which is equivalent to two bytes.

half-word boundary—In the IBM 360 Computer Series and several other systems, any address ending in a 0 bit which is divisible by binary 2 denotes a natural boundary for an item of 2 bytes

length. Items of this type must be referenced by an address falling on a boundary of the corresponding type.

Hamming code—One of the error-correction code systems in use today, named after the inventor.

handshaking—In a synchronous transmission scheme, the slang-type term used to describe the process by which predetermined configurations of characters are exchanged by the receiving and transmitting equipment to establish synchronization.

hands-on background—Relates to the prior work experience of individuals developed by actually operating the hardware and often used as a criteria of programmer capability and knowledge.

hardware—1. The electric, electronic, and mechanical equipment used for processing data consisting of cabinets, racks, tubes, transistors, wires, motors, and such. 2. Any piece of automatic data processing equipment (slang).

hash—1. Considered to be computer or program garbage specifically recorded on tapes to fill or comply with restrictions on conventions of starting procedures, block sizes, and others. 2. Same as garbage.

hash total—1. The development of a summation for purposes of verification of one or more corresponding fields of a file that would usually not be totalled. 2. A control developed from a specific number in each record processed that has no significance other than as a control. 3. A sum of numbers in specified fields of a record or of a batch of records used for checking purposes. No attention is paid to the significance of the total. Examples of such numbers are customer numbers or part numbers.

header—Refers to a specific file record that contains common, constant, or identifying information indicating groups of records which are to follow. Also the first part of a message containing all necessary information for directing the message to its destination.

head, erase—A magnetic head designed to be used to erase or obliterate the old information prior to writing new information.

header card—A Hollerith card which is designed to identify types and characteristics of records maintained on the following cards.

heading—Refers to a string of characters, usually placed at the beginning of a message, designed to represent message routing and destination information, and which is machine readable.

head-per-track—Refers to equipment with separate read/write heads that are fixed over each track of information on a memory disk surface. The reliable read/write technique used in high speed magnetic drums has been combined with the low cost, large scale storage capacity of the disk. Electronic switching replaces slow and costly mechanical arm accessing.

head, recording—A head designed to be used to transfer data to a storage device such as a drum, disk, tape, or magnetic card.

hertz—A unit of frequency equal to one cycle per second.

hexadecimal number system—Refers to a type number system using the equivalent of the decimal number sixteen as a base.

hierarchy—A specified ranking or ordering of items, e.g., a series or group of items classifed by rank or order.

higher order language—Most often this term refers to a computer programming language that is less dependent on the limitations of a specific computer; for instance pseudo-languages; problem oriented languages; languages common to most computer systems, such as ALGOL, FORTRAN, and COBOL; and the assembly languages.

high-low limits—A designation of the maximum and minimum values of data expected. These values are used to check the program and results.

high order—Pertaining to the weight or significance assigned to the digits of a number; e.g., in the number 123456, the highest order digit is one; the lowest order digit is six. One may refer to the three high-order bits of a binary word as another example.

hit—1. A term used in mechanical retrieval systems to represent the search for and the location of an answer found by the machine. 2. In file maintenance, the location of a match between a detail record and a master record. 3. Also, the occurrence or match of transaction items with file items in the process of file maintenance.

hold—The function or procedure designed to retain information in one storage device after transferring it to another device, in contrast to clear.

holistic masks—A unique set of characters which reside within a character reader and which are designed to theoretically represent the exact replicas of all possible input characters in the machine's repertory. Only perfect specimens will be accepted.

Hollerith code—An alphanumeric punched card code invented by Dr. Herman Hollerith in 1889, in which the top three positions in a column are called "zone" punches (12, 11, and 0, or

Y, X and 0, from the top downward), and are combined with the remaining punches, or digit punches (1 through 9) to represent alphabetic, numeric, and special characters. For example, A is a combination of a Y (12) and a 1 punch; an L is a combination of an X (11) and a 3 punch, etc.

Hollerith strings—Hollerith strings can be used as arguments of functions and can be stored with floating-point or fixed-point variable names in an arithmetic assignment statement. In FORTRAN, a Hollerith string is specified in writing the character count followed by an H, and then the string of characters. A string must have eight characters, or less, when stored with a floating-point variable name; it must have four characters, or less, when stored with a fixed-point variable name. If used as an argument, the string can be any length. When strings are less than the maximum (eight for real, four for integer), they are stored left-justified and blanks are filled in for the missing characters. (Some computers)

horizontal parity check—A procedure designed for the comparison of the number of bits tallied and totalled along channels as related to a previously determined quantity.

host computer—A computer that is connected to a stored-program multiplexor and which is the base or independent computer upon which the multiplexor is dependent for certain vital functions as program read-in, etc. In an arrangement of this sort, the multiplexor could have stand-alone capacity in the event the host computer is not always available.

housekeeping operation—A general term for the operation that must be performed for a machine run usually before actual processing begins. Examples of housekeeping operations are: establishing controlling marks, setting up auxiliary storage units, reading in the first record for processing, initializing, set-up verification operations, and file identification.

HSM—Abbreviation for high-speed memory.

hunting—Refers to continuous attempts on the part of an automatically controlled system to seek or discover desired equilibrium conditions. The systems usually contain a standard method for determining deviation from this standard, and a method of influencing the system such that the difference between the standard and the state of the system is brought to zero. (Related to servomechanism.)

hypertape units—Refers to a brand of high speed tape units which use cartridges and house the supply and take-up reels to permit automatic loading.

hysteresis—1. Concerns the lagging in the response of a unit of a system behind an increase or a decrease in the strength of a signal. 2. Also relates to a phenomenon demonstrated by materials that make their behavior a function of the history of the environment to which they have been subjected.

* – * – *

IAL, International Algebraic Language—The computer language which preceded ALGOL.

ICC—Abbreviation for International Computation Center. Sponsored by UNESCO in Rome. Its purpose is to make computer services available to member nations.

I-conversion—Refers to a type of FOR-

MAT specification in FORTRAN used to convert fixed-point (integer) data for I/O operations.

identifier—1. A specific symbol designed to identify, indicate, or name a body of data. 2. A key.

IFCS—Abbreviation for International Federation of Computer Sciences.

IFIPS—Abbreviation for International Federation of Information Processing Societies. The predecessor of IFIP.

ignore—1. Refers to a typewriter character used to indicate that no action whatsoever is being taken; e.g., in teletype or flexowriter code, a character code consisting of holes punched in every hole position is an ignore character. This convention makes possible erasing any previously punched character. 2. An instruction requiring nonperformance of what normally might be executed; i.e., not to be executed. This instruction should not be confused with a NO OP or Do-Nothing instruction, since these generally refer to an instruction outside themselves.

image—An exact logical duplicate stored in a different medium.

immediate access—Pertaining to the ability to obtain data from or place data in a storage device or register directly, without serial delay due to other units of data, and usually in a relatively short period of time.

immediate address—The designation of an instruction address that is used as data by the instruction of which it is a part.

immediate address instruction—A particular type of instruction containing the value of the operand in its address part rather than the address of the operand. It is used most often for incrementing a count by a fixed amount, or masking a partial-word field of data, or for testing a special character for identical characteristics with the immediate character in the instruction.

inclusive OR—Refers to the Boolean operator used to give a truth table value of true if either or both of the two variables it connects are true. If neither is true, the value is false.

increment—The quantity by which another is modified. An increment is usually positive; however, a negative quantity when added, is also called an increment.

incremental computer—Refers to a particular special-purpose computer that is specifically designed to process changes in the variables themselves, e.g., digital differential analyzer.

incremental plotter control—Used to provide for high-speed plotting of points, continuous curves, points connected by curves, curve-identification symbols, letters, numerals under program control.

incremental tape units—Refers to various types of magnetic tape modules requiring a tape-flow for the process of reading or writing.

index—1. A table of computer words or fields containing addresses of records located in file storage. 2. An ordered reference list of the contents of a document, such as names, subjects, etc. 3. A symbol or number used to identify a particular quantity in an array of similar quantities; e.g., the terms of an array represented by x (1), x (2) . . . x (100) have the indexes 1, 2, . . . 100 respectively. 4. Pertaining to an index register.

indexed list—Refers to a FORTRAN instruction used in read and write statements to form special indexed arrays.

indexing—1. The indexing method of random-access file organization in which a part of the file is set aside as an index in order to locate information in other parts of the file. 2. The modification of an instruction by the contents of an index register in order to obtain a new effective address. 3. The storing of copy in electronic form permits rapid and automatic indexing for information-retrieval purposes.

indexing, association—Refers to a study concerning two approaches—the automatic generation of word-association maps based on lists of words from the text, and representations based on the number of times words appear in the text.

index, permutation—Relates to an index capable of alphabetically listing all of the major, plus minor words of a title or document so that each word appears once as the first word, followed by the other words rotated in a circular fashion. This is done so that the documents can be retrieved by numerous permutations.

index register—A register that contains a quantity for modifying addresses (synonymous with B-register and B-box).

index-word—1. Refers to a storage position or register, the contents of which may be used to modify automatically the effective address of any given instruction. 2. An index based on the selection of words as used in a document, without giving thought to synonyms and more generic concepts related to the term selected.

indicator—A device often used as a control unit when it is designed to determine the selection from alternative processes. It can be set into a prescribed state according to the results of a previous process. An example is an overflow indicator. The state of such indicators may be displayed on a control panel for the benefit of programmers and operators.

indicator, end-of-file—Refers to a device, associated with each input and output unit, that makes an end-of-file condition known to the routine and operator controlling the computer.

indicator, machine check—Relates to a type of protective device that is turned on when certain conditions arise within the machine. The machine can be programmed to stop or to run a separate correction routine or to ignore the condition.

indicator, overflow—A type of signaling device that is used to indicate the occurrence of an overflow; for instance, a number too large to be contained in a given register.

indicator, read-write check—A particular device which has been incorporated into certain computers to indicate upon interrogation whether or not an error was made in reading or writing. The machine can be made to stop, try the operation again, or follow a special subroutine, depending upon the result of the interrogation.

indicators, comparison—Examples of comparison indicators are: high, low, and equal. They are set on the basis of comparisons of operands in the arithmetic or index registers with operands in memory. The equal indicator is also set and reset by add and subtract instructions. If the result of an addition or subtraction is zero, the equal indicator is set. If the result is not zero, the equal indicator is reset.

indirect addressing—1. A method of computer cross reference in which one memory location indicates where the correct address of the main fact can be found. 2. Any level of addressing other than the first level of direct addressing. 3. Translation of symbolic instructions into machine-language instructions on a computer other than that for which the program was written.

infix notation—A technique used to form one-dimensional expressions (e.g., arithmetic, logical, etc.) by alternating single operands and operators. Any operator performs its indicated function upon its adjacent terms which are defined, subject to the rules of operator precedence and grouping brackets which eliminates ambiguity.

information efficiency—A computed ratio of the actual negative entropy to the maximum possible entropy, using the same set of signs.

information function—A special mathematical function which describes a source of information.

information link—The physical means of connecting one location to another for the purpose of transmitting information.

information retrieval—1. A method for cataloging vast amounts of data, all related to one field of interest, so that one can call out any or all of this data at any time it's needed with accuracy and speed. 2. A branch of computer science relating to the techniques for storing and searching large or specific quantities of information that may or may not be a real-time system.

information theory—That area of mathematical theory concerned with the information rate, channels, channel width, noise and other factors affecting information transmission. Initially developed for electrical communications, it is now applied to business systems, and other phenomena that deal with information units and flow of information in networks.

inhibit—1. To prevent the occurrence of an event. 2. To prevent a device or logic element from producing a specified output.

inhibition rules—Priority and inhibition rules are usually designed to be implemented in the time-sharing hardware to resolve possible conflicts when two interrupts occur simultaneously or when a second interrupt occurs before a previous one is completely processed.

initialize—The establishment or origination of the basic conditions or start-up state. Such procedures might be used to set an initial value for the address of an operand, establish the initial control value for a loop, set all registers to a preset value prior to running, begin a bootstrap operation with a control digit or word, etc.

initial program loader (IPL)—Specific routines designed to load the initial section of an operating system or other programs and surrender control of the machine to the program which is loaded.

in-line data processing—Data processing in which all changes to relevant records and accounts are made at the time that each transaction or event occurs. The process usually requires random access storage.

input—1. Information or data transferred or to be transferred from an external storage medium into the internal storage of the computer. 2. Describing the routines with direct input as defined in (1), or the devices from which such information is available to the computer. 3. The device or collective set of devices necessary for input as defined in (1).

input block—1. Refers to that section of internal computer storage reserved for the receiving and processing of input information. (Synonymous with input area.) 2. An input buffer. 3. A block of computer words considered as a unit and intended or destined to be transferred from an external source or storage medium to the internal storage of the computer.

input device, optical reader—A type of device which reads printed and typewritten material, and inputs data directly without converting it into punch tape, punch cards, or other intermediate formats. Optical reader recognizes all letters of the alphabet, standard punctuation, 0 to 9, and special symbols used in programmed functions. It handles documents and continuous fanfold sheets. This high-speed reader can be used simply as an input device, or it can be used as a complete small system for data processing and storage.

input/output—1. Commonly called I/O. A general term for equipment used to communicate with a computer. 2. The data involved in such communication. 3. The media carrying the data for input/output. 4. The process of transmitting information from an external source to the computer or from the computer to an external source.

input/output area—Same as working storage.

input/output buffer—A storage device that permits data-word transfers to and from memory to proceed without main program attention. May be programmed so that when input-output transfer is complete, the computer generates an internal interrupt.

input/output, buffered—Most types of peripheral equipment are designed to utilize an input/output buffer register for storage of data to be transferred to the computer so that various devices can

be operated simultaneously at their maximum speed. The processor does not wait for a device to complete its cycle before continuing the program.

input/output channel—A specific channel which permits simultaneous communications and independently so between various storage units or any of the various input or output units. Such a channel is the control channel for most peripheral devices and quite often performs various checks on data transfers such as validity checks, etc.

input/output channels, buffered—See input/output section buffered.

input/output channel selection—Refers to the capacity of a computer to designate a particular channel for I/O operations.

input/output, concurrent—Refers to the acceptance, listing, and processing of all requests for I/O functions from the operating programs. This function of the executive system makes possible the concurrent operation of several programs using the same I/O channels without the danger of one program interfering with another program's I/O functions. Requests for I/O functions are submitted to the executive in the form of a parameter which specifies the location of an execution packet which defines the function to be performed. An attempt is made to recover from I/O errors whenever feasible.

input/output control—1. There are several controls which direct interactions between the processing unit and input and output equipment. One is used to control actions with tape, card, and printer equipment. A second control is specifically designed for random processing of records stored on direct access devices. 2. A program which assigns equipment, controls the I/O devices, controls data transfers between memory and the I/O device, and controls the buffering of data for the device.

input/output control, interleaving—The I/O control is capable of linking up to 64 input and output stations by lines to the central processor. It calls the stations, and collects and distributes the input/output data. It also controls the interleaving of data during a data interrupt, senses the status of I/O devices and skips instructions based on this status, traps IOT (input output transfer) instructions initiating a program break, and generates real-time signal pulses for use by external peripheral equipment (some computers).

input/output control systems (IOCS)—Refers to a group of computer routines designed to automatically control the performance of input-output operations and direct other work or functions, such as, error correction, checkpoint, label processing, restart, and others.

input/output equipment—Pertains to those specific units of the total computing system which are designed to accept data and output the results of computing and processing in a form readable either by humans or other processing units.

input/output, hybrid computer—This particular input/output group of programs consists of a system monitor and programs to control operation of analog/digital conversion equipment and special devices such as an oscilloscope display or a digital plotter.

input/output interface control module (IO)—Refers to the microcircuit modules which use all computer inputs and outputs, with the number and type determined by system applications and the peripheral equipment used. There is also a provision to directly connect an I/O interface with a memory module, under program control to allow an efficient method of resolving conflicts in memory access.

input/output interrupt—Through the use of input/output interrupt, the input/output equipment can be kept running at full capacity with relatively small amounts of central-processor time required for input/output control. The operation of each input/output unit is under the direct control of an associated synchronizer. The performance of a particular input/output operation is initiated by a central-processor instruction which transfers a control word (function specification) to a fixed memory location associated with the input/output synchronizer concerned.

input/output, programmed—Program control information transferred between the central processor and an external device provides the fastest method of operating on data received from peripheral equipment. The programmed input/output channel permits input directly to the accumulator where the data can be acted on immediately, thus eliminating the necessity for a memory reference by either the channel or the program. Likewise, output data may be sent directly from the accumulator to an external device.

input/output, random access—Refers to an I/O control capability allowing efficient random processing of records stored on a direct-access device. Random access I/O efficiency is achieved by the system in two ways: (1) Seeks are issued in an order which minimizes the average seek time, rather than in the order in which they are requested.

(2) Seeks are overlapped with other processing. Because records must sometimes be processed sequentially (for example, when a report is being written), the ability to call for records sequentially is also available.

input/output, remote message—Pertains to an I/O control for obtaining messages from and sending messages to remote terminals. For remote-message control, the I/O control handles the following functions: receipt of messages from remote terminals; sending of messages to remote terminals; automatic dial-up; and code conversion. The user supplies the system with line-control specifications and installation-oriented routines to analyze message headers.

input/output routines—Used for simplifying the programming of input and output functions for standard peripheral equipment.

input/output section, buffered—This allows the processor to continue with computation while input and output communications are proceeding. The transfer of data to or from the central processor is conducted via input/output channels which communicate directly with the magnetic-core memory. Access to the memory is time-shared between the operating program and input/output data transfer. Access also is automatically controlled by the I/O rate of the external device; it is not a programming consideration. Any cycle of the memory time is available for input/output data transfer in preference to its use by the program. The input/output system is provided with program interrupt features so that testing of the condition of the external devices by the running program is not necessary, although possible, if desired.

input/output traffic control—1. Refers to the direction of the time sharing of the main memory by the various peripheral devices and the central processor. This control element makes possible the concurrent performance of central processor computing and up to eight simultaneous input/output operations. For example, the computer can simultaneously read or write tape, read cards, punch cards, store information in a random-access disc storage unit, read information from a random-access drum device, print two separate reports, and compute. 2. The coordination of peripheral simultaneity with internal computation is performed by the central processor element called the input/output traffic control.

input, real-time—Relates to real-time systems which have instantaneous input or entry and acceptance, most often determined by the requirements of another independent system, i.e., they are on-line inputs flowing directly to the computer as the activity occurs.

input units—Pertains to electronic machines that feed or introduce data into the system. Such machines can be paper tape readers, card readers, magnetic document sorter-readers, optical readers, and others.

input work queue—Refers to a list or line of jobs ready for processing but not yet begun or in process. Usually these tasks are input on a first-come first served basis. Such an input queue consists of programs, data, and control cards settled and waiting in the input job stream. Schedulers and special operating systems handle and control such queues differently.

inquiry—As related to computing a designed request for specific information from storage; e.g., a request for the number of available airline seats or a machine statement to initiate a search of library documents.

inquiry and communications systems—Refers to those computer systems which are now equipped with facilities for diversified on-site and long distance inquiry and data-communications networks. Centralized records and data-processing operations can be tied in with information sources at remote locations and will provide instant on-line response to interrogations and input data from a large number of inquiry stations. Communication networks may include standard teletype stations, and electric typewriter stations. (Burroughs)

inscribing—In reference to optical character recognition, the preparation of source documents for automatic reading which includes both handwritten and printed characters.

insertion, switch—Pertains to the inputting of information into a computer system by an operator who operates the switches manually.

instantaneous access—Refers to directly obtaining data from, or placing data into a storage device or register without serial delay due to other units of data, and usually in a relatively short period of time.

instruction—A set of characters, together with one or more address (or no address), that defines an operation and which, as a unit, causes the computer to operate accordingly on the indicated quantities; a machine instruction to specific functions. Types: actual, arithmetic, blank, branch, control, direct, effective, execution, executive, extract, halt, hold, jump, machine, macro, programmed, and pseudo.

instruction address—The address of the storage location where the instruction word is stored. The next instruction to be performed is determined by the control program of the instruction addresses, and the machine control automatically refers to these addresses.

instruction-address registers—Usually refers to the three control-memory registers (instruction-address register 1, instruction-address register 2, and an interrupt register) which are used to store the addresses of instructions. Instruction-address register 1 directs the sequential retrieval of instruction characters from their storage locations in main memory. Instruction-address register 2 which exists only in the basic set of control registers can be loaded with the address of another instruction by the programmer. A single program instruction can interchange the contents of the two instruction-address registers, providing a convenient means of branching to and returning from any position in the program. The interrupt register can be loaded with the starting address of a routine to be executed when a program-interrupt condition exists. The controlling program is interrupted automatically upon receipt of a signal from an external device or a program instruction.

instruction, breakpoint—1. Pertains to an instruction which will cause a computer to stop or to transfer control in some standard fashion to a supervisory routine which can monitor the progress of the interrupted program. 2. An instruction that will cause the computer to stop or take other special action, when a particular switch is set.

instruction code—The list of symbols, names and definitions of the instructions that are intelligible to a given computer or computing system.

instruction, conditional jump—Same as conditional branch.

instruction counter—Same as control register.

instruction, effective—To alter a presumptive or unmodified instruction when using a stored program computer. Such alteration produces a complete instruction and when it is actually executed it is called an effective instruction or an actual instruction. The modification process uses words or parts of words specifically called modifiers or index words. These are added to or combined with the presumptive or unmodified instruction by means of arithmetical or logical operations.

instruction format—1. The process of allocating bits or characters of a machine instruction to specific functions. 2. Instructions are coded in a two-address, variable-length format. However, one or perhaps both addresses may often be omitted, thereby saving memory space and speeding up instruction execution. 3. The allocation of instructions according to some particular machine or installation conventions or rules. 4. An allocation of characters of various instructions differentiating between the component parts of the instructions, such as, address part, operation part, etc.

instruction, logical—An instruction whose function is to carry out a logical operation, such as an AND, OR, NOR.

instruction, machine—An instruction that the particular machine can recognize and execute.

instruction, macro—1. A particular kind of source-language statement that can produce a variable number of machine instructions. 2. Usually symbolic mnemonic type instructions that programmers can write in a source program to call for special or library routines that perform wanted functions as open, seek, close, etc. Macro instructions result in one-for-many instructions and are extensively used.

instruction, micro—Refers to instructions in a micro-programmable machine which perform many of the hardware functions such as gating, testing, and branching.

instruction modification—Refers to changing the operation-code portion of an instruction or command such that if the routine containing the instruction or command is repeated, the computer will perform a different operation.

instruction, no-op—1. Relates to the instruction that specifically instructs the computer to do nothing but process the next instruction in sequence. 2. A blank instruction. 3. A skip instruction.

instruction, one-address—Refers to one consisting of an operation and exactly one address. The instruction code of a single-address computer may include both zero and multiaddress instructions as special cases.

instructions, IOT—This permits the computer to communicate with external devices, send control information, and transfer data. Certain processor commands, such as the clock instructions, are also in the IOT (input/output and transfer) class. The IOT instruction is microcoded to simplify programming for I/O transfers. For example, clearing the AC (accumulator) and loading a device buffer are done in one instruction.

instruction, skip—Refers to the instruction having no effect other than directing the processor to proceed to another instruction designated in the storage portion. (Synonymous with skip, and no-op instruction.)

instruction, symbolic—1. An instruction in an assembly language directly translatable into machine code. 2. An instruction using symbols to represent or express the operator part and the address parts.

instruction, table-look-up—Pertains to an instruction specifically used to allow reference to systematically arranged, and stored data.

instruction word—1. In most computers a grouping of letters or digits processed by the computer as a distinct unit to signify the provision of definitions of operations to be performed or the description of further data. 2. A part of a word or all of a word which is executed by the computer as an instruction.

instruction, zero-address—Refers to the instruction specifying an operation in which the location of the operands are defined by the computer code, so that no address need be given explicitly.

interface—1. One common boundary between automatic data-processing systems or parts of a single system. In communications and data systems, it may involve code, format, speed, or other changes as required.

integer—A signed or unsigned number with no fractional part.

integer constants (FORTRAN)—An integer constant is a number without a decimal point, using the decimal digits 0, 1, . . . , 9. A preceding + or − sign is optional, and an unsigned integer constant is assumed to be positive.

integer programming—Relates to a class of optimization problems where the values of all of the variables are re-

stricted to integers. Normally, the optimization problem without this integer restriction is a linear program; the integer restriction is a linear program; additional adjectives indicate variations — for example, integer quadratic programming.

integer variables (FORTRAN)—An integer variable consists of a series of not more than six alphameric characters (except special characters), of which the first is I, J, K, L, M, or N.

integrated data processing (IDP)—1. A system that treats as a whole all data-processing requirements to accomplish a sequence of data-processing steps, or a number of related data-processing sequences, and that strives to reduce or eliminate duplicating data entry or processing steps. 2. The processing of data by such a system in which all operations are in some way connected or associated with a computer.

integrator, summing—The term referring to an analog computer amplifier which forms the time integral of the weighted sum of the input voltages or currents as an output.

intelligence, artificial—Refers to the pursuit of computer and related techniques to supplement the intellectual capabilities of man. As man has invented and used tools to increase his physical powers, he now is beginning to use artificial intelligence to increase his mental powers. In a more restricted sense, the study of techniques for more effective use of digital computers by improved programming techniques.

interface modules (CLT's)—These modules are furnished to interface CLT's with currently available modems in addition to telegraph facilities for which no modem is necessary. Where required, interface modules conform to EIA specifications. The modular concept of the standard communication subsystem permits the addition of new interface modules as new offerings are made available by the common carriers. Jacks are provided on each telegraph interface module which permit a teletypewriter to monitor all data passing through the interface.

interference, adjacent-channel—Refers to the placing of two modulated carrier channels so close together in frequency, that one or both sidebands extend from one channel into the other.

interleave—Merging segments of one program into another program so that the two programs can, in effect, be executed simultaneously; e.g., a technique used in multi-programming.

interleaving, input-output control—See control module, input-output.

interleaving, multiprocessing—Refers to special process of addressing adjacent storage modules in an even/odd fashion. It significantly reduces storage-access conflicts in a multiprocessor system, and thereby increases overall system performance. With interleaving, the modules are divided into even and odd locations (although the addressing structure within the modules themselves remains unchanged). Thus, in a fully expanded eight module system, modules 0, 2, 4, 6 are referenced for even addresses while modules 1, 3, 5, 7, are referenced for odd.

intermediate memory storage—Used as an electronic scratch-pad for holding working figures temporarily until they're needed, and for releasing final figures to the output.

intermediate subcarrier—Refers to a carrier which may be modulated by one or more subcarriers and which is used as a modulating wave to modulate a carrier.

International Algebraic Language—The forerunner of ALGOL. (Synonymous with IAL.)

interpret—1. The process of printing on a punched card the graphic symbols of the information punched in that card. 2. To translate non-machine language into machine language. 3. To decode. 4. The translation of coded characters into standard letters, numbers, and symbols.

interpretive language—Refers to a distinct program writing language used to translate and execute each source language expression serially, i.e., before translating and executing the following one, much as an interpreter of languages or speeches might do.

interpretive trace program—Pertains to a trace or diagnostic program used to perform a desired check on another program and may include instructions as its output, and intermediate results of those instructions can be arranged in the order in which the instructions are executed. When such a trace program is an interpretive type, it is called an interpretive trace program.

interrecord gap—1. Refers to the blank portion between records on magnetic tape. 2. An interval of space or time, deliberately left between recording portions of data or records. Such spacing is used to prevent errors through loss of data or overwriting, and permits stop-start tape operations.

interrogators, video-data—Refers to those that are comprised of keyboard and separable associated display, which provide a valuable terminal facility for conventional communications lines. Up to eight interrogator units can be serviced by one interrogator control-terminal outside line, using as many as sixteen prerecorded formats, with up to a 480-character display. Transmission rate is up to 180 cps (some computers).

interrupt—1. A break in the normal flow of a system or routine such that the flow can be resumed from that point at a later time. An interrupt is usually caused by a signal from an external source. 2. An interrupt is a special control signal that diverts the attention of the computer from the main program, because of a particular event or set of circumstances, to a specific address which is directly related to the type of interrupt that has occurred. 3. To stop current control sequence; i.e., to jump when affected by signals from on-line peripheral equipment or to skip as triggered by results of programming test techniques.

interrupt handling—Occurs when an interrupt condition exists; the control program saves the interrupted program's registers and status, and routes control to routines that handle the interrupt cause. When the interrupt is handled, the original program's registers and status are restored, and control is restored so that the original program continues as if no interrupt had taken place.

interrupt, input/output—Its use will allow the input/output equipment to be kept running at full capacity with relatively small amounts of central-processor time required for input/output control. The operation of each input-output unit is under the direct control of an associated synchronizer. The performance of a particular input/output operation is initiated by a central-processor instruction which transfers a control word (function specification) to a fixed-memory location associated with the input-output synchronizer concerned. After the microseconds required to execute the initiate instruction, the central processor is free to initiate the operation of other input/output units or to execute other instructions. When the input/output unit is ready to perform the specified operation, its synchronizer accesses and decodes the function specification, which causes the unit to begin executing the specified operation. The synchronizer performs all data transfers, data and equipment checking, and other required control functions. (UNIVAC)

interrupt, internal and external—Refers to a special control signal which diverts the attention of the computer to consider an extraordinary event or set of circumstances; i.e., it causes program control to be transferred to a special subordinate which corresponds to the stimulus. Many levels of control can be exercised by the numerous forms of interrupts provided. The interrupts from external sources serve primarily to synchronize the computer program with the readiness of peripheral devices, including other computers, to transmit or receive data. Internal interrupts serve primarily to synchronize the computer program with termination of input-output transfers and to signal the occurrence of an error.

interrupts and control logic—The synchronization of input/output activities and responses to real-time situations is accomplished through interrupts. The interrupt is a control signal that may be received from a peripheral subsystem (external interrupt) or from the control section of the central processor. Each interrupt has a unique fixed address in central store. These interrupt locations are programmed to enter interrupt response subroutines in the executive system.

interrupts, multiprogramming—In some computers a set of control signals which are referred to as interrupts. Whenever certain conditions exist, a control signal will direct the central computer to execute the word (instruction) at a specified address in central store. Each interrupt is activated by unique conditions and directs the computer to a correspondingly unique address in central store. The occurrence of an interrupt terminates guard mode, program lockin, and central-store address assignments.

interrupts, priority ordered—Some time-sharing computers are capable of having over 200 priority ordered interrupts for external lines. This extensive interrupt capability permits a terminal to be attached to more than one interrupt line. If the attached interrupts cover a range of priorities, by selectively arming and disarming the external interrupt lines, the executive program can change the relative priority of a terminal's attention requests allowing different classes of service or response to be given to the terminal.

interrupt, trapped program—Certain conditions can cause the program of the computer to be interrupted: (1) memory parity error, (2) add overflow, (3) programmed I/O channel, (4) operator, (5) external device, (6) multilevel priority interrupts, and (7) power failure. An interrupt trap associated with each event may be set under program control to either respond when the event occurs or to ignore it.

interspersed gang punching—The dual punching of cards with fixed data in one or more cards simultaneously within a larger group of cards.

interval timer—By using this the control program provides the facility with the ability to keep track of the time of day and to interrupt periodically as rquired. More than one interval can be controlled at once. For example, a five-second interval between successive polling of a teleprocessing line can be specified, and at the same time a two-minute limit on the duration of a new program undergoing test can be in effect.

INTRAFAX—Closed-circuit facsimile systems called INTRAFAX leased to government, military, and industrial users by Western Union.

IOCS—An abbreviation for input/output control system. Specialized program which is usually related to large scale computer operations.

IPC—Abbreviation for industrial process control.

IPL—An abbreviation for Information Processing Language.

IPL-V—Refers to the abbreviation for Information Processing Language—Five. A list-processing language researched principally by Newell, Simon, and Shaw to manipulate tree structures.

IRL—Abbreviation for information retrieval language.

ISO (International Standards Organization) code—Codes authorized by the ISO to represent alphabetic, numeric, and special characters.

iterative—To describe a procedure or process which repeatedly executes a series of operations until some condition is satisfied. An iterative procedure can be implemented by a loop in a routine.

Iverson notation—A special symbol set

developed by Dr. Kenneth Iverson describing the formal structure of computer languages. Used in APL.

* _ * _ *

jitter—1. Refers to the short-time instability of a signal. The instability may be in either amplitude or phase, or both. The term is applied especially to signals reproduced on the screen of a cathode-ray tube. The term "tracking jitters" is used to describe minor variations in the pointing of an automatic-tracking radar. 2. The loss of synchronization caused by mechanical or electrical changes.

job control language (JCL)—Used to declare the environment in which a job is to be run, and optional output desired.

job flow control—Contains the processes: I/O transition between jobs and job segments, unit assignments, initial loading and initialization when the computer is first turned on; control between jobs; and control over the type of operation mode, ranging from simple stacked jobs through teleprocessing systems performing concurrent operations.

job-processing monitor—Refers to computer programs that are processed by routines contained in the monitor system. The operations that may be processed upon a program are: compilation, assembly, loading, segmenting, execution, and dumping. One or all of these operations may be required to process a program. Other factors, such as inputs and outputs necessary to the program, may be required in order to successfully perform an operation. The information defining the processing of a program plus the operations performed upon the program comprise a job. The operating system processes all programs on a job basis. Job processing is controlled by two system routines: the monitor and the executive. The executive accepts control information for each job. This information is placed in the monitor which controls the sequence of operations performed on the job. The monitor is resident in memory to accept control information routines necessary for performing the various operations are contained in a master file. The monitor loads and executes each routine as it is needed. Each routine, in turn, returns control to the monitor upon completion. When all operations have been completed for the job, the executive is loaded into memory to accept control informlation for the next job. In order to achieve automatic job processing, all computer programs must return to the monitor upon completion. This is done with a call to the subroutine EXIT as the last executable statement of the program. Programs having more than one completion point must call EXIT at each point. (UNIVAC)

job stacking—Pertains to the capability of a monitor system for batch processing both FORTRAN compilations and assemblies. Assemblies or compilations, i.e., jobs, can be stacked behind one another. After the operator specifies the operation, assembling or compiling proceeds automatically through one job after another until an end-of-run card is encountered signifying the end of the run.

JOVIAL—A type of language designed for real-time command and control by System Development Corp.

JUG—Refers to the Joint Users Group which is a group of computer users sharing common interests, software and computers.

jump, conditional—Pertains to a particular instruction designed to cause the proper one of two (or more) addresses to be used in obtaining the next instruction, depending upon some property of one or more numerical expressions or other conditions.

jump, unconditional—Same as unconditional branch.

justify—1. The process used to adjust exactly, as by spacing, or to align a set of characters horizontally (or vertically) to right or left margins. To develop exact format or spacing in words, fields, items, or data as designed by context of exact specifications. 2. To move a data item so that a particular part of the item assumes a particular position relative to some reference point in a storage medium; for instance, to adjust the print on a printed page so that the left, right, or both margins are aligned; also to shift the item in a register to position specifically the most or least significant digit.

justify, left—The process of formatting a left margin for the type on a printed page. Typewriters produce left justified copy.

justify, right—The process of formatting a right margin for the type on a printed page. More difficult and expensive than left justification.

* — * — *

K—A special symbol which stands for the numeral 1000. For example: 32 K would be equivalent to 32,000.

Karnaugh map—Refers to an arrangement in tabular form which facilitates combination and elimination of duplicate logical functions by listing similar logical expressions.

key—1. A character group usually forming a field, utilized in the identification or location of an item. A marked lever manually operated for copying a character; e.g., typewriter paper-tape perforater, card punch manual keyboard, digitizer or manual word generator. 2. That part of a word, record, file, etc., by which it is identified or controlled. 3. The field by which a file of records is sorted into order; e.g., the key for a file of employee records by a number, department, or letter.

keyboard entry—1. Pertains to an element of information inputted manually, usually through a set of switches or marked punch levers, called keys, into an automatic data processing system. 2. A medium for achieving access to, or entrance into, an automatic data processing system.

keyboard inquiry—The checking of program progress, storage contents, or other information by keyboard maneuvering.

keyboard send/receive set (KSR)—Refers to a combination transmitter and receiver with transmission capability from keyboard only.

keyboard, supervisory—The supervisory console contains the operator's control panel, a keyboard and typeprinter, and a control unit for the keyboard and typeprinter. Optionally, a paper-tape reader and punch may be connected to the computer through the same control unit. Information transfer between the computer and any single device is performed and output channel assigned to the console auxiliaries. Two switches mounted on the control unit permit selection of the paper-tape reader of the keyboard, and the paper-tape punch on the type printer (some computers).

keyboard time-out—A feature causing the keyboard to lock if more than 15 seconds elapse between the sending of characters. If a time-out occurs during the typing of a line, any information typed on that line up to that point will be discarded. To avoid this loss of information, the user may press and release shift before the 15-seconds limit has been reached; this action may be repeated as necessary to prevent a time-out. By pressing shift, the user can prevent a time-out without affecting the input information.

key, load—Refers to a control key, or similar manual device, which is used to input data or instructions into a computer or control system. The instructions are usually composed of computer routines.

key, protection—Refers to various indicators designed to allow the program access to sections of memory which the program may use, and a denial of access to all other parts of memory. Thus, this is a memory-protection device with a key which is numbered by the computer. Usually such keys are for most locations in memory, and when a storage key differs from the program protection key, the program can be interrupted and taken over by a supervisory program to handle the problem which arises.

keypunch—1. A special machine to record information in cards or tape by punching holes in the cards or tape to represent letters, digits, and special characters. 2. To operate a device for punching holes in cards or tape.

keypunch and verifier operator—Various individuals who are trained to operate numerical and alphabetical keypunch and verifying machines to transcribe routine or easily identified data from various documents onto punched cards.

keypunch, printing—A card-printing device that prints each number or letter on the card as it punches the card.

key, sorting—The record fields which determine, or are used as a basis for determining, the sequence of records in a file.

key, start—Refers to a specific push button located on the control panel designed to initiate or resume the operations of the equipment after an automatic or programmed stop.

key, stop—Refers to a specific push button located on the control panel designed to cause a halt in the processing but this often only after the completion of an instruction being executed at a given moment.

key-verify—The process using the punch card machine known as a verifier, which has a keyboard to make sure that the information supposed to be punched in a punch card has actually been properly punched. The machine signals when the punched hole and the depressed key disagree.

keyword—A significant or informative word in a title, abstract, body, or part of the text that generally are utilized to describe a document. A keyword or set of keywords may describe the contents of a document, label the document, and/or assist in identifying and retrieving the document.

keyword-in-context index (KWIC)—This lists available programs arranged alphabetically by the keywords in the program titles. There is an index entry for each significant keyword in the title. Certain words are not accepted as indexing words but will be printed as part of the title.

A KWIC index is prepared by highlighting each keyword of the title in the context of words on either side of it and aligning the keywords of all titles alphabetically in a vertical column.

key, write—Concerns a specific code in the program status double-word that is designed to be used in conjunction with a memory lock to determine whether or not a program may write into a specific page of actual addresses.

kilobit—An abbreviation for one thousand binary digits.

kilobauds—Relates to various types of new and higher capacity data channels, i.e., for special applications, some channels capable of 20 kilobauds are now available.

* — * — *

label—1. A device for identification used for introducing a record, groups of records, or an address; a number, symbol, tag, or slip. 2. A name (symbol) which indicates an instruction or data group. Usually this is a mnemonic label for easy recognition. 3. A set of symbols used to identify or describe an item, record, message, or file. Occasionally it may be the same as the address in storage. 4. A string of alphameric information placed at any location for informational and instructional purposes. 5. To assign a symbol, acronym, or word, as a means of identification, to a body of data, tape, card, deck, block; to create a specialized associated record or filing "handle."

label, file—Relates to a specific set of alpha-numeric characters that uniquely identifies the contents of a particular roll of magnetic tape or a portion of magnetic tape. Usually the file label is written on magnetic tape as a block which contains the file name, reel number, date written, and date expired.

label, operational—Refers to a procedure in which tape files are identified, as far as the operator is concerned, by means of an operational label. An operational label may be any combination of letters and digits to a maximum of six characters. Two special characters are also used consisting of the character * and the character—to indicate a scratch tape and an empty (or malfunctioning) tape unit, respectively.

label record—One used to identify the contents of a file or reel of magnetic tape.

language, absolute—1. Refers to a specific set of symbols, characters, or signs, and the rules for combining them, designed to convey instructions or information to a computer. 2. Also, a particular language for writing instructions in a form to be executed by the compiler; the language can be directly interpreted by the control section of the machine. 3. Information or data is expressed in code that can be read directly, used or written by the computer or peripheral machines without further processing.

language, algorithmic—Concerns a specific arithmetic language designed so that numerical procedures may be precisely presented to a computer in a standard form. The language is intended not only as a means of directly presenting any numerical procedure to any suitable computer for which a compiler exists, but also as a means of communicating numerical procedures among individuals.

The language itself is the result of international cooperation to obtain a standardized algorithmic language. The

International Algebraic Language is the forerunner of ALGOL. (Synonymous with ALGOL, and clarified by International Algebraic Language.)

language, artificial—One specifically designed for ease of communication in a particular area of endeavor, but one that is not yet natural to that area. This is contrasted with a natural language which has evolved through long usage.

language, assembly—The standard machine oriented programming language (e.g., EASY, ARGUS) belonging to an assembly system.

language, command—1. The specific language designed to be recognized by the executive and utilized to issue control commands to the system. 2. A source language designed and structured with procedural instructions. Such a language has capabilities of causing the execution of many functions, most of which are basic or used repetitively.

Language, (COBOL) Common Business Oriented—The most widely used programming language of the business problem-oriented type designed and developed by a committee representing the Department of Defense together with various manufacturers and major computer users... with a purpose of organizing standardized form and terminology which programmers could more efficiently use on equipment manufactured by many different manufacturers.

language, executive control—1. A set of control commands, carefully minimized, yet capable of performing all of the desirable or mandatory functions required in a modern executive system. The command language is open ended and easily expanded, so that features and functions may be added as the need

arises. 2. The basic format of an executive control statement is quite simple, and is amenable to a large number of input devices. Statements are not restricted to card image format, and may be of variable lengths. Each statement consists of a heading character for recognition purposes, followed by a command (which categorizes the statement), followed by a variable number of expressions. The end of a statement is signified by the end of a card, a carriage return, or an equivalent signal, depending on the type of input device.

language listing, symbolic-assembly—Refers specifically to a binary output program of the compiler which is optional at compile time. The listing contains the symbolic instructions equivalent to the binary-code output of the compiler. Such an assembly language output listing is useful as a debugging aid. By including certain pseudo-operation codes in "in-line" assembly language, the assembly language output can be assembled by the assembler (if output is obtained on either cards, paper tape, or magnetic tape). This will allow modification of programs at the assembly language level.

language, machine—1. The basic operating language, i.e., information recorded in a form that may be made available to a computer. Punched paper tape may contain information available to a machine, whereas the same information in the form of printed characters on a page is not available to a machine. 2. Information that can be sensed by a machine.

language, machine-independent—One which is not written for application or use with any specific computer or system or class of computers. Such languages are usually problem-oriented and widely accepted, such as FORTRAN, COBOL, ALGOL, etc.

language, machine-oriented—1. Relates to various languages designed for interpretation and use by a machine, without a translation being necessary. 2. Also refers to a system for expressing information that is intelligible to a specific machine; e.g., a computer or class of computers. Such a language may include instructions that define and direct machine operations, and information to be recorded or acted upon by these machine operations. 3. The set of instructions expressed in the number system basic to a computer, together with symbolic operation codes with absolute addresses, relative addresses, or symbolic addresses. (Synonymous with assembler language, related to object language, and contrasted with problem-oriented language.)

language, meta—Refers specifically to a formal language designed to use special symbols to describe the syntax of computer languages, for example, Backus normal form.

language, native—Usually relates to a communication language or coding system for use between machine units or modules which is peculiar to or usable for a particular class or brand of equipment.

language, natural—Most often considered to be a language whose rules reflect and describe current usage rather than prescribed usage.

language, object—Refers to the basic language which is the output of an automatic coding routine. Usually object language and machine language are the same. Sometimes however, a series of steps in an automatic coding system may involve the object language of one step serving as a source language for the next step, and so forth.

language, problem-oriented—1. Refers to various languages designed for convenience of program specification in a general problem area rather than for easy conversion to a machine-instruction code. The components of such a language may bear little resemblance to machine instructions. 2. Also refers to machine-independent languages designed so that one needs only to state the problem not the how of solution. (Related to program generators, and contrasted with procedure-oriented language.)

language, procedure-oriented—Refers to various machine-independent languages developed to describe how the process of solving the problem is to be carried out, e.g., FORTRAN. (Contrasted with problem-oriented language.

language, source—Refers to the basic original form in which a program is prepared prior to processing by the machine.

language theory parsing—Refers to various procedures designed to break down the components of a sentence into structural forms.

language translation—The transformation or translation of information from one language to another.

language translator—1. A program which converts a language to equivalent statements in another computer language, usually for a different computer. 2. A routine which aids in the performance of natural language translations such as French to English. 3. Any assembler or compiling program which brings forth same or equivalent output from human-readable statements.

laser—A tremendously condensed directed lightbeam. An invention with endless applications that will probably enter the world of computers soon. Laser action will take place using optical fibers as the active transmission lines. This optical-transmission technique could raise the speed of operation to rates measured in gigacycles (billions of cycles) per second.

latency—1. In various serial storage devices, latency is referred to as the time required to locate the first bit (or character) in a particular storage location. 2. Also the delay while waiting for information called for the storage to be delivered to the arithmetic unit, i.e., access time minus the word time.

leader—Refers to an unused or blank length of tape located at the beginning of a reel of tape preceding the start of the recorded data.

learning (computer)—1. Refers to various processes or techniques by which computers modify programs according to their own memory or experience, i.e., changes of logic paths, parameter values. An example is the now famous chess-playing computer. 2. As related to process-control, an analog computer can alter its parameters by a continuous process according to temperatures or other guage reports it receives. Examples are adoptive autopilots for aircraft, which explores different alternatives.

leased line, leased circuit—A service category designed so that connections to separate points are permanently in existence for the duration of the contract.

left justified—In most instances data is considered left justified when the left-hand digit or character (or its sign) occupies the left-hand position of the space allotted for that data.

length, field—Refers to the distinct physical extent of a field. On a punch card it refers to the number of columns. On a tape it refers to bit positions.

length, variable—Concerns the determination of the number of characters which may be available in a particular storage location or data element. Since it is variable, it is possible that each successive block may have a different, varying, numbers of words, but the word packing density usually remains constant.

length, word—1. The number of bits or characters specified as a physical unit by a programmer. 2. The size of a field. 3. The number of bits or other characters in a word.

letter code—In the basic Baudot code, the designed function that causes machines to shift to lower case. This code is used to "rubout" errors in tape, as it is made up of intelligence pulses in each of the five channels, and causes receiving machines to print nothing.

level, addressing—A process to develop the number of steps of an indirect address which has been applied to a particular program. First level is considered direct addressing, i.e., the address part of the instruction word has the address in storage of the operand. In second level addressing (indirect), the address part of the instruction word gives the storage location where the address of the operand may be found.

lexeme—Refers to the specific written word, particle, or stem that denotes the meaning.

librarian—In most systems this is a program designed to create, maintain, and make available the collection of programs, routines and data that make up an operating system. Librarian functions may include system generation and system editing.

library, program—1. The available collection of computer programs and routines. 2. An assemblage or organized set of computer programs, routines, or common or specifically-designed software, i.e., catalog of program titles, abstracts, etc., reels of magnetic tapes or cabinets of punched cards, tapes containing various programs or routines, source or object programs classified for intelligence or retrieval, etc.

light, NIXIE—A patented tube or glowing bulb designed with the particular capability of converting a binary number as a pattern of pulses into a visual number. The light or tube is used on various panels, consoles, or other types of visual devices to display decimal numbers indicating register contents or storage locations or other information for the programmer or operator which is subject to rapid characters.

light pen (stylus)—1. Quite basically this is considered part of a visual display (CRT) which provides a "window into the computer." Most models can display as a series of points, a message of thousands of characters of information, of tables, charts, graphs and the lines and curve of drawings. The light pen (stylus) available with the display can detect information that has been displayed on the screen and enables the operator to change the information under program control. When this penlike device is pointed at information displayed on the screen, it detects light from the cathode-ray tube (CRT) when a beam passes within its field of view. The pen's response is transmitted to the computer which, in turn, relates the computer action to the section of the image being displayed. In this way, the operation can delete or add text, maintain tighter control over the program, and choose alternative courses of action. 2. An optional device which when used in conjunction with the incremental display, can greatly extend its usefulness. It is a highspeed, photosensitive device with which the operator can cause the computer to change or modify the display on the cathode-ray tube. As the pertinent display information is selected by the operator, the pen signals the computer by generating a pulse. Acting upon this signal, the computer can then instruct other points to be plotted across the tube face in accordance with the pen movements, or exercise specific options previously programmed without the need for separate input devices.

limiter—Refers to a device designed to reduce the power of an electrical signal when it exceeds a specified value. The amount of reduction or compression increases with an increase of the input power.

LINC (Laboratory Instrument Computer)—A proprietary program, LINC performs several of the functions that external devices or people are normally required to perform. Data recording, analog-to-digital conversion, experiment monitoring, control, and analysis are built-in capabilities of the computer. LINC gives direct assistance to the research worker in many ways. (DEC)

line, delay—Refers to various devices designed to be capable of retarding a pulse of energy between input and output, based on the properties of materials, circuit parameters, or mechanical devices. Examples of delay lines are material media such as mercury, in which sonic patterns may be propagated in time; lumped-constant electrical lines; coaxial cables; transmission lines; and recirculating magnetic-drum loops. (Related to magnetic delay line.)

line printing—Refers to basic computer printing of one line of characters across a page; i.e., 100 or more characters simultaneously, as continuous paper advances line by line in one direction past type bars or a type cylinder that contains all characters in all positions.

linkage—1. Those specific instructions that are related to the entry and re-entry of closed subroutines. 2. The interconnections between a main routine and a closed routine; i.e., entry and exit for a closed routine from the main routine.

linkage editor—A specific routine designed for standard services to convert outputs of assemblers or compilers to forms which can be loaded and executed by combining separately developed object modules, or incorporating all or parts of previously processed load modules into a new load module. The linkage editor also replaces or inserts, control sections, creates overlay facilities, or resolves symbolic cross references between various input modules. Usually linkage editors are run before programs are ready for load in OS, DOS, or TOS operations, i.e., disk and tape operating systems.

linkage macro-instruction—A basic macro-instruction designed to provide logical linkage between programs and subroutines and that will save data needed by another program.

LIPL—Abbreviation for Linear Information Processing Language—a version or subset of IPL, a high-order programming language.

LISP (List Processing)—Refers to various types of interpretive languages developed for manipulation of symbolic strings of recursive data, i.e., used to develop higher-level languages.

list—1. A string of items written in a meaningful format that designates quantities to be transmitted for input/output. 2. An individual series of similar items, as the names of cities and the current population of each; i.e., a one-dimensional array of numbers. 3. To print every relevant item of input data.

list, chained—A system relating to a set of items designed to contain an identifier for the next item in a particular order, but such order does not have any particular relation to the order in which they are stored.

listing, assembly-language—Refers to a specific binary-output program of the compiler which is optional at compile time. The listing also contains the symbolic instructions equivalent to the binary-code output of the compiler. Such an assembly-output listing is useful as a debugging aid. By including certain pseudo-operation codes in in-line assembly language, the assembly-language output can be assembled by the assembler. (If output is obtained on either cards, paper tape, or magnetic tape.) This will allow modification of programs at the assembly-language level.

list processing—A particular method for programming using list structures to organize storage. Computer storage is organized into many lists or structures of data items, each with a symbolic name, a reader, starting record and a number of entries.

list processing languages—Particular languages developed by symbol manipulation and used primarily as research tools rather than for production programming. Most have proved valuable in construction of compilers and in simulation of human problem solving. Other uses have been generalized and verification of mathematical proofs, pattern recognition, information retrieval, algebraic manipulation, heuristic programming and exploration of new programming languages.

list, push-down—A list of items designed so that the last item entered is the first item of the list, and the relative position of the other items is pushed back one.

list structure—Refers to specific sets of data items combined because each element contains the address of the successor items or element, i.e., a predecessor item or element. A characteristic of such lists is that they grow in size according to the limits of fixed storage capacity, and it is relatively simple to insert or delete data items anywhere in a list structure.

literal—1. The symbol, word, or number which names, describes, or defines itself and not something else that it might represent. 2. An item of data with its value as stated or listed. Example would be 490, a literal; thus, 490 is its value.

load—1. The process of filling internal storage of a computer with information from auxiliary or external storage. 2. To enter or add to the internal storage of a computer various information from auxiliary, intermediate, or external storage.

load-and-go—Refers to a fundamental computer operation and/or compiling technique designed so that the pseudo-language is directly converted to machine language and the program run without an output machine-language program being created.

loader, bootstrap—See bootstrap loader.

loader, system—The system loader is designed to load binary object program output from compilations and assemblies into specific sections of computer memory. The system loader is capable of loading binary main programs, binary subprograms, library subroutines, and input-output drivers. The linkage between these programs is performed automatically during loading. The system loader loads input-output drivers from the specified logical equipment for a program and performs all linkages within the monitor. Programs may be loaded from cards, paper tape, or from the master file. Intermixed programs may be loaded in part of each of these devices in one load operation. The loader is resident in upper computer memory and is capable of overlaying itself in part with library subroutines. Common data-storage areas are placed in the loader area to allow complete overlay of the loader. Thus, a program may use all of computer memory. No memory storage is lost because of the size of the loader. (ASI)

load mode—For most systems, in load mode, data transmission is designed so that data delimiters are carried along with the data transmitted as in contrast with move mode.

load point—Refers to a precise and preset point at which magnetic tape is initially positioned under the read-write head to start reading or writing.

locate mode—For many systems this is a specific method of communicating with an input/output control system (IOCS) by using a method designed so that the address of the data involved, but not the data themselves, is transferred between the IOCS routine and the program, thus sparing the programmer from having to incorporate detailed, machine-level I/O logic in every one of his routines, since IOCS in memory communicates with the running program and performs I/O as directed by the program. But, locate-code operations require that the computer be equipped with index registers or base registers which enable run-time address computation to proceed while individual computer instructions are being interpreted.

location—1. A position of unit storage in the main internal storage that stores one computer word; a storage register. 2. A place in main memory or auxiliary storage where a unit of data may be stored or retrieved.

locations, protected—Concerns specific locations which are designed or reserved for special purposes, and in which data cannot be stored without undergoing a screening procedure to establish suitability for storage therein.

logger—A machine that automatically records physical processes with respect to time.

logical circuit—One of many types of switching circuits such as AND, OR, NAND, etc., gates which can perform various logic operations or represent logic functions.

logical connectives—Refers to the fundamental operators gates, switches or words, such as AND, OR, OR ELSE, IF THEN, NEITHER NOR, and EXCEPT, that make new statements from given statements and also have the property that the truth or falsity of the new statements can be calculated from the truth or falsity of the given statements and the logical meaning of the operator.

logical decision—1. In computers these are the decisions concerning the choice or ability to choose between alternatives. Basically this amounts to an ability to answer yes or no with respect to certain fundamental questions involving equality and relative magnitude; e.g., in an inventory application, it is necessary to determine whether or not there has been an issue of a given stock item. 2. The operation of selecting alternative paths of flow depending on intermediate program data.

logical design—1. Refers to the basic logic and its implementation for the system, machine, or network. 2. Also concerns the planning of a computer system prior to its engineering design. 3. Computer design from the view-point of data flow within the computer without consideration of the hardware. 4. Design that deals with the logical and mathematical interrelationships that must be implemented by the hardware.

logical element—Refers to the basic and the smallest building blocks in computers or data processing systems that can be represented by logical operators in an appropriate system of symbolic logic. Typical logical elements are the AND gate and the OR gate; they can be represented as operators in a suitable symbolic logic.

logical expressions—A logical or logic expression consists of logical constants, variable logic elements, function references, and combinations of those operands, separated by specific logical operators, and parentheses. A logical expression often contains arithmetic expressions, separated by relational operators, and again separated from other elements as specified by logical operators and parentheses. Logic expressions are most often used in logical

IF statements but can also be used in logical assignment statements and as arguments of functions. The logical expression may take on only two values, true or false, when a logical expression appears in a FORTRAN statement it is evaluated according to the rules given below. It will always yield one of the two values, TRUE or FALSE.

logical IF—A FORTRAN IV statement designed to cause an execute when the logical expression is true, or will bypass the statement if it is false.

logical number—Concerns the various numbers assigned to peripheral units during autoload or system generation time. Such numbers can be altered whenever convenient, in contrast to a physical unit number.

logical record—One where the scope, direction, or length is governed by the specific nature of the information or data which it contains instead of by some feature or limitation of the storage device that holds it. Such records differ in size from the physical records in which they are contained. Physical records might be limited to 400-character physical record size (example, an airline standard), but many logical records might require fewer or more than the limit.

logical variable—A variable which may have only the value "true" or "false". (FORTRAN IV)

logic formal—Most frequently this refers to an objective study of the structure, form, and design of valid arguments. It disregards, for this purpose, the meaning and importance of the terms of the argument itself.

logic shift—A shift which is similar to a cyclic shift and designed so that it can affect all positions, i.e., a nonarithmetic shift.

logic, symbolic—1. Refers to the fundamental study of formal logic and mathematics through the use of a special written language which seeks to avoid the ambiguity and inadequacy of ordinary language. 2. Also concerns the mathematical concepts, techniques, and languages as used in definition (1), whatever their particular application or context. (Synonymous with mathematical logic, and related to logic.) 3. Relates to the exact reasoning about relations, using symbols that are efficient in calculation. A branch of this subject known as Boolean algebra has been of considerable assistance in the logical design of computing circuits.

log, real-time clock—This built-in clock, while used for a wide variety of programming-time purposes, is also used to log the receipt times of a periodic real-time input data. Each input message and its receipt time may be recorded together. This clock is also used in connection with the preparation of statistical and analytical reports dealing with the frequency of certain transactions.

longitudinal check—Refers to a process, procedure or system of error control based on the check to determine if some present rules for the formation of the group of bits in the same numerical order in all the character signals in a block are observed.

loop—The repetitious execution of a series of instructions caused by having the last instruction in the series return the machine to the first instruction in the same series.

loop, closed—The complete signal path in a control system represented as a group of units connected in such a manner that a signal started at any point follows a closed path and can be traced back to that point.

loop, dynamic—Refers to a specific loop stop designed to consist of a single jump instruction which causes a jump to itself. A loop stop is usually designed for operating convenience, such as to indicate an error.

loop, high speed—Such loops are found in magnetic drums and disk storage devices which have a section that has a faster access than that provided by a complete revolution of that drum or disk, i.e., a read head and a write head spaced some distance apart on the same track so that data written by one head is read by another head a short time later and sent back to the write head. In consequence, a fixed-length loop of data revolves and may be changed by gating. The delay is similar to that of a delay line.

loop, nesting—In most systems nesting loops usually contain a loop of instructions which then also contains inner loops, nesting subroutines, outer loops, and rules and procedures relating to in and out procedures for each type.

loop, open—A specific but basic loop in a control system in which there is no self-correcting action for misses of the desired operational condition as there is in a closed loop system.

loop, recirculating—Usually concerns drum computers, and is a small section of memory which has much faster access than the remainder of memory.

low order—That which pertains to the weight or significance assigned to the digits of a number; e.g., in the number 123456, the low order digit is six. One may refer to the three low-order bits of a binary word as another example.

lowpass—A type of pass which relates to the operation of a circuit or a device, as a filter which permits the passage of low frequency signals and attenuates high frequency signals.

L P (linear-programming)—Linear programming (LP) is a mathematical technique designed and developed so that the best allocation of limited resources may be determined by manipulation of a series of linear equations. Each factor in the problem is evaluated against all other factors in relation to the long-range goals, thus yielding optimum parts of action for management consideration.

LPM—Lines per minute.

Luhn scanner—The scanning device invented by the IBM employee, H. P. Luhn. It is designed for photoelectrical scanning of punched cards as they are fed through the machine and with some search capabilities.

* – * – *

machine address—The direct, absolute, unindexed address expressed as such, or resulting after indexing and other processing has been completed.

machine, asynchronous—Refers to various machines which have operating speeds not related to any fixed or specific frequency of the system. Therefore, since no fixed period or interval signals the next event, it may be begun at the end of a prior one, without regard to the time it might take.

machine code—1. Composed of the absolute numbers, names, or symbols assigned by the machine designer to any part of the machine. 2. Same as operation code.

machine cognition—Refers to optical machine reading and pattern recognition. Certain machines have capability to optically sense a displayed character and to select from a given repertoire of characters, the specific character which is nearest in shape to the character which is displayed. The various shapes of characters are based on statistical norms, and if different shapes arise new characters join the repertoire. This suggests a type of artificial learning, i.e., perception and inerpretation are based on experience. Optical character recognition must be part of the scheme. Machine learning is based on artificial perception or machine cognition.

machine cycle—1. A fundamental concept which refers to the specific time interval in which a computer can perform a given number of operations. 2. Generally considered to be the shortest complete process of action that is repeated in order. 3. The minimum length of time in which the foregoing can be performed.

machine-independent—Refers to a phrase or concept used to indicate that a procedure or a program is conceived, organized, or oriented without specific reference to the operating characteristics of any one data-processing system. Use of this phrase usually implies that the procedure or program is oriented or organized in terms of the logical nature of the problem, rather than in terms of the characteristics of the machine used in solving it.

machine instruction—1. Upon machine recognition, a code element causes a predefined sequence of operations. 2. An instruction that the particular machine can recognize and execute.

machine language—1. The particular set of symbols, characters, or signs, and the rules for combining them, that conveys instructions or information to a computer. 2. Information or data is ex-pressed in code that can be read directly, used or written by the computer or peripheral machines without further processing (same as machine-oriented language and related to object language).

machine logic—1. Hardware techniques of problem approach and function execution; the way a system is designed to do its operations; what those operations are, and the type and form of data which can be used internally. 2. The capability of an automatic data processing machine to make decisions based upon the results of tests performed.

machine-oriented programming system—A specific system that uses a language that is oriented to the internal language of a specific computer. Systems that are considered to be machine oriented are assembly systems and macro systems.

machine, self-organizing—Refers to a unique and special class of machine or system that may be characterized loosely as containing a variable network in which the elements are organized by the machine itself, without external intervention, to meet criteria of successful operation. (Synonymous with self-organizing system.)

machine tool control—Most often refers to numerical control systems. A powerful and versatile program for production of tapes for computer controlled point-to-point and contouring machines.

machine tools, numerically controlled—Machinery, controlled by a computer in manufacturing operations. Some numerically controlled machines use paper tape which has been prepared by a specially programmed computer to control the movement of complex machine tools. Computers can control drafting machines, conveyor belts, and many other complicated physical processes.

machine translation—Transmitting automatically from one representation to another representation. The translation may involve codes, languages, or other systems of representation (related to automatic dictionary).

machine, Turing—A unique and useful mathematical abstraction of a device that operates to read from, write on, and move an infinite tape, thereby providing a model for computerlike procedures. The behavior of a Turing machine is specified by listing an alphabet; i.e., collection of symbols read and written, a set of internal states, and a mapping of an alphabet and internal states which determines what the symbol written and tape motion will be, and also what internal state will follow when the machine is in a given internal state and reads a given symbol.

macro code or macroprogram macro—Refers to groups of source-language statements, routines, or programs that is understandable to a processor or compiler with or without aid of an interpretative routine. Production of many-for-one instructions in machine language; an open-ended sequence of machine instructions, may be linked to consecutive or closed subroutines.

macroexpansion, conditional—Concerns a program design in which a certain number of lines of coding within a macroinstruction will be included or excluded during expansion, depending upon certain conditions.

macro generation—Generally concerns compilers, i.e., the many-for-one concept or process of generating several machine-language instructions from one

macro statement in source programs.

macrolibrary—Relates to groups of prepared and specialized but unspecific programs which are located in mass storage and which may be selectively found by an assembler which reads them, particularizes them by replacing general parameters with specific parameters, and incorporates them into programs.

magnetic card—See card, magnetic.

magnetic card storage—See card, magnetic.

magnetic cell—1. This is the basic unit of storage capable of storing a single bit or representing the site of a no bit area where an existing bit will represent a magnetic field or direction of a magnetic force. 2. Refers to a binary storage cell designed so that the two values of one binary digit are represented by different patterns of magnetism, and in which means of setting and sensing the contents are stationary with respect to the magnetic material.

magnetic character—Refers to a character imprinted with ink and designed with magnetic properties. These characters are unique in that they can be read directly by both humans and machines.

magnetic core—1. The basis of most internal storage, i.e., a magnetic material, usually toroidal in shape, which is pulsed or polarized by electric currents carried in a wire or wires wound around it. This central unit is capable of assuming and remaining at one of two conditions of magnetization, thus providing storage, gating, or switching functions. See core memory. 2. In most computers it is a small doughnut-shaped ferrite designed and constructed for on or off magnetization and used to store information in the computer. 3. Also refers to a miniaturized ring of ferromagnetic substance that may be instantaneously magnetized to a negative or positive flux and remains so until changed by further computer operations.

magnetic disc (disk)—A circular plate which is flat with a magnetic surface on which data can be stored by selective magnetization of portions of the flat surface.

magnetic document sorter-reader—Refers to special properties of the ink, used to print data on documents, which can be given small charges of electricity. As a by-product of reading these electrical impulses, the sorter transmits the data to the memory of the computer for processing. Magnetic ink character recognition (MICR) was developed through the efforts of the banking profession and the machine manufacturers.

magnetic drum—A rapidly rotating cylinder, the surface of which is coated with a magnetic material on which information may be stored in the form of small polarized spots.

magnetic-drum storage—1. One of the basic memory devices consisting of a rotating cylindrical drum surfaced with a magnetic coating. Binary data are stored as small magnetized spots arranged in close tracks around the drum. A magnetic reading and writing head is associated with each track so that the desired track can be selected by electric switching. Data from a given track are read or written sequentially as the drum rotates.

magnetic stripe recording—Refers to many types of magnetic recording, i.e., the magnetic material is depositied in strip form on a document or card, the term magnetic stripe recording is most often used.

magnetic strip file—Designed for use in mass storage systems and also a file storage device which uses strips of material with surfaces that can be magnetized for the purpose of storing data.

magnetic tape—A storage device externally located in the form of a ferrous oxide coating on a reel of metallic or plastic tape upon which bits may be recorded magnetically as a means of retaining data.

magnetic-tape plotting system—1. An example of a particular system is: the magnetic-tape plotting units produce an X-Y plot from data recorded on magnetic tape by a digital computer. Information read from the tape is used to drive a digital incremental plotter, which reproduces the data in either a continuous curve or discrete points. Versatility of the system permits the use of subroutines for generation of any desired symbols, letters, numerals, or scale markings. 2. Most systems are very versatile, reliable, and almost completely automatic. Zero position, scale factor adjustment, curve identification, symbol selection, axis generation, etc., are handled entirely by subroutines with the computer. For this reason, the plotting system may be operated by unskilled personnel. The operator is required only to select the desired plot by means of the automatic SEARCH feature, then initiate the plotting action by pressing either the single- or multiple-plot button. Plots can be produced up to 29½ inches in width and 120 feet in length. Adapters are available for on-line operation for most large computers. They are also designed for off-line operation with virtually any medium or large-scale digital systems. These systems produce completed graphs from data recorded on magnetic tape.

magnetic wire—Refers to a wire made of or coated with a magnetic material and used for magnetic recording and storage.

magnitude—1. Refers to a measurement of size or mass. The absolute value of a number. 2. Also relates to the size of a quantity as distinct from its sign. Thus +10 and −10 have the same magnitude.

main frame—The main part of the computer; i.e., the arithmetic or logic unit. The central processing unit (CPU).

main memory—Basically, the fastest storage device of a computer and the one from which instructions are executed (contrasted to auxiliary storage).

main path—Refers to the principal line of direction taken by a computer in the execution of a routine, directed by the logic of the program and the nature of the data.

maintenance, file—Procedures for periodically modifying files to incorporate changes that occurred during a given period.

maintenance, preventive—Concerns that specific maintenance of a computer system, that attempts to keep equipment in top operating condition and to preclude failures during production runs.

maintenance, remedial—Concerns that specific maintenance performed by the contractor following equipment failure; therefore, remedial maintenance is performed, as required, on an unscheduled basis.

management, data base—A basic concept which refers to a systematic approach to storing, updating, and retrieval of information stored as data items usually in the form of records in a file, where

many users, or even many remote installations, will use common data banks.

management information—Very generally this is the required data or program (system) results considered the primary prerequisites for decision making with regard to business operations and control.

manipulated variable—In specific instances this is a process that is desired to regulate some condition, i.e., a quantity is altered by the computer in order to initiate a change in the value of the regulated condition.

mantissa—The name given fractional part of a logarithm; e.g., in the logarithm 2.5, 2 is the characteristic and 5 is the mantissa.

manual entry—Concerns the manual insertion of data, usually for remote typewriter units or keyboard modules or terminals.

manual mode—The mode designed so that all automatic features are off and the computer is prepared to accept operator instructions directly from the control console.

map—1. The process of transforming information from one form to another. 2. To establish a correspondence between the elements of one set and the elements of another set.

map, memory—A hardware-implemented printout provided for dynamically relocating, protecting, and executing programs in scattered fragments of memory.

mapping—1. Refers to procedures for a transformation from one set to another set. 2. A correspondence.

marker, beginning-of-information (BIM)—A convenience item for operators, this is a reflective spot on the back of a magnetic tape, 10 feet from the physical beginning of the tape which is sensed photoelectrically to indicate the point on tape at which recording may begin.

marker, destination-warning—Another operator convenience item, it refers to a reflective spot on the back of a magnetic tap, 18 feet from the physical end of the tape, which is sensed photoelectrically to indicate that the physical end of the tape is approaching.

marker, end-of-tape—That special mark, character, long blank or other coding which indicates the end of a tape or recording, i.e., often times this is a reflective strip and easy-to-see, or a transparent section, or, in paper tape, a special bit pattern.

mark, record—A basic programming feature, usually a special character used in most computers either to limit the number of characters in a data transfer, or to separate blocked or grouped records in tape.

mark sensing—A technique used to detect special pencil marks entered in special places on a card, and automatically translating the marks into punched holes.

mark, tape—Refers to a specific character that is written on tape to signify the physical end of the recording on tape.

mask—1. A fundamental concept which refers to a machine word that specifies which parts of another machine word are to be operated on. Also called extractor or filter. 2. That specific act of replacing characters in the accumulator with characters from a specified storage location that corresponds to the "ones" position in the mask, which is in a specific storage location or register. 3. To extract a selected group of characters from a string of characters.

master/slave system—Concerns that spe-cific computer configuration designed for business or scientific use (as production automation) in which one computer, usually of substantial size or capability, rules with complete control over all input-output and schedules and transmits tasks to a slave computer. The latter computer often has a great capacity, and it performs the computations as directed and controlled by the master unit.

mathematical model—A conceptual tool which relates to the general characterization of a process, object, or concept, in terms of mathematics, thus enabling the relatively simple manipulation of variables to be accomplished in order to determine how the process, object, or concept would behave in different situations.

mathematical parameter—Usually concerned with math models. A secondary variable in an application. For example, the analytic geometry description of a line, $y = ax$ plus b can be replaced by the parametric expression $y = a^t x + b$ where t is regarded as a parameter. The constants, a and b, and the dependent variables, x and y, are not considered as parameters.

MATH-PAC—Refers to various mathematical and statistical programs for simplifying such scientific and engineering applications as solution of simultaneous linear equations, matrix algebra, multiple linear regression, roots of a polynomial, and least squares polynomial fit. (General Electric)

matrix—1. An array of numbers that is rectangular—subject to mathematical operations, such as addition, multiplication, and inversion, according to specified rules. Any table is a matrix of circuit elements such as diodes, wires, magnetic cores, and relays, arranged and designed to perform a specified function.

mean-time-between-failures—Concerns the particular measurement limit of the ratio of operating time or equipment to the number of observed failures as the number of failures approaches infinity.

media conversion—1. Generally most program libraries have complete sets of routines to perform media conversions of all kinds. Media conversion is efficiently completed in the multiprogramming mode rather than with off-line equipment or smaller computers. 2. Also concerns small, tightly coded subroutines operating under control of the executive system perform one-line conversion of data between card, printer, punch, and tape equipment concurrently with other programs. Low-speed devices use magnetic drum as a large buffer area between themselves and operating programs. Use of the magnetic drum as a buffer provides increased throughput capability as programs using these drum buffers effectively "read" or "print" information at drum transfer speeds.

mega—(1,000,000) (or 1024K for memory devices).

memories, associative—Associative-memory capability is developed by high-speed memory searches within computers and is based on content or subject matter rather than being limited to locating data through specified "addresses."

memory—Any device into which a unit of information can be copied, which will hold this information, and from which the information can be obtained at a later time (the terms memory and storage are interchangeable). Memory types include disk, core, drum, or relay memories. Extremely rapid access-storage elements from which instructions are executed and data operated on are referred to as main memory as contrasted to auxiliary-memory modules.

memory address register—1. That particular register which contains the address of the selected word in memory. See register. 2. Also refers to the location in core memory that is selected for data storage or retrieval is determined by the memory address. Some registers can directly address all 4096 words of the standard core memory or of any preselected field of extended core memory.

memory address, virtual—Refers to new systems and is often interpreted as addressing, but it is (1) a particular character relative to the beginning of a page, (2) a particular page relative to the initial point of that segment, and (3) a particular large memory segment or book. Thus programs can be addressed into noncontiguous areas of memory in relatively small blocks.

memory buffer register—1. A register designed so that a word is stored as it comes from memory (reading) or just prior to its entering memory (writing). See register. 2. Also concerns the memory which serves as a buffer register for all information passing between the processor and the core memory, and serves as a buffer directly between core memory and peripheral equipment during data-break information transfers. The memory buffer is also used as a distributor shift register for the analog-to-digital converter.

memory cycle—A fundamental operation referring to or consisting of reading from and writing into memory.

memory dump—1. The procedure that

lists the contents of a storage device, area, or selected parts of it. 2. Same as storage dump.

memory (dynamic allocation)—In many large systems, each time a subroutine is called using this feature, the unique storage area for that subroutine is assigned to the first storage available. Thus, all subroutines called on the same level will share the same storage area. This results in a significant storage saving in many cases. In addition, a recursive subroutine call is possible because a new storage area is assigned each time a subroutine is entered. This feature, together with in-line symbolic coding, provides real-time capability.

memory guard—Refers to various electronic or program guards inhibiting or preventing access to specific sections of storage devices or areas especially concerning the main or internal memory of the central processor.

memory hierarchy—1. A combination of memories with differing sizes and speeds and usually having different cost-performance ratios. A hierarchy might consist of a very high-speed, small semiconductor memory, a medium-speed core memory and a large, slow-speed core. 2. Due to a speed mismatch between core memory and semiconductor logic and between core and other random-access storage media (drums or disks), memory system innovations have arisen. Program and data parts can be scattered in both main memories and in disks or drums for swapping between main and auxiliary storage automatically on demand (demand paging). Normally copies of all pages in main memory are retained on an auxiliary drum or disk and, when changes are made in page contents while in main memory, copies

are written back onto the drum or disk when no longer needed. Access to semiconductor memories are in nanoseconds (billionths), to magnetic core memories in microseconds (millionths), and to disk and drum in millisecond (thousandths) with such differences in speed usually inversely related to cost; i.e., the slowest memories are the lowest cost per bit storage. Splitting memories into sections, and then interleaving the accessing to alternate sections is a procedure for cutting down the speed mismatch between logic and core memories.

memory location—A specific position in a computer storage device.

memory, main—This is the fundamental internal storage unit and is usually the fastest storage device of a computer and the one from which instructions are executed. (Contrasted to auxiliary storage.)

memory map—A hardware-implementation which provides for dynamically relocating, protecting, and executing programs in scattered fragments of memory.

memory, nonvolatile—When power is removed from the system, this storage medium retains its information.

memory overlays—In many large systems the monitor remains resident in lower memory at all times. Object programs are loaded into memory, starting at the end of the monitor. The program loader resides in upper memory. Object programs cannot be loaded into the loader area. This area can be overlayed by common storage. Part of the loader can also be overlayed by library subroutines.

memory, permanent—Refers to that specific type of storage of information that remains intact when the power is turned off. Also called nonvolatile storage.

memory, photo-optic—A specific memory or storage unit that uses an optical medium. For example, a laser might be used to record on photographic film.

memory protection—A method specifically designed to insure that the contents of main memory within certain designated but variable bounds will not be destroyed or altered. Special programming devices or hardware thus guard against the effects of equipment malfunction and program bugs in real-time systems.

memory, random-access (RAM) (bank)—Used to provide storage of on-line account records containing all information—account balance, available balance, unposted dividends and previous nobook transactions, account holds, etc., required for complete processing of transactions and inquiries, as well as for updating of passbooks.

memory, rapid—Refers to those specific sections of the whole memory from which information may be obtained in the shortest possible time.

memory, read-only—Concerns those various types of memory that cannot be altered in normal use of the computer. Usually, a small memory that contains often-used instructions such as micro-programs or system software.

memory, regenerative—A memory device whose contents gradually vanish if not periodically refreshed.

memory register—A specific register in computer storage as in contrast with a register in one of the other units of the computer.

memory, scratch-pad—Refers to an internal unit of high-speed memory used to store the location of an interrupted program and to retrieve the latter after the interrupting program has been completed.

memory, thin-film—1. Relates to various procedures of computer storage that utilizes a film (only a few millionths of an inch thick) of metallic vapor that has been deposited on a thin glass plate. The film can be polarized in a billionth of a second (a nanosecond) for fast-memory access. 2. Also refers to a storage device made of thin disks of magnetic material deposited on a nonmagnetic base. Its operation is similar to the core memory.

memory, virtual—A multiprogramming technique designed to permit the user to treat secondary (disk) storage as an extension of core-memory, thus giving the virtual appearance of a larger core memory. A type of memory with the capability of using a type of algorithm of the paging or segmenting type. In this manner a larger memory is simulated than actually exists in core.

memory, volatile—Storage medium of the type in which information can be destroyed when power is removed from the system.

merge-match—A process of comparison of two files, usually based on key words designed to place them in a pre-arranged sequential order of those records which match to the arbitrarily selected key words. And further, the resulting segregation of those records which do not match are mated to combine or join two different units of equipment.

merge/sort—A routine set which arranges random items in an ordered sequence. These routines can also be used to combine two or more ordered sequences into a single file.

merging sort—The process for forming of a single file of sequenced records from two or more files of sequenced records.

message—1. Generally refers to a finite

98

sequence of letters, digits, symbols, etc. 2. In communication, a transmitted series of words or symbols that are designed and intended to convey information. In message switching, a message consists of a header, text, and an end-of-message symbol. 3. In computing, a group of words, variable in length, transported as a unit; a transported item of information.

message switching—There exists a need for message switching communication systems among large corporations spread out over a large number of widely separated locations. Where communications traffic is high, a computer-controlled switching system is needed. In this type of application, the data flow pattern involves message traffic between a number of terminals and a central switching center. The sending terminal transmits each message to the center, which stores it temporarily, performs any processing or code conversion functions that may be required, and then transmits the message to one or more designated receiving terminals. Large networks may utilize two or more switching centers which are interconnected by high-speed communications links.

MICR (Magnetic Ink Character Recognition)—A check-encoding system employed by banks for the purpose of automating check handling. Checks are imprinted (using magnetic ink) with characters of a type face and dimensions specified by the American Banking Association. There are fourteen characters—ten numbers (0-9) and four special symbols—which are used to provide amount, identifying, and control information.

microcode—1. A coding system using sub-operations not ordinarily accessible in programming; e.g., coding that makes use of parts of multiplication or division operations. 2. A list of small program steps. Combinations of these steps, performed automatically in a prescribed sequence, from a macro operation like multiply, divide, and square root.

microfilm computer output (COM)—Refers to various microfilm devices, especially printers that are designed to take output directly from the computer, thus substituting for line printer or tape output.

microfilm displays—A specific example is a Burroughs system. The DIGIPRINT system, consisting of a symbol generator, line generator, CRT, and memory, is a low-cost alpha-numeric and graphic information-recording system that operates from any digital-data source. Computer generated data consisting of symbol and format commands is converted by the DIGIPRINT system to a CRT display which is photographed with the system's special digitally controlled 16-mm microfilm camera (35-mm option). The camera can also simultaneously photograph an "overlay" that contains basic continuing entries. Up to 10 overlays can be stored. Thus when the recorded information is retrieved, it is "printed" on the forms or maps that were used as overlays. This is a projected microfilm display. The unit is compatible with 63 kc tape drives on a real-time basis.

A camera/monitoring system is provided to permit quick confidence checks during long runs. Slave monitors are also available in the form of display consoles using 10", 16", or 21" cathode-ray tubes.

The DIGIPRINT system supplies its own page formatting without burdening the data source with this requirement. It provides automatic positioning of 135 symbols per line, up to 80 lines per page.

microprogramming—1. Refers to a programmers technique of using a certain special set of computer instructions that consists only of basic elemental operations which the programmer can combine into higher-level instructions as he chooses, and can then program using only the higher-level instructions. 2. Specifically refers to machine-language coding in which the coder builds his own machine instructions from the primitive basic instructions built into the hardware.

microsecond—One millionth of a second. One second = 1,000,000 microseconds.

MICR scan—Refers to procedures for sensing of characters, marks, or codes printed in magnetic ink. The technique was developed by American Bankers' Association and is used on bank checks. The character size, shape, and ink are standardized by the USA Standards Institute.

milestone—Refers to a specific task or event that cannot be considered completed until all tasks that feed into it are completed.

millisecond (ms)—The abbreviation for millisecond, one thousandth of a second. Written mathematically as 10^{-3} seconds, and also abbreviated msec.

(MIS) management-information system—A communications process in which data are recorded and processed for operational purposes. The problems are isolated for higher-level decision-making, and information is fed back to top management to reflect the progress or lack of progress made in achieving major objectives. An MIS gives the executive the capability of controlling the operation of a firm on a real-time basis.

mnemonic—Pertaining or intending to assist the human memory. A mnemonic term, then, is an abbreviation or acronym that is easy to remember.

mnemonic-operation code—Concerns various basic operation codes designed so that the names of operations are abbreviated and expressed mnemonically to facilitate remembering the operations they represent. A mnemonic code normally needs to be converted to an actual operation code by an assembler before execution by the computer. Examples of mnemonic codes are ADD for addition, CLR for clear storage, and SQR for square root.

mod—An abbreviation for modifications made in programs after they are written; each modification is thus properly identified to indicate it is the latest by using a mod number. For example: mass storage operating system, mod Z, version 3.

mod/demod—Abbreviated form for modulating and demodulating units.

mode—1. A particular operation method, e.g., the binary mode, the interpretive mode, the alphameric mode, etc. 2. The most frequent value in the statistical sense. Types: access, analysis, binary, byte, card, compute, freeze, hold, job-program, manual, and recording.

mode, burst—Generally relates to a mode of communications between the processor and I/O device operating through the multiplexor channel. In burst mode, the receiving unit continues to fetch bits until the unit is finished.

mode, conversational—Refers to a specific mode of operation designed so that real-time man-machine communications are maintained. In this mode the system is used exclusively for servicing remote terminals.

MODEM—1. An often used acronym for MOdulator DEModular unit. 2. A specific MODEM is a device that converts data from a form which is compatible with data-processing equipment to a form that is compatible with transmission facilities, and vice-versa.

mode, noisy—Usually relates to various floating-point arithmetic procedures associated with normalization in which "1" bits, rather than "0" bits, are introduced in the low-order bit position during the left shift.

modifier—Generally defined as a quantity used to alter the address of an operand; e.g., the cycle index.

modularity—1. A popular computer system concept which refers a set of conditions in the determination of the design of the equipment and programming systems such that the hardware and softwear components can be readily identified, altered, or augmented without replacements of particular units or sections. 2. Also concerns various operating system programs which conform to specific standards, so that control programs will have an identical interface with all processing programs. These standards are well documented so that user-written programs can follow the same conventions. The user is free to supplement supplied programs to meet special situations. By following the rules indicated in the standards, portions of control or processing programs can be changed or replaced in modular fashion.

module—1. Generally refers to a segment of core storage. 2. Also relates to a piece of peripheral equipment with specific capacity for storage (memory). 3. Sometimes this concerns an interchangeable plug-in item containing components.

4. In some sales literature it is an incremental block of storage or other building block for expanding the computer capacity.

modulo—Refers to mathematical operations that yield the remainder function of division. Thus 39 modulo 6 = 3.

monadic operation—Refers to operations performed on one operand, e.g., negation. (Synonymous with unary operation.)

monitor—A CRT receiver usually found in the control room of a transmitter station.

monitor operating system—In larger systems the monitor exercises primary control of the routines that compose the operating system. It is this monitor or operating system which turns the computer into a flexible tool allowing the user to achieve maximum use of the hardware's advanced design features.

monitor, real-time—The monitor, operating or executive system is an operating and programming system designed to monitor the construction and execution of programs, to optimize the utilization of available hardware, and to minimize programmer effort and operator intervention. The executive or monitor system, as a monitor, provides for concurrent processing and real-time operation in a classical monitor environment. The executive system is of modular construction, tailored to each user's equipment configuration and applications requirements. Extensions to the system for peripheral devices and application programs may be added, altered, or deleted as required.

monitor, remote-computing system—In multiprogramming systems when the computer is available for batch processing, the computer operator will indicate to a subsystem under the system monitor or executive that files on the auxiliary disk-storage device are to be processed. Under control of the subsystem, the files will be transferred from disk-storage or tape, which is then used as the system-input unit for normal processing under the system monitor. The result of this processing, which is contained on the system output unit, can be handled in either of the following ways: (1) it can be transferred to disk storage for subsequent transmission to a terminal, or (2) it can be printed on an offline printer and mailed to the terminal.

monte-carlo method—1. Those procedures that involve statistical sampling techniques in order to obtain a probabilistic approximation to the solution of a mathematical or physical problem. 2. The branch of linguistic study which deals with the history and functions of derivational forms and inflections. 3. A statistical trial and error calculating technique used when a great number of variables exist, and successive repeated calculations are required to establish probabilities.

morphology—Refers to that specific branch of linguistic study that deals with the history and functions of derivational forms and inflections.

MQ register—A register which is treated as an extension of the accumulator register in multiply and divide operations. Same as the extension register.

multicomputing, real-time—Refers to the many types of real-time command and control situations requiring maximum reliability. They can combine two or more computers in multicomputer systems. Two or more essentially independent computing systems communicate directly, with access to each other's memory. Capable of tremendous computing power, such systems have the added advantage of reserve equipment. Typical real-time applications demanding this degree of reliability include manned-space vehicle launching, and airport traffic control.

The concept of individual modules for processor, memory, and controller provides multiprocessor and multicomputer systems with multiple functions without undue duplication of hardware.

multiplexor—Can be considered a specialized computer, with stored program capability, designed for handling input-output functions of a real-time system.

multiple access—A system where output or input can be received or dispatched from more than one location.

multiple module access (MMA)—In many processor systems an MMA unit is positioned between each storage module and the several processors which may reference it to resolve potential storage-access conflicts. This unit is designed to furnish five priority-ordered processor connection paths. Should an access conflict occur between processors, the MMA will grant storage access to the processor having the relative highest priority attachment to the MMA, then to the next, and so on. Communications between processors and a single storage module can therefore be conducted on an asynchronous basis—if the storage module is "busy" servicing one processor, a passive wait cycle is induced in others of lower priority that may be referencing it.

multiple precision—Using two or more computer words to represent a single numeric quantity or numeral, i.e., with twice as many or more digits as are normally carried in a fixed-length word used to keep track of several parts of each numeral, precision is enhanced especially in matrix manipulation which often requires the use of multiple precision arithmetic.

multiple regression—A special analysis program for determining the mathematical relationships and relative significances of manufacturing parameters associated with a given problem.

multiplexed operation—A simultaneous operation sharing the use of a common unit of a system in such a way that it can be considered an independent operation.

multiplier, analog—Refers to a specific type of analog device designed to develop the analog product from two or more analog input signals, i.e., the output variable is proportional to the product of the input variables.

multiplier-quotient register—Refers to a specific register designed so that the multiplier for multiplication is placed therein, and in which the quotient for division is developed.

multiprocessing—1. The use of several computers to logically or functionally divide jobs or processes, and to execute various programs or segments asynchronously and simultaneously. 2. Two or more processors in a system configuration; one processor to control the system, with the others subordinate to it. All processors have direct access to all memory; each can perform computations and request input/output on individual programs stored in system core memory. Devices request memory access and wait until memory is available. They start immediately upon receipt of a memory access, and need not wait for the next clock cycle.

multiprocessing, sharing—Refers to the design of some systems which permit communications between individual processors by several means. The processors may share a control unit connected to a file device so that information may be communicated through the file. On all models a channel-to-channel adapter may interconnect two system channels. Shared-processor storage enables two interconnected processors to share main storage. In many systems two processors may communicate through shared large-capacity core storage. A direct-control feature can be used to signal directly from one processor to another. This feature would not, in general, be used to transfer any volume of data, but only to set up conditions for an interrupt of the processor receiving the signal.

multiprocessor, overlapping—Refers to the specific processor designed to be capable of determining whether its current operand and next instruction lie in different storage modules. It is also designed to determine if this situation is present, and of retrieving these two words in parallel, at an effective 100% performance increase. Since the I/O controller is not required to reference instructions in main storage except on command transfers, it does not have, nor does it need, the overlapping feature. The overlapping feature permits the separation of the instruction and data of a program into separate physical banks. Furthermore, the basing register of the processor allows either the instruction or data area of a program to be relocated independently—a significant advantage in core compacting to overcome fragmentation (some systems).

multiprogramming—A particular method

for handling numerous routines or programs simultaneously by overlapping or interleaving their execution; i.e., permitting more than one program to time-share machine components.

multiprogramming executive system— Many larger systems operate in a multiprogram or multiprocessing environment. In order to initiate and preserve this, the executive or monitor routine must be in complete control of the total system. Special hardware features are provided to permit this control. The multiprogramming and multiprocessing capabilities of these systems are often based upon guard mode operations, i.e., the setting aside of certain instructions, registers, and storage locations for the exclusive use of the executive routine, assuring protection against the interaction of unrelated programs (some systems).

multisequential system—A particular computing system which works much like a multiprocessor, i.e., one computer controlling several satellite computers and one which is capable of interleaving the execution of instructions which can also execute more than one instruction at a time, i.e., one capable of concurrent working of several computers.

multivibrator, free-running—Specifically refers to an oscillator which develops preplanned or desired shapes of signals most often of nonsinusoidal shapes. Operations are dependent upon two interacting circuits, i.e., two tubes or transistors connected so that one governs the operation of the other.

* _ * _ *

nanosecond—One billionth second. Nanosecond speeds were first in-

troduced to the data processing industry with a thin-film memory computer.

N/C (numerical-control) machines—A punched paper or plastic tape with magnetic spots is used to feed digital instructions to a numerical-control machine, i.e., an automated cutting or forming machine thus guided. Tolerances as fine as 1/10,000 of an inch are achieved on unattended units. Tapes are developed with digital computer programs.

nest—A subroutine or block of data embedded into a larger routine or block of data.

network—1. Refers to various series of interconnected points in computer systems. 2. Also, the interconnection of a number of points by communications facilities.

next-available-block register—Refers to that specific address register of available blocks of core storage that are chained together for use by the line control computer, i.e., for the allocation of incoming information.

nine edge—The lower or bottom edge of a card. This edge is most commonly used for entering the equipment first because of the external equipment requirements.

NIXIE display indicators—Refers to the popular Burroughs bulbs or NIXIE indicator tubes. The tubes are all-electronic, gas filled, cold-cathode indicators that display numerals, letters, or special symbols. These devices are the industry's most widely used electronic readout and are ideal for converting electromechanical or electronic signals directly to readable characters. NIXIE tube assemblies and display systems fall into two distinct categories, numeric and alpha-numeric. The numeric types are generally used in digital voltmeters, frequency counters, and other devices where digital information of a decimal nature must be displayed. The alphanumeric types are used in schedule boards, arrival-departure displays, computer readout panels, stock-quotation systems, and in other applications where a minimum of 36 characters (ten numbers and 26 letters) are required.

noise—1. Generally concerns various meaningless extra bits or words that must be ignored or removed from the data at the time the data is used. 2. Relates to errors introduced into data in a system, especially in communication channels. 3. Generally this is due to random variations of one or more characteristics of any entity such as voltage, current, and data. 4. Loosely, any disturbance tending to interfere with the normal operation of a device or system.

noise, broadband (white)—Specifically relates to the thermal noise that is uniformally distributed across the frequency spectrum at a wide range of energy levels.

noise generator—A special device designed to generate a random signal of known statistical properties of amplitude distribution and spectral density.

noisy mode—Most often refers to a floating-point arithmetic procedure associated with normalization in which digits other than zero are introduced in the low-order positions during the left shift.

nondestructive readout—1. A particular storage area that cannot be erased and reused, e.g., punched cards or perforated paper tape. 2. A reading process that does not destroy the data in the source. 3. A reading of the information in a register without changing that information.

nonlinear programming—A term covering all types of constrained optimization problems except those where the objective function and the constraints are all linear. Special types of nonlinear programming for which some theory has been developed are convex programming, concave programming, and quadratic programming.

no-op instruction—Concerns particular instructions that specifically instruct the computer to do nothing but process the next instruction in sequence, i.e., a blank instruction, a skip instruction, or a waste instruction. (Synonymous with waste instruction and skip.)

normalize—1. Refers to various programming techniques, i.e., to adjust the exponent and fraction of a floating-point quantity so that the fraction lies in the prescribed normal, standard range. 2. In mathematical operations this is a procedure to reduce a set of symbols or numbers to a normal or standard form. (Synonymous with standardize.) 3. To alter or position into a regular or standard format as to right- or left-justify.

normalized—Specifically, a mantissa is considered normalized if its first digit is not zero.

notation, infix—A unique notation for programmers designed for expressing arithmetic and logic statements by alternating single operands and operators. Most operators guide or follow particular system conventions for precedence and grouping brackets to avoid ambiguity.

notation, Polish—1. Refers to various distinct techniques or devices created by the Polish Logician, J. Ludasieqez for treating algebraic statements by manipulating strings of operations. 2. A specific form of prefix notation.

notation, prefix—A technique of forming one dimensional expressions without need for brackets by preceding with a string or vector of operators, an operand string or vector that may itself contain operators upon operands.

N-type—1. Concerns various semiconductor crystals doped to provide excess electrons. 2. A symbol in flowcharting depicting several options.

null—1. In math or set theory an absence of information, as contrasted with zero or blank for the presence of no information. 2. Refers to a condition of no deflection from a center or end position.

null representation—An empty or blank representation, for example, on a paper tape which controls a printer, a null representation does not cause movement of the printing position, as does a space character.

null string—Generally an empty string.

number, base—Concerns the quantity and type of characters designed for use in each of the digital positions of a numbering system. In the more common numbering systems the characters are some or all of the Arabic numerals as follows:

System Name	Characters	Radix
BINARY	(0,1)	2
OCTAL	(0,1,2,3,4,5,6,7)	8
DECIMAL	(0,1,2,3,4,5,6,7,8,9)	10

unless otherwise indicated, the radix of any number is assumed to be 10. For positive identification of a radix 10 number, the radix is written in parentheses as a subscript to the expressed number, i.e., $126_{(10)}$. The radix of any nondecimal number is expressed in similar fashion, e.g., $11_{(2)}$ and $5_{(8)}$.

number, binary—A number which usually consists of more than one figure, i.e., one representing a sum, in which the individual quantity represented by each figure is based on a radix of two. the figures used are 0 and 1.

number, biquinary-coded decimal—A number which usually consists of successive pairs of digits, i.e., each pair is a biquinary number; e.g., if the digits of a decimal number are 3671, the biquinary-coded decimal number would be 03 11 12 01. Left digit (1) of each pair of digits has a weight of 5.

number, hexadecimal—Refers to a specific numeration system designed to use the radix of 16, i.e., 16 symbols are used, 0 through 9 plus the characters K, S, N, J, F, and L for digits beyond 9, and each hexadecimal digit thus can be represented by a group of four binary digits, which is called a tetrad.

number, real—Generally relates to set theory, i.e., an element of a set of all positive and negative numbers, including all types, integers, zeros, mixed, rational, irrational, etc., but not imaginary or complex.

number, self-checking—A programming technique, i.e., a number, with a suffix figure related to the figure(s) of the number, used to check the number after it has been transferred from one medium or device to another. (Related to check bit modulo-n, and error-detecting code.

number, serial—Concerns specific numerals usually designed to be attached to a device, machine, item, or a sequence or position of an item relative to other items, i.e., numbers representing a label or identifier.

numbers, floating point—In many cases, the solution of a problem requires values of numbers that are either too large or too small to be expressed by the computer. The physical size of the number can be reduced by "scaling" or shifting the number to the right or left a predetermined number of places so that the most significant bits of the number may be used. For instance, the decimal number 6,510,000 may be expressed as 0.651×10^7, 0.0651×10^8, 0.00651×10^9, etc. The exponent of the number-system base is the scale factor or the number of places the number is shifted.

number system—1. Generally considered to be a defined set of numbers, as integers, fractions, decimals, real or noninteger numbers, etc., not to be confused with systems of numeration. 2. An integer is a whole number as differentiated from a fraction or a decimal. A decimal may be used but it cannot have digits other than zeros to the right of the decimal point and still be classified as an integer. In some cases a noninteger may be a solution but only the integer portion of the number has meaning. All are members of number systems.

number, uniform random—Refers to various sets of digits designed and constructed in such a sequence that each successive digit is equally likely to be any of n digits to the base of the number.

numerical analysis—The particular study of techniques of obtaining useful quantitative solutions to problems that have been expressed mathematically, including the study of the errors.

numerically controlled machine tools—Machinery, controlled by a computer, in manufacturing operations. Some numerically controlled machines use paper tape which has been prepared by a specially programmed computer to control the movements of complex machine tools. Computers can control drafting machines, conveyor belts, and many other complicated physical processes.

* — * — *

object code—One which is produced by a compiler or special assembler which can be executed on the target computer.

object computer—A computer system which uses the object program to thus execute the instructions, as contrasted to a computer that might be used to merely compile the object program from the source program.

OCAL—An acronym for: On-line Cryptanalytic Aid Language.

odd-even check—1. In an odd check, a bit (1) is carried along as a check if the total number of ones in the machine word is even, and 0 if the total number of ones in the machine word is odd. In an even check, the bit values are 0 for even and 1 for odd. Words are considered to be even parity or odd parity with check bit depending on the number of numeric ones which are permitted by the computer conventions. 2. Same as parity check.

OEM—Frequently used abbreviation for Original Equipment Manufacturer.

off-line—A system or peripheral equipment or device in a system in which the operation or peripheral equipment is not under the control of the central processing unit.

off-line equipment—Those devices not in direct communication with the central processing unit of a computer (synonymous with auxiliary equipment).

off-line mode—Refers to a procedure or way of computer operation; it means and concerns the devices that are not hooked up together. Perhaps the printer is printing the payroll checks, while the computer is solving a completely unrelated mathematical problem. Both are independent operations.

one-pass operation—In most systems only one pass is made over the source language yielding a binary program. This is true regardless of the input/output configuration. For users without magnetic tape units, this is especially useful. They do not have to reload cards or paper tape for a second pass. However, a two-pass option is included for more comprehensive listings and smaller binary decks.

ones complement—A radix minus-one complement with the radix equal to two.

one-to-one translator—Refers to various direct translating programs which generally produce only one instruction in the object language for each instruction in the source language.

on-line data processing—Those peripheral equipment or devices in direct communication with the central processing unit of a computer (clarified by off-line equipment).

on-line diagnostics—Refers to error detection, i.e., the running of diagnostics on a system while it is in line but off-peak to save time and to take corrective action without closing down the system.

on-line equipment—Refers to various units of the processing equipment usually of compatible computer speed or with buffers to transpose differing speeds, that are directly connected to the main processing unit.

on-line plotter—Plotters have become popular tools for engineers, scientists,

etc. A local or remote digital incremental plotter—in either on-line or off-line operation with a digital computer—provides a high speed plotting system with high degrees of versatility and reliability. As regards on-line operation with medium-size computers, a small adapter unit converts the computer output signals to a form suitable for driving a plotter. No modification to the basic computer circuitry is required. Adapters are available for all standard medium-scale digital computers. The plotter can be used for off-line operation with virtually any medium or large-scale computer.

on-line process optimization—An essential element of process control is the task of ensuring operating conditions or combinations of conditions for optimum profit. On-line analog computers can be used to adjust one or more process conditions to compensate for uncontrolled variations so that operation is maintained at the optimum level.

on-line, real-time operation (OLRT)—Refers to a particular system operation designed so that input data to the system are given directly from the measuring devices, and the computer results are thereby obtained during the progress of the event. For instance, the data that are received from measurements during a run, with real-time computation of dependent variables during the run, enables the computer to make changes in its output.

OP code—A command usually given in machine language, i.e., operations code.

open-ended—1. Refers to those qualities by which the addition of new terms, subject headings, or classifications do not disturb the preexisting system. 2. Concerns systems having the capability of being extended or expanded.

open-loop system—One in which the computer does not directly control a process or procedure, but instead displays or prints information for the operator to assist in determination of required action. Most real-time systems are basically open-loop systems.

open-routine—Relates to various routines that can be inserted directly into a larger routine without special linkages or calling sequences.

open shop—Refers quite generally to a computing installation at which computer programming, coding, and operating can be performed by any qualified company employee.

operand—1. Any quantity entering into or arising from an operation. An operand may be an argument, a result, a parameter, or an indication of the location of the next instruction. 2. A piece of data upon which an operation is performed. 3. The address or name portion of an operation, e.g., x is the operand of the operation (AND x).

operation code—1. Refers to various symbols or coding techniques that designate a basic computer operation to be performed. 2. Concerns combinations of bits specifying absolute machine-language operators, or the symbolic representation of the machine-language operator. 3. Also, that part of an instruction that designates the operation of arithmetic, logic, or transfer to be performed.

operation code, augmented—A unique and specific code which is further defined or limited by information found in another position of an instruction, i.e., an instruction word but one which has addresses considered as the operation code.

operation codes, mnemonic—Refers to the procedure for writing of operation codes in a symbolic notation which is easier to remember than the actual operation codes of the machine.

operation cycle—That part of a machine cycle where the actual execution of the instruction takes place. Some operations (e.g., divide, multiply) may need a large number of these operation cycles to complete the operation, and the normal instruction/operation alternation will be held up during this time. Also called execution cycle.

operation decoder—Concerns specific switching circuits designed to interpret the operator portion of the machine instruction to be executed, and set other circuitry for its execution.

operation, dyadic—An operation performed on two operands.

operation field—The instruction format part which specifies the procedure or process which is to be performed.

operation, floating-point—Refers to numerical calculations which use arithmetic points, binary or decimal, which are moveable, though not necessarily the same for each number.

operation, full-duplex—Very basically, full-duplex (or duplex) operations refer to communication between two points in both directions simultaneously.

operation, half-duplex—Half-duplex operations refer to communication circuits which operate in only one direction at a time, with or without a break feature. The break feature enables the receiving station to interrupt the sending station.

operation, input/output—1. In many large systems each channel is often capable of operating in three different transfer modes: input, output, or function. Usually the input and output modes are employed when transferring data to or from the central computer. The function mode is the means by which the central computer establishes the initial communication path with a peripheral subsystem. During this mode of transmission, the central computer sends one or more function words to a peripheral subsystem directing the specified units to perform the desired operation. 2. The input/output section acts as an autonomous processor which runs independently of the instruction-execution cycle, scanning the input channels for the presence of input or output word transfer requests and transferring data between the channels and central storage, controlled by the input/output access-control location associated with the channels.

operation, iterative—Refers generally to the standard, usual, or automatic repetition of the solutions. For example, a set of equations with successive or changed combinations of initial conditions, or simply the use of different parameters and the use of the same computing program.

operation, jump—A basic instruction designed so that the computer departs from the regular sequence of instruction executions and jumps to another routine or program, or even some preceding or forward instructions to thus alter control, repeat a process or loop, etc.

operation, loop—Refers to a particular loop which has an associated set of instructions designed to restore modified instructions or data to their original or initial values at each entry to the loop, or sequence of instructions which may be obeyed repetitively.

operation mode, real-time—In many large systems real-time is a mode of operation designed so that data necessary to the control and/or execution of a transaction can be processed in time for the transaction to be affected by the results of the processing. The essence of real time is concurrency—simultaneity. Real-time is refinement in the integration of data-processing with communications. Real-time eliminates slow information-gathering procedures, dated reporting techniques and lax communications; insures that facts within the system are as timely as a prevailing situation, as current as the decisions which they must support. Real-time system usually provide answers when answers are needed, deliver data instantly whenever the need for that data arises. Incoming information is edited, updated, and made available on demand at every level of responsibility. Imminent departures from established standards are automatically detected, and management is notified in time for action.

operation, multiplexed—Refers to simultaneous operations which are designed to share the use of a common unit of a system in such a way that it can be considered as an independent operation.

operation, parallel—Generally concerns simultaneous performance of several actions, usually of a similar nature, through provision of individual, similar, or identical devices for each such action. Most often parallel operation is performed to save time over serial operation. Parallel operation usually requires more equipment.

operation, real-time on-line (OLRT)—Refers to particular systems operations designed so that the input data to the system are given directly from the measuring devices. Computer results and output are thereby obtained during the progress of the event. For example, the data that are received from measurements during a run, with real-time computation of dependent variables during the run, enables the computer to make changes in its output.

operation, red-tape—1. Relates to various administrative or overhead operations or functions that are required to maintain control of a situation, e.g., for a computer program, housekeeping involves the setting up of constants and variables to be used in the program (synonymous with red tape). 2. Also, a general term used to describe coding which reserves, restores, and clears memory areas.

operation, serial—Relates to the flow of information through a computer system in time sequence designed to use only one digit, word, line, or channel at a time. (Contrasted with parallel operation.)

operation, unary—An operation on one operand, e.g., negative. (Synonymous with monadic operation.)

operator—1. Designates what operation to perform, e.g., ADD is the operator of the operation (ADD x). 2. In the description of a process, that which indicates the action to be performed on operands. 3. The person who actually manipulates the computer controls, places information media into the input devices, removes the output, presses the start button, etc.

operator interrupt—In large monitor systems the operator-interrupt trap is armed and the fixed-interrupt location is patched each time the monitor receives control. As an operator interrupt occurs, control is given to a routine in the monitor. This routine signifies to the operator the type-in is desired, by ringing the bell, returning the carriage, and typing.

operator intervention section—Refers specifically to that portion of the control equipment in which operators can intervene in normal programming operations on control.

operator's console—This provides capability of manual intervention and monitoring of computer operation.

operator's control panel—A fundamental part of a computer, the operator's control panel contains all the switches and indicators for the operation of the central processor. Most permit bit-by-bit register display and manual entry into the registers by convenient indicator pushbuttons. The control panel is used primarily for initial set-up prior to a program run or for debugging purposes, rather than to exercise control over a running program. Control of an operating routine is maintained by the use of the on-line typewriter or by sense switches.

operators, postfix—Refers to a specific notation system in which the operator appears after the operand, for example, $AB + = A + B$. It is used in Polish Notation.

operator, store—In many large systems storage of information in the PRT (Program Reference Table) is completed through the use of relative addresses. Storing operations are often carried out in the following manner. To store a value in the PRT, a literal (an integer with a value from 0 to 1023) equal to the relative address of the pertinent PRT location must be the top word in the stack. The information to be stored must be the second from top word in the stack. With these conditions existing, a store operator can be executed and the following actions will occur automatically.

optical arena, multifont—Refers to basic optical character reading equipment designed with the ability to discern many fonts or formats of characters, usually from hard copy.

optical character reader—Refers to specific units designed to read numerical data printed in widely used type styles on paper or card documents at rates up to 480 characters per second, and documents at rates of 400 per minute. The printed data automatically is translated into machine language for direct input to the processor (some units).

optical character recognition (OCR)—Refers to the computer entry identification of graphic characters by use of photosensitive devices.

optical-display plotter—A specific example follows: The major element of one plotter unit is a console with a 12-inch-square display screen (a 21-inch cathode-ray tube) on which tables, graphs, charts, alpha-numeric characters, or the lines and curves of drawings can be displayed as a series of points. When the full display area is used, 3848 alpha-numeric characters—the contents of a page of information—can be viewed. A built-in electronic marker helps the operator edit messages. When the display console is used as a point plotter, it can plot graphs, charts, and drawings with the precision of a square matrix of 1024 points, or more than one million individually addressable points.

Buffer storage for the unit is available in 4096- and 8192-character capacities. These buffer-storage units hold points, lines, and position instructions which may be read from or written at a maximum rate of 238,095 characters a second (some systems).

optical-display terminal—A specific example follows: Information is placed into the computer through the alpha-numeric keyboard and is simultaneously displayed on its video screen. The unit then displays a reply to the inquiry on its screen. Information is displayed at various rates, such as 600 characters a second, about 40 times faster than that produced for an operator by means of a type-out. Some viewing areas have a 30-line capacity of 40 characters each. To erase the display, once the permissible number of characters has been displayed and the inquiry has been answered, requires only a push of the "erase" button. Most often, the standard 36 alpha-numeric characters (A through Z, 0 to 9) plus 23 special characters are available (some systems).

optical document reader—An input device which can read documents as a human would so that data can be directly and easily put into the computer for processing. Although optical document readers cannot read all human script as yet, they can read a large variety of hand-printed and typed documents, for example, bank checks with the account numbers in magnetic ink and specially formed numbers made by the raised letters on credit cards.

optical font—Refers to one of the media types that can be used as computer input. An optical font is a specific variety of type which can be sensed by a computer input device and translated into electronic form within the computer.

optical mark-page reader—Optical mark-page readers can be attached to a system for direct reading of marks made by an ordinary lead pencil in specified positions (like the marks made for electronic test scoring) on 8½ by 11-inch sheets of paper. The sheets can be read at a maximum rate of 2000 per hour, or one each 1.8 seconds. The reader is normally attached to the multiplexor channel and operation is in the multiplex mode. Applications for the reader are in payroll, order entry, accounts payable, inventory control, sales analysis, general ledger work, and many other phases of business, government, and institutions.

optical reader–1. Generally this is a system based on the principle that the special shape of each character printed on the input media is capable of being identified by a reading device. For example, the audit-journal from a cash register, if printed in a distinctive optical font, could be used as the input media to a computer. As the optical reader reads each character from the input media, it translates the data into electrical impulses that in turn are transmitted to the computer for processing. 2. A specific unit designed to read printed and typewritten material directly, without converting it into punchtape, punchcards, or other intermediate formats. It recognizes all letters of the alphabet, standard punctuation, 0 through 9, and special symbols used in programmed functions. It handles documents, and continuous fanfold sheets.

optimization, nonlinear–Refers to various mathematical techniques or procedures designed for the determination of a maximum, minimum, or an attempted optimum value or values of variables or functions of variables which are subject in the model to predetermined nonlinear constraints or limitations as expressed by sets of in-

equalities or equations. This is contrasted to linear optimization in which constraints are linear, i.e., in a certain sense, proportional.

optimization, on-line process–See on-line process optimization.

optimization, process–Refers to an extensive P-C (processor-controller) program used in larger systems and based on the model of the process which directs the DAC (Data Acquisition and Control) system. Process data is continuously collected and analyzed for computation of optimum operating instructions. These instructions are given to the process operator via an on-line typewriter.

options–In practically all systems, during the execution of any program, including a processor program, options are available to the programmer in the construction, extension, or printing of the results. For example, updated source code can replace or augment the original code, with listings completely or partially inhibited. Other options control the execution, punching, and timing of the programs.

order, high–A concept which relates to the weight or significance assigned to the digits of a number; e.g., in the number 123456, the highest order digit is one; the lowest order digit is six. One may refer to the three high-order bits of a binary word as another example. (Contrasted with low order.)

order, low–That which pertains to the weight or significance assigned to the digits of a number; e.g., in the number 123456, the low order digit is six. One may refer to the three low-order bits of a binary word as another example.

orderly close-down–Refers to the procedure for the stoppage of the system in such a way that ensures an orderly restart and no destruction of messages. When a system is forced to stop, an orderly close-down provides that all records are updated that should be updated and that no records are erroneously updated again when the restart is made. Furthermore, all incoming and outgoing transmissions are completed, with a message sent to the terminals which notifies the operators of the close-down.

OR gate—One of the basic elements or electrical gates or mechanical devices which implement the logical OR operator. An output signal occurs whenever there are one or more inputs on a multichannel input. An OR gate performs the function of the logical "inclusive OR operator." (Synonymous with OR circuit.)

origin—1. Generally refers to the absolute storage address of the beginning of a program or block. 2. In relative coding, the absolute storage address to which addresses in a region are referenced.

ORSA—Operations Research Society of America.

Orthoscanner—1. Honeywell input device designed to read printed documents and to regenerate and read defaced information. It reads orthocode (a series of small vertical bars). 2. This system recognizes characters in the form of a printed code of vertical bars (orthocode). In this form 600 decimal digits can be scanned per second, with a document rejection rate of about one-tenth of one percent. The orthocode contains orthocorrections digits that make possible automatic regeneration of lost data. (Honeywell)

OS—The abbreviation for Operating System.

out, fan—Refers to the versatile number of circuits designed to be supplied with input signals from an output terminal of a circuit or unit. The changes of digital circuits depend basically on the number of devices that can drive or be driven by one circuit of a specific type, and the number of elements that one output can drive is related to the power available from the output and the amount of power required for each input.
input.

output—1. Results from the computer such as answers to mathematical problems, statistical, analytical or accounting figures, production schedules, etc. 2. Information transferred from the internal storage of a computer to secondary or external storage; information transferred to any device exterior to the computer. 3. The state or a sequence of states occurring on a specified output channel. 4. The device or collective set of devices used for taking data out of a device. 5. A channel for expressing a state on a device or logic element.

output, asynchronous (transmission)—In many large systems this refers to the timing on asynchronous output-data transfers which are not time critical. Since each output-data character is preceded by a start bit and followed by a stop bit, the time interval between characters will appear to the transmission facilities as nothing more than an extra-long stop bit. Although no information is lost if a data character is not transferred from the central processor to the asynchronous output CLT within the "character availability interval," a failure to do so will result in a reduced transmission rate.

output bus drivers—In many systems

most major output signals from the standard computer used in programmed and data-break information transfers are power amplified by bus-driver modules to allow them to drive a very heavy circuit load.

output register buffer—Refers to various buffering or transfer devices that receive data from internal storage and transfer it to an output media such as magnetic tape.

overflow—1. With respect to an arithmetic operation, the generation of a quantity beyond the capacity of the register or location which is to receive the result; over capacity; the information contained in an item of information which is in excess of a given amount. 2. The portion of data that exceeds the capacity of the allocated unit of storage. 3. Overflow develops when attempts are made to write longer fields into a field location of a specific length; a 12-digit product will overflow a 10-digit accumulator.

overflow areas, file—As regards file systems and in random addressing, the overflow area is an available storage location that is chained to a particular pocket so that when that pocket is full, the generated addresses use the overflow area.

overflow check indicator—Refers to a specific device that is designed to be turned on by incorrect, or unplanned for, operations in the execution of an arithmetic instruction, particularly when an arithmetic operation produces a number too large for the system to handle.

overflow (FORTRAN)—In most FORTRAN systems, overflow occurs when the characteristic of a floating-point number exceeds the machine capacity (generally 10^{+38}). In assembler language, overflow occurs when a fixed point number is divided by zero or when an algebraic sum is larger than the accumulator register can hold.

overflow, link (L)—Refers to a specific one-bit register that serves as an extension of the accumulator. The content of this register can be program sampled and program modified. Overflow into the link from the accumulator can be checked by the program to greatly simplify and speed up single- and multiple-precision arithmetic routines.

overlapping—A concurrent operation process or procedure in which various phases of two consecutive instructions are executed simultaneously, i.e., multiplication can take place while reading from storage is also being completed.

overlapping, multiprocessor—In many large systems the processor is designed to be capable of determining whether its current operand and next instruction lie in different storage modules. It is also capable, if this situation is present, of retrieving these two words in parallel, at an effective 100% performance increase. Since the I/O controller is not required to reference instructions in main storage, except on command transfers, it does not have, nor does it need, the overlapping feature.

The overlapping feature permits the separation of the instruction and data of a program into separate physical banks. Also, the basing register of the processor allows either the instruction or data area of a program to be relocated independently—a significant advantage in core compacting to overcome fragmentation (some systems).

overlay—1. The particular method of repeatedly using the same blocks of internal storage during different stages of a problem; e.g., when one routine is no longer needed in internal storage, another routine can replace all or part of that storage. 2. The use of one area in storage to successively store more than one different subroutine or program part. 3. A technique for bringing routines into high-speed storage from some other form of storage during processing, so that several routines will occupy the same storage locations at different times. Overlay is used when the total storage requirements for instructions exceed the available main storage.

overlays, monitor—In many larger executive systems the monitor remains resident in lower memory at all times. Object programs are loaded into memory starting at the end of the monitor. The program loader resides in upper memory. Object programs cannot be loaded into the loader area. This area can be overlayed by common storage. Part of the loader can also be overlayed by library subroutines.

overpunch—1. A hole punched in one of the three top rows of an IBM card and which, together with the second punch in one of the nine lower rows, identifies an alphabetic or special character. Also called zone punch. 2. To add holes in a card column that already contains one or more holes (synonymous with zone punch, and related to zone bits).

* _ * _ *

pack—1. A basic procedure used to develop the combination or consolidation of several short fields into larger field. 2. Procedures to combine two or more units of information into a single physical unit to conserve storage. For example, the fields of an employee's pay number, weekly pay rate, and tax exemptions may be stored in one word, each of these fields being assigned a different location within the word. 3. The procedure which reduces the amount of storage required to hold information by changing the method of coding data or blanks. For example, storing two or more data items into a single word by using a contiguous subfield, or by dividing words into convenient parts, etc.

packed decimal—A system technique of data representation. Two digits per character can be used to increase speed and capacity in fields where alphabetics and special characters are not being used.

pad, scratch—Refers to a useful and informal term referring to or designating a unique internal storage area, designed to be reserved for intermediate results, various notations, or working . area, quickly erasable storage.

page—An important concept or programming device, it concerns a quantity or determination of main-memory capacity and used when allocating memory and for partitioning programs into units or control sections. A page is quite standardized, usually 512 to 4096 bytes or words and/or 8 to 64 lines of source program coding, as used for displaying the coding on CRT's (cathode ray tubes) i.e., in CRT's used in conversational time-sharing a single page of program can be displayed at one time for the programmer or user inspection, the size varying with the size and capacity of the CRT, and not related to the memory page stated above (some systems).

paging—The breakdown of a program and data into fixed blocks, often 1,000 words so that transfers between disk and core can take place in page units rather than as entire programs.

paper tape, chadless—A paper tape with the holes partially punched. It is commonly used in teletype operations.

parallel access—1. Pertains to simultaneous access to all bits in a storage location comprising a character or word. Equal access time for any bit, character, or word in a storage device. 2. The process of obtaining information from or placing information into storage where the time required for such access is dependent on the simultaneous transfer of all elements of a word from a given storage location (synonymous with simultaneous access).

parallel arithmetic—A process designed so that simultaneous operations are performed on all digits of a number and in which partial sums and numbers are formed or shifted.

parallelism—Refers to various concurrent operations of several parts of a computer system. This could be simultaneous processing of multiple programs or simultaneous operation of multiple computers.

parallel processing—Concerns the operations of a computer designed so that programs for more than one run are stored simultaneously in its storage, and executed concurrently. 2. See multiprocessing, concurrent processing, and multiprogramming.

parallel transfer—All bits stored in one string of flip-flops are transferred simultaneously to another string, using one wire (or a pair of wires) for each flipflop.

parity check—A check by summation in which the binary digits, in a character or word, are added, and the sum checked against a single, previously computed parity digit; i.e., a check tests whether the number of ones in a word is odd or even (synonymous with odd-even check, and related to redundant check and forbidden-combination check).

parity check, horizontal—Refers to a specific parity check applied to the group of certain bits from every character in a block.

partial word—Concerns a type of programming device designed to permit the selection of a portion of a machine word for processing.

password—The unique set of digits or characters assigned to a user as part of his identification number in communicating with the computer.

pattern recognition—The recognition of shapes or other patterns by a machine system. The patterns may be either a physical shape or a speech pattern.

PAX (Private Automatic Exchange)—A dial exchange providing private telephone service to an organization, and that does not allow calls to be transmitted to or from the public telephone network.

PCMI—An abbreviation for Photo-Chromic MicroImage, which is a trademark of National Cash Register Company (NCR), and describes a microimage process developed by NCR which can develop reductions of 1:40,000 in area, i.e., 1.6 billion words or 7.5 billion characters can be stored on less than 2 square inches of the surface of a film.

pencil—System for storing retrieving and manipulating line drawings.

pen, light—An important terminal operator's tool, it is an optional device, used in conjunction with the incremental display, that can greatly extend its usefulness. It is a high speed, photo-sensitive device that can cause the computer to change or modify the display on the cathode-ray tube. As the pertinent display information is selected by the operator, the pen signals the computer by generating a pulse. Acting upon this signal, the computer can then instruct other points to be plotted across the tube face in accordance with the pen movements, or exercise specific options previously programmed without the need for separate input devices.

perception, artificial—See artificial cognition.

peripheral buffers—Relates to various magnetic-core buffers which reside outside the main processor memory to compensate for speed differences between slower electromechanical input/output devices and processor speeds. Operations are overlapped, with all units operating simultaneously at rated speeds. Buffering eliminates the need for more expensive, multiple I/O channels, and eliminates complex I/O timing considerations from the programming job.

peripheral interrupt—Concerns a specific stop resulting from the signal of readiness for or completion of a task by a peripheral device.

permuted-title index—Same as index, permutation.

phase class name—Refers specifically to non-terminal codes in formal language theory (BNF), such as ⟨identifier⟩, ⟨letter⟩, etc. BNF means Backus Normal Form.

PL/1 (programming language)—Compilers used in compiling object programs from source programs written in a new pro-gramming language. This language has some features that are characteristic of FORTRAN and incorporates some of the best features of other languages, such as string manipulation, data structures, and extensive editing capabilities. Further, it has features not currently available in any language. The language is designed to take advantage of recent developments in computer technology and to provide the programmer with a flexible problem-oriented language for programming problems that can best be solved using a combination of scientific and commercial computing techniques. It is designed to be particularly useful for the increasing number of semicommercial, semiscientific applications such as information retrieval and command and control applications.

plotter, XY—Concerns various devices used in conjunction with computers to plot coordinate points in the form of a graph, usually on a real-time current basis.

plotting board—See board, plotting.

pointer—Usually refers to a specific table/look-up technique that permits each datum (X_1) to be stored with a pointer pointing to a list of associated functions of X_1, as a variant technique to ordered or sequential or even indirect addressing techniques.

Polish, Cambridge—Refers to concepts used in the LISP language, i.e., some operators are allowed to have more than two operands.

Polish notation—1. A distinct technique or device created by the Polish logician, J. Lukasieqez for treating algebraic statements by manipulating strings of operations. 2. A specific form of prefix notation.

port—Usually refers to the specific entry channel to which a data set is attached. The port is in the central computer, and each user is assigned one port.

precision, double—Pertaining to a quantity having twice as many digits as are normally carried; i.e., a double precision number requires two machine words in a fixed-word machine.

precision, multiple—Using computer words of two or more to represent a single numeric quantity or numeral, i.e., with twice as many or more digits as are normally carried in a fixed-length word used to keep track of several parts of each numeral, precision is enhanced especially in matrix manipulation which often requires the use of multiple precision arithmetic. See: double precision.

precision, single—Refers very specifically to the number of words or storage positions used to denote a number in a computer. Single-precision arithmetic is the use of one word per number; double precision, two words per number, and so on. For variable word-length computers, precision is the number of digits used to denote a number. The higher the precision, the greater the number of decimal places that can be carried.

prefix notation—A technique of forming one dimensional expressions without need for brackets by preceding with a string or vector of operators, an operand string or vector that may itself contain operators upon operands.

presumptive instruction—Concerns various types of instructions that will most likely be modified before they are used for the final program.

primary storage—The main internal storage.

primitive—Refers to the most basic or fundamental unit of data, i.e., a single letter digit, element, or machine code as primitive when related to the ultra sophisticated codes or languages now available. Also refers to first or second generation computer equipment, and in a few more years, perhaps to the 3rd.

printer, electrostatic—Now becoming very common, these are devices for printing an optical image on paper, in which dark and light areas of the original are represented by electrostatically charged and uncharged areas on the paper. The paper is dusted with particles of finely powdered dry ink and the particles adhere only to the electrically charged areas. The paper with ink particles is then heated, causing the ink to melt and become permanently fixed to the paper.

printer, line—One where an entire line of characters is composed and determined within the device prior to printing.

printing keypunch—A card-printing device that prints each number or letter on the card as it punches the card.

print positions—Usually concerns the maximum number of characters which can be printed on a single line.

priority interrupt—In many large systems priority interrupt levels must be assigned using the interaction of functions with each other as a primary basis. Most on-line systems designers ensure that all possible interrupts are operating compatibly when worst-case conditions occur. Debugging can become a "horrendous" task; consequently these problems must be solved during the design of the system, not during program and hardware checkout. It may be necessary to reassign the priority levels of key interrupts dynamically under program control. Hardware solutions to this have ranged from large banks of flip-flops to core switching matrices. At least two advances are required in the priority interrupt area to make effective use of the higher performance hardware being developed for on-line systems use. They are time-related priority assignments and externally weighted priority. Adequate solutions have not been found to meet all foreseen requirements, although designers are learning to make use of what is available to make the computer react to the on-line environment.

priority interrupts, multilevel—In many large systems, interrupt provisions have been made to facilitate the priority requirements of various subroutines. Specifically, the interrupt requests of these subroutines are handled by the central processor in the sequence of the highest priority. If a priority subroutine requests an interrupt, it will have priority over all subroutines of lower priority, even though they have previously requested an interrupt.

priority interrupt table—Refers to circumstances when a computer does not have a fully automatic interrupt handling capability, a table is set up that lists the priority sequence of handling and testing interrupts.

privileged instructions—A very important concept concerning protection against one problem subprogram misusing another problem subprogram's I/O devices. This is provided by restricting all I/O commands to the supervisor state. A subprogram requests I/O action by issuing a supervisor call instruction. The supervisory subprogram can then analyze this request and take the appropriate action.

problem-oriented language—1. One of the source languages oriented to the description of a particular class of prob-

lems. 2. A specific language designed for solutions of a particular class of problems. COBOL and FORTRAN programs are designed for various classes of problems whether scientific or commercial types, and although they require elaborate and extensive translation and compilation, they are relatively simply developed and quite easily understood even by the novice computer personnel.

procedure-oriented language—One of the source languages oriented to the description of procedural steps in machine computing.

process control—1. Refers to a fundamental type of operation which pertains to systems whose purpose is to provide automation or continuous operations. This is contrasted with numerical control that provides automation of discrete operations (e.g. machines). 2. Also refers to automatic control of continuous-manufacturing industrial processes by using, for example, hybrid computers.

processor interrupt—In many larger systems as the computer is sequencing through a set of instructions, there are definite times when it is desirable to interrupt the program for such things as handling a machine error, an I/O device, a supervisor call, or a program exception such as an arithmetic overlfow. Often electronic circuitry instead of complex programming recognizes and handles these interrupts. And, this results in the most efficient utilization of the processor. Interrupts are automatic procedures that alert the system to conditions arising that may affect the sequence of instructions being executed. To make possible the operation of a system in a nonstop environment, and to increase the efficiency of I/O equipment, the system must have the ability to switch to the appropriate routine when a supervisory call or exceptional condition arises, and then resume the processing that has been interrupted. Records of the complete status of the system are automatically stored as soon as an interrupt occurs, together with an identification of the cause of the interrupt.

processor, satellite—The processor designed especially and primarily for card-to-tape conversion, printing of tape contents, and other selected, high-volume operations; frequently used to support and add to the capacity of a large processor to further increase its productivity.

processor unit, central (CPU)—The principal and most basic unit of the computer. It controls the processing routines, performs the arithmetic functions, and maintains a quickly accessible memory. It also contains the operators console in most smaller systems.

production, language theory—In formal language theory (BNF), refers to translations of input strings into output strings.

program, background—Refers to very specific programs that are of lower priority than the foreground or main program and are at halt or standby while the main program runs.

program compilation—A fundamental concept concerning various programs written in the languages of ALGOL, COBOL, FORTRAN IV, or the other assembly languages. These are compiled at several thousand statements per minute without sacrificing object code efficiency and such compiler or translation programs are becoming universally available.

program, interpretive—Refers to highly specialized programs which relate and handle the execution of programs by translating each instruction of the source language into a sequence of computer instructions and allow these to be executed before translating the next instruction, i.e., the translation of an instruction is performed each time the instruction is to be obeyed. If the interpretative program allows for programs written for one type of a computer to be run on a different type, it is often called a simulator program.

program loader—In many computer systems, during the execution of a processing program, and as a result of many different actions of the control programs, additional programs or program segments may be brought into main storage. A program loader alters all necessary addresses in the object program to allow loading at an address of main storage assigned by the control program. The loader has the capability to load separately assembled program segments as if they were a single program, to call in segments from the system program library and combine them with other programs, to link one program segment with another through the use of symbolic references, and to enable different program segments to refer to common data areas. The loader can also perform program overlays, and enable patching of object programs (some systems).

program, macro-generating—Refers to particular types of generating programs designed and developed to construct the group of instructions in the object language appropriate to a particular macro-instruction in the basic source language.

programmer-defined macros—Those coding segments, which are used frequently throughout a program, can be defined at the beginning and referenced by a mnemonic code with parameters. This increases coding efficiency and readability of the program.

programming language, automatic (APL)—Refers to a language designed to permit the computer to aid in doing part or the majority of the coding and programming.

programming, micro—A procedure now resuming popularity. This refers to programmer technique of using a certain special sets of instructions for automatic computers that consist only of basic elemental operations, and combining them into higher-level instructions. A programmer may then program using only the higher level instructions; e.g., if a computer has only basic instructions for adding, subtracting, and multiplying, the instruction for dividing would be defined by microprogramming.

program relocation, dynamic—Refers to the procedures of moving of a partially executed program to a different location in main memory without detrimentally affecting the ability to complete normal processing.

program segmenting—Most larger systems now use programs that do not fit into memory. They may be segmented by use of the source-language linking statements. This allows sections of the program to be loaded and executed independently. Common storage is used by each link for passing data.

programs status word (PSW)—In many larger systems the PSW is stored at a fixed location, the address of which depends on the type of interruption.

The system then automatically fetches a new PSW from a different fixed location, the address of which is also dependent on the type of interruption. Each class of interruption has two fixed locations in main storage—one to receive the old PSW when the interruption occurs, and the other to supply the new PSW that governs the servicing of that class of interruption. After the interruption has been serviced, a single instruction uses the stored PSW to reset the processing unit to the status it had before the interruption (some computers).

PROSPORO—A fill-in blanks process control system developed by IBM and Humble Oil.

protection key—See key, protection.

pseudoinstruction—1. A particular symbolic representation in a compiler or interpreter. 2. A group of characters having the same general form as a computer instruction, but never executed by the computer as an actual instruction (synonymous with quasi-instruction).

psuedo-op—1. A symbolic representation in a compiler or interpreter. 2. A group of characters having the same general form as a computer instruction but never executed by the computer as an actual instruction. 3. An instruction written in an assembly language designating a predetermined and limited group of computer instructions for performing a particular task.

pseudo-random sequence—Because some sequences of numbers may be random, in a satisfactory way, for some types of calculations, but not for others, various techniques have been designed to determine numbers by chance, most by mathematical manipulations. Most of these are psuedo-random sequences.

pulse modulation—The use of a series of pulses designed to convey the information contained in the modulating function. The characteristics of a train of pulses may be modified in one of several ways to convey information including amplitude (PAM), position (PPM), and duration (PDM).

pulse train—Refers to particular groups of pulses which occur or happen in time sequence at a point in a circuit, i.e., an amplitude vs. time plot of the pulses appears as though the pulse group occurs in space sequence or along a line, thus the terms pulse string or pulse train.

punched card—A card capable of being punched with holes to represent letters, digits or characters.

* – * – *

quadratic programming—Maximization of an objective function that is quadratic, subject to linear constraints. This is one of the few convex programming problems, aside from linear programming, that have solution algorithms that terminate in a finite number of steps.

qualifier—Generally, this is a name used to qualify another name with an action similar to an adjective in English grammar, i.e., to give additional information about a name or to distinguish the named thing from other things having the same name.

quantizer—Devices used to convert an analog measurement into digital form.

quasi-instruction—1. A symbolic representation in a compiler or interpreter. 2. A character group with the same general form as a computer instruction, but never executed by the computer as an actual instruction. Same as pseudo-instruction.

query—In larger or time-sharing systems, this is a specific request for data, instructions, characteristics of states of switches, position in a queue, etc., while the equipment is computing or processing.

queue—A line or group of items waiting for the attention of the processor, usually in core, that are chained together by address words in consecutive order and then acted on by the processor.

queue, input—Refers to a group or a queue of new messages that are in the system and are waiting for processing. The Main Scheduling Routine will scan them along with other queues and order them into processing in order.

queue, output—Generally these are messages that are in a line or are queued and which have been produced by the system and are waiting to be scheduled for transmission.

queue, push-down—A last in, first out, method of queuing in which the last item attached to the queue is the first to be withdrawn.

queue, sequential—A type of procedure using the first-in, first-out method of queuing items waiting for the processor.

queuing analysis—Refers to the specific study of the nature and time concerning the discrete units necessary to move through channels; e.g., the time and length of queue at service centers of grocery check-out stands, harbors, airports, etc. Queuing analysis is employed to determine lengths of lines and order, time, discipline of service.

queuing theory—A probability theory form useful in studying delays or line-ups at servicing points.

QUIKTRAN—A subset of FORTRAN

including built-in functions augmented by powerful and versatile operating statements for complete control maintenance. Special codes for easy parameter insertion and changes, such as assigning new values to variables, and for deletion and replacement plus cross-referencing and selective output, make this an outstanding innovation to computer science (IBM).

* _ * _ *

raceway floor—A type of raised floor which provides for concealment of cables and connections to thus improve support to the equipment, with the convenience of the removal of certain floor panel for servicing or inspection.

radio frequency (RF)—A frequency residing above the audio range and below the frequency of visible light.

radix—Refers to the number system base. It is a quantity that defines a system of representing numbers by positional notation; the number of digit symbols required by a number system. Examples:

System	Radix
decimal	10
octal	8
quinary	5
binary	2

radix notation—1. An annotation which consists of a decimal number in parentheses, written as a subscript to a number, its decimal value indicating the radix of the number; e.g., $11_{(2)}$ indicates the number 11 is in the radix of two; $11_{(8)}$ indicates the number 11 is in the radix of eight. 2. A number written without its radix notation is assumed to be in the radix of ten (synonymous with base notation).

radix number—The number of characters for use in each of the digital positions of a numbering system. In the more common numbering systems the characters are some or all of the Arabic numerals as follows:

System Name	Characters	Radix
binary	(0,1)	2
octal	(0,1,2,3,4,5,6,7)	8
decimal	(0,1,2,3,4,5,6,7,8,9)	10
quinary	(0,1,2,3,4)	5

Unless otherwise indicated, the radix of any number is assumed to be 10. For positive identification of a radix 10 number, the radix is written in parentheses as a subscript to the expressed number, i.e., $12_{(10)}$. The radix of any nondecimal number is expressed in similar fashion, e.g., $11_{(2)}$ and $5_{(8)}$ (synonymous with base and base number).

radix point—Refers to the dot that marks the separation between the integral and fractional parts of a number. In the decimal number system, the decimal point; in the binary number system, the binary point.

random access—1. Refers the fundamental access to storage under conditions in which the next location from which data are to be obtained is in no way dependent on the location of the previously obtained data. 2. Pertains to the process of obtaining data from, or placing data into, storage when there is no sequential relation governing the access time to successive storage locations. 3. Refers to a quality or type of memory device that allows data to be written in, or read from, the memory through direct locating rather than locating through reference to other data in the memory. No search is required;

the machine can proceed directly to the desired memory location.

random-number generator—Concerns a special machine routine or hardware device designed to produce a random (unbiased) number or a series of random numbers according to specified limitations.

random number, normal—A system in which numbers are selected by pure chance from a set of numbers distinctly characterized, and in which each number has an equal choice of being selected. The distribution of numbers in the set follows a normal or Gaussian distribution.

random numbers—A grouping or unbiased succession of digits or numbers developed entirely as a result of a random or chance process. A particular satisfaction of various statistical criteria is considered an adequate test of randomness, principally the tests which show total absence of bias in any form in the selection process.

random walk method—A variation of the Monte Carlo statistical system or method in which a problem is developed for a probabilistic solution. The "walk" factor consists of a series of traverses of long line segments. The directions, and oftentimes lengths, vary at random. The probability of reaching a defined point by a walk of this type at a given time is often given by a function that is for other interests.

range check—Refers to a type of procedure designed for controlling the accuracy of data by verifying that the value of a piece of data falls between certain pre-established maximum and minimum values.

range of a DO statement—Refers to all FORTRAN statements included in the repetitive execution of a DO loop operation.

range, proportional—Refers generally to the band, or set of values of a specific condition which is being controlled and which will cause the controller to operate over its full linear range. A proportional range is most often expressed by engineers or design teams in terms of percentage of full scale of the associated instrument.

rapid-access memory—Generally in computers having memories with different access times, this specific section has much faster access than the remainder of the memory, in some systems this is semiconductor memory.

rate action—Relates to a type of control action designed so that the rate of correction is made proportional to how fast the condition is going awry. This is also called derivative action.

rate, clock—Relates to a specific time rate at which pulses are emitted from the clock, i.e., the clock rate determines the rate at which logical or arithmetic gating is performed with a synchronous computer.

rate, reset—Concerns the specific number of corrections per unit of time made by the control system.

rate sampling—A calculation concerning the time developed during the sampling of physical quantities for measurement, i.e., to obtain data to feed into a computing system so that the results of the computations can be made available to complete a specific task or purpose. Some examples are on-line processing for controlling weather data, timesharing of equipment, future positions for missile guidance, etc.

rate, scan—A calculation of the frequency at which data is compared or read to various predetermined sets of criteria for the purpose of seeking certain data.

rating, carrier-to-noise—Refers to a specific ratio in decibels of the value of the carrier to that of the noise after selection and before any non-linear process such as amplitude limiting and detection.

ratio, activity—Refers to the calculation of that ratio which pertains to the number of file elements which are: records, for example, for which changes or transactions are made during a specific updating run or in a given period, to the total number of records or elements in the file. If out of a total of 100 records, 20 are updated in a specific month, the activity ratio is thus 20% for this file.

ratio, recall—In information retrieval systems a calculation of the ratio of the number of pertinent documents retrieved by a single query to the total number of pertinent documents in the total collection as determined by the query criteria.

ratio, signal-to-noise—Refers to a calculation of ratio of an amount of signals conveying information to the amount of signals not conveying information.

read, destructive—Concerns the sensing of data through the use of a process which inherently destroys (erases) the record of the data which has been read. In some core storage, reading is destructive, but such data is usually regenerated after each readout. In tapes, drums, discs, etc. reading is most often accomplished without destruction. The changing of the sequence or location or items in a collection, matrix, or array.

reader, badge—Refers to various devices designed for the automatic collection of data. The badge reader is usually activated by the insertion of a specially shaped badge or card.

reader, page—Generally refers to optical character readers which can process cut-form documents of differing sizes and which might be able to read information in reel form.

reader, paper-tape—A fundamental device designed to sense and translate the holes or information on tape into machine code.

read head—Refers to a specific electromagnetic device that is used for reading data from a medium, such as tape, disks, drums, cards, or an optical sensor.

reading access time—Refers to a measurement of the elapsed time before data may be read or used in the computer during the equipment read cycle.

read, nondestructive—Refers to a type of reading of the information in a register that is completed without changing that information.

read/write channels—In many large systems the data path and movement between the main memory and a peripheral device is completed by a programmer-assigned read/write channel. This channel is not a fixed connection to any one unit but is rather a floating link that can be used by any device. As opposed to the conventional method of complex and costly high-speed and low-speed transmission lines, the read/write channel can be assigned to any device regardless of speed or mode of data transfer.

read/write check—Checking specifically the accuracy of reading, writing, sensing, punching, recording, etc., completed by comparing or sensing what has been written and comparing and/or sensing what was expected to be read and/or written, i.e., running punched cards through key-verifiers or a comparator.

read/write head—Refers to a small electromagnetic unit used for reading, recording, or erasing polarized spots that represent information on a mag tape, drum or disk.

real number—Generally concerns various elements of sets of all positive and negative numbers, including all types: integers, zeros, mixed, rational, irrational, etc., but not imaginary or complex.

real time—1. This pertains to the actual time during which a physical process transpires. 2. Pertaining to the performance of a computation during a related physical process to obtain results needed to guide that process. 3. A method of processing data so fast that there is virtually no passage of time between inquiry and result. Each inquiry may be communicated to the system separately, and the result received immediately.

real-time buffer (single character)—In many systems each buffer permits teletype communication with many remote locations. Because the buffer operates on one character at a time, many teletypes may be communicating with the processor simultaneously at full speed in either direction through the same buffer.

real-time clock—Refers to various registers and circuitry which automatically maintain time in conventional time units for use in program execution and event initiation.

real-time control system—Refers to modern computer systems that process data and make the necessary decisions in real time (immediately). For example, the automatic control of manufacturing processes by a computer in an oil refinery.

real-time information system—A system designed to provide information about the process it is describing fast enough for the process to be continuously controlled by an operator using this information (for example, a scientist controlling the path of a space rocket).

real-time, on-line operation (OLRT)—The immediate processing of data in synchronism with a physical process, in such a fashion that the results of the data-processing are useful to the physical operation.

real-time operation—1. Refers to concurrent operations for data processing (computing) and physical processing in such a way that the results of the computing operations are available whenever needed by the physical processing operations, and vice versa. 2. A system designed for paralleling data processing with a physical process so that the results of the data processing are immediately useful to the physical operation. 4. Relates to operations performed in a computer simultaneously with a physical process so that the answers obtained are useful in controlling the process.

real-time processing communication—Most real-time systems are combined data processors and communicators of transaction data between remote locations and a central computer, via communication lines, and allow the data to be processed while the business transaction is actually taking place. Generally, a real-time system may be thought of as a communications-oriented data-processing system which is capable of performing batch-processing functions while concurrently processing inquiries or messages, and generating responses in a time interval directly related to the operational requirements of the system.

real-time relative addressing—In larger systems relative addressing is a feature of great significance, specifically multi-programming, time-sharing, and real-time operations. It allows storage assignments to be changed dynamically to provide contiguous storage for operation of another program, and permits programs to dynamically request additional main storage according to processing needs. An additional advantage is that system programs stored on mass storage may be brought in for operation in any available area without complicated relocation algorithms. Relative addressing is provided for through basing registers contained within the processor. A separate register controls the basing of the program instruction and the data bank, and a third register controls the selections of the appropriate basing register.

real-time, remote inquiry—In many time-sharing systems on-line inquiry stations permit users to interrogate the computer files and receive immediate answers to their inquiries. In industry, for example, the stations can be located at dozens of remote locations such as office, factory, warehouse, and remote branch locations. Such a system permits all levels of industrial management to obtain immediate answers to questions about inventories, work-in-process, sales, etc.

real-time satellite computer—Refers to specific satellite computers in the real-time system which relieve the larger computer system of time consuming input and output functions as well as performing preprocessing and post-processing functions such as validity editing and formatting for print.

real-time simulation—Relates to particular operations of a simulator or simulation program, such that the instants of occurrence of many basic events in the simulator occur at the same times as they would in the system being simulated or as in the real world, or faster.

real variables (FORTRAN)—A real variable in a FORTRAN system consists of a series of alphanumeric characters (except special characters) of which the first is alphabetic but can not be one of the integer indicators, i.e., I, J, K, L, M, or N.

recognition, character—Refers to the advancing technology of using optical machines to sense and encode information into a machine language i.e., characters that are written or printed to be read by human beings.

recognition, pattern—Refers to the recognition of various shapes or other patterns by a machine systems. Patterns may be such as physical shapes or speech patterns.

record—1. A set of one or more consecutive fields pertaining to a related subject, as an employee's payroll record. Although a record need not be a block in length, such an arrangement is often useful. 2. A listing of information, usually in printed or printable form; one output of a compiler consisting of a list of the operations and their positions in the final specific routine and containing information describing the segmentation and storage allocation of the routine. 3. To make a transcription of data by a systematic alteration of the condition, property, or configuration of a physical medium, e.g., placing information on magnetic tapes or a drum by means of magnetized spots. 4. To group related facts or fields of information treated as a unit. Types: data, label, logical, master, physical, trailer, transaction, unit.

record gap—1. Refers to that specific space between records on a tape, usually produced by tape acceleration or deceleration during the writing stage of processing. 2. Concerns a specific gap used to indicate the end of a record.

record header—Refers to specific records which contain the description of information designated in a classification or group of records, which follow this initial document. Also known as header table.

record, home--Usually refers to the first record in a chain of records, i.e., the home record is designed to be used with the chaining method of file development or organization.

recording density—Refers to the measurement of the number of bits per a given unit length of a linear track in a recording medium.

recording double-pulse—Refers to a specific method for magnetic recording of bits, in which each storage cell comprises two regions, magnetized in opposite senses with unmagnetized regions on each side.

record, label—Refers to various records used to identify the contents of specific files or reels of magnetic tape.

record manual, product reference—One page of the master product file.

record mark—Refers to special characters designed to be used in some computers either to limit the number of characters in a data transfer, or to separate blocked or grouped records in tape.

record, master—The basic updated record used in the next file-processing run, a master record is most often a magnetic tape item. Visual copies for possible analysis and alteration are usually developed.

record name—In COBOL, the title, designation or name given to a record within a file and assigned the level number 01. Data names for elements within a record have lower-level numbers, 02, 03, etc.

record, physical—A punched card is a physical record. Magnetic tapes and disks have physical records as bounded by beginnings and ended by interrecord gaps (IRGs), i.e., physical records on these media are simply the start/stop boundaries while punched paper tape and drums have other special boundaries.

record, trailer—Refers to a specific record that follows a group of records and contains pertinent data related to the group of records.

record, unit—1. A single card containing one complete record; currently, the punched card. 2. A printed line with a maximum of 120 characters; a punched card with a maximum of 72 characters, a BCD (binary-coded decimal) tape record with a maximum of 120 characters.

record, variable length—A fundamental concept concerning a record which has a loose or unfixed number of constituent parts, i.e., blocks, words, etc., are subject to particular installation or chief programmer rules, constraints, conventions, or by the equipment design.

recursion—Refers to procedures for the continued repetition of the same operation or group of operations.

recursive definition—A definition which defines something partly in terms of itself.

recursive process—In data processing, this refers to a method of computing values of functions in which each stage of processing contains all subsequent stages, i.e., the first stage is not completed until all other stages have been completed.

redact—Refers to a procedure to edit or revise input data.

red-tape operation—1. Refers to general computer operations that do not directly contribute to the solution; i.e., arithmetical, logical, and transfer operations used in modifying the address section of other instructions, in the counting cycles, and in the rearrangement data. 2. Specifically, those internal operations that are necessary to process the data, but do not contribute to any final solution.

reduction, data—1. Relates to the art or process designed to change masses of raw test or experimentally obtained data, usually gathered by instrumentation, into useful, ordered, or simplified intelligence. 2. Refers to the process of transforming raw data into intelligible form by smoothing, adjusting, scaling and ordering experimental readings.

redundancy—1. As regards the communication of information, redundancy is the fraction of the gross-information content of a message that can be eliminated without the loss of the essential information. Numerically, it is one minus the ratio of the net information content to the gross information content, expressed in percent. 2. Refers also to an extra piece of information used to assist in determining the accuracy of moved digits or words in a computer. (Clarified by redundancy check.)

redundancy check—Refers to a specific checking technique based on the presence of extra (redundant) information which is used only for checking

purposes. Parity checking, check digits, control totals, and hash totals are all examples of redundancy checks.

reentrant program—A program so written that after interrupting a lower-priority program, will allow the latter to be restarted from the point of interruption.

re-entry point—Refers to a specific branch-point at which an instruction or a program is re-entered from a subroutine or main program. This position is called the re-entry point.

reference address—1. Refers to specific addresses that are designed to convert related addresses to machine-language addresses. 2. Specifically an address used as a reference for a group of related addresses.

reference edge, document—That specific edge of a source document in character recognition, which provides the basis of all subsequent reading processes.

reflected-binary code—Usually refers to any binary code in which sequential numbers are represented by binary expressions, each of which differs from the preceding expression in one place only. (Synonymous with reflected code and cyclic code.)

regenerate—Refers to a specific procedure designed to restore information that is electrostatically stored in a cell, on the screen of a cathode-ray tube in order to counteract fading and other disturbances that are prevalent with this type of information.

regenerative repeater—Refers to communications and a repeater in which retransmitted signals are practically free from distortion.

REGENT—A problem-oriented programming system and report-program generator that is designed to reduce substantially the time and effort necessary to translate general-data processing and reporting requirements into detailed computer instructions. It demands little knowledge of computer coding or instructions other than the basic rules of writing in the simplest form of the PAL assembly language. Essentially, the REGENT report-program generator is a program which, on the basis of a series of statements provided to it, produces another program which will produce a report or other output of the desired kind. These statements are written on the standard PAL coding form and then keypunched into cards. (UNIVAC)

register—1. A temporary storage device used for one or more words to facilitate arithmetical, logical or transferral operations. Examples are the accumulator, address, index, instruction, and M-Q registers. 2. The hardware for storing one or more computer words. Registers are usually zero-access storage devices. Types: address, bonds, buffer memory, circulating, control, current-instruction, memory, memory address, memory buffer, return code, shift, standby, storage, and switch.

register, address—Refers to a basic register that stores an address.

register, arithmetic—Concerns that particular register located in the logic unit of a computer which holds the operands required for a specific operation, i.e., it can hold the addend for addition or the multiplier for multiplication or particular words to be compared or shifted, etc.

register, check—A specific register designed to store information temporarily where it may be checked with the result of a succeeding transfer of this information.

register, circulating—1. A specific type of shift register in which the stored information is moved right or left, and the information from one end is reinserted at the other end. In the case of one-character right shift, the rightmost character reappears as the new leftmost character and every other character is shifted one position to the right. 2. Refers to a specific register in which the process, as in the preceding statement, is continuously occurring. This can be used as a delaying mechanism.

register, console display—An example follows: There are binary displays on many computer operator's consoles. One display bit indicates the memory word parity; other display bits may indicate: (1) the next instruction, (2) the contents of any memory location, (3) the contents of the accumulator, (4) the contents of index registers, (5) the status of the traps. When the computer halts, the display register will indicate the next instruction word, while a register will contain the address of the halt instruction that stopped the computer. To display anything else, the appropriate push-button display switch must be pressed. When the DISPLAY M (memory button) is pressed, the contents of the memory location specified by a register will be displayed. When either the DISPLAY or other buttons are pressed; the contents of other registers or the condition of the traps are displayed. The display register is also used as an entry register. Buttons are provided which may clear all or various parts of the display register. The contents of the display register may be entered in any memory location. Pushing any of the ENTRY buttons will accomplish entry of the display register contents into the appropriate memory location or register.

register, control–1. An especially important register which holds the identification of the instruction word to be executed next in time sequence, following the current operation. The register is often a counter that is incremented to the address of the next sequential-storage location, unless a transfer or other special instruction is specified by the program. (Synonymous with program counter, and contrasted with program register.) 2. Refers also to the accumulator, register, or storage unit that stores the current instruction governing a computer operation; an instruction register.

register, current-instruction–The specific control-section register designed to contain the instruction currently being executed after it is brought to the control section from memory. Also called instruction register.

register, flip-flop–Chain-like connections of flip-flops used to store binary digits. If digits are stored serially, data may be fed from one end and shifted bit-by-bit. If chained in parallel, all flip-flops can be set to the desired state simultaneously.

register, index–A register designed to contain a quantity for modifying addresses. (Synonymous with B-register and B-box.)

register, instruction–Generally this temporary storage device is designed to retain the instruction code of the instruction currently being executed.

register, memory-address (MA)–A special location in core memory is selected for data storage or retrieval and is determined by the MA. This register can directly address all words of the standard core memory or in any preselected field of extended core memory.

register, memory-buffer (MB)–Refers to the MB which serves as a buffer register for all information passing between the processor and the core memory, and serves as a buffer directly between core memory and peripheral equipment during data break information transfers. The MB is also used as a distributor-shift register for the analog-to-digit converter.

register, multiplier-quotient–Refers to a specific register in the arithmetic or logic portion of a computer in which the multiplier for multiplication is placed and in which the quotient for division is formed.

register, next available block–A specific type of address register of available blocks of core storage that are chained together for use by the line control computer, i.e., for the allocation of incoming information.

register, output buffer–Refers to the specific buffering or transfer device which receives data from internal storage and transfers it to an output media such as magnetic tape.

register, operation–1. Concerns an important register in which an operation is stored and analyzed in order to set conditions for the execution cycle. 2. Also, a temporary storage device which retains the operation number while that number is being analyzed. 3. Relates to a register which stores the operation code of the instruction or program in process.

register, program–1. Refers to various registers in the control unit that store the current instruction of the program and control computer operation during the execution of the program. 2. Also, a temporary storage device or area which retains the instruction code of the instruction being executed.

register, sequence control–Concerns a

specific hardware register designed to be used by the computer to remember the location of the next instruction to be processed in the normal sequence, but subject to branching, execute instructions, and interrupts.

registers, general—These are generally very fast registers designed to be used for any general purpose (usually as scratch pad). More recently they are being used in place of special registers such as the accumulator.

register, shift—Refers to a specific register designed so that the characters may be shifted one or more positions to the right or left. In a right shift, the rightmost character is lost. In a left shift, the leftmost character is lost.

regression, multiple—A special analysis program for determining the mathematical relationships and relative significances of manufacturing parameters associated with a given problem.

relative address—1. A fundamental computer concept relating to an address of a machine instruction that is referenced to an origin; e.g., R + 15 is a specific address relative to R, where R is the origin; the other R + machine addresses do not need to be named. 2. A label used to identify a word in a routine or subroutine with respect to its relative position in that routine or subroutine. A relative address is translated into an absolute address by addition of some specific address for the subroutine within the main routine.

relative addressing—A procedure or method of addressing in which the absolute address is obtained by means of the address modification, either simulated or actual, and is performed by the addition of a given number to the address part of an instruction, i.e., the

address part of the presumptive instruction is known as the relative address.

relativization—A particular technique by which the next written instruction address and operand address are given relative addresses. The relative address is translated automatically to an absolute address during execution of the program.

relay—An often used electromagnetic switching device, designed to have multiple electrical contacts, and which is energized by electrical current through its coil. It is used to complete electrical circuits.

reliability—1. The techniques used to measure the ability to function without failure. 2. The amount of credence placed in the result. 3. A word to indicate a measurement of trustworthiness and dependability, and frequently used to imply reliability factor or coefficient.

relocate—1. A procedure designed to modify the instructions of a routine in such a way that the routine can be moved to another location and then executed at that location. 2. A method to modify the addresses relative to a fixed point or origin.

relocation, base address—Refers to the specific ability to augment memory references by the contents of a specific base register, alterable only in the supervisor mode.

relocation dictionary (RLD)—1. The part of an object program that identifies all of the addresses of a program which must be changed when the program is to be relocated. 2. Part of a load module containing directions which enable a fetch program to properly initialize all relocatable address constants within the text section (TXT), by accounting for the actual starting address of the load module in storage and the incremental difference between the desired address and the initial address of the module.

remote batch—See batch, remote.

remote-computing monitor system—When the computer is available for batch processing, the computer operator will indicate to a subsystem under the system monitor that files on the auxiliary disk-storage device are to be processed. Under control of the subsystem, the files will be transferred from disk-storage or tape, which is then used as the system-input unit for normal processing under the system monitor. The result of this processing, which is contained on the system output unit, can be handled in either of the following ways: (a) It can be transferred to disk storage for subsequent transmission to a terminal, or (b) it can be printed on an off-line printer and mailed to the terminal.

remote computing system, exchange device—In many larger systems, the exchange device controls the flow of information between the computer and the terminals. Characters typed at the terminals are formed into statements within the exchange device and then are sent to the computer, one statement at a time. The computer returns an answer to the exchange device, which, in turn, sends it to the proper terminal. An exchange device is also designed to allow each terminal to send or receive data independent of all other terminals.

Programs are permanently stored in disk storage. When the user indicates that a program he has constructed is to be saved, the remote computing system places it in disk storage. Thereafter, the program will be available to the user whenever needed.

remote device—Relates to various input/output units, or other pieces of equipment, which are outside of the computer center but connected by a communication line. In a typical on-line, real-time communications system, the remote device is usually a teletypewriter, an audio answer back device, or a CRT visual display unit.

remote inquiry—On-line inquiry stations permit people to interrogate the computer files and receive immediate answers to inquiries. In commercial operations they can be located at dozens of remote locations such as office, factory, warehouse, branch locations hundreds of miles away. Such an on-line real-time system permits all levels of industrial management to obtain immediate answers to questions about inventories, work in process, sales, and other facts for effective management.

remote message, input/output (I/O)—Refers to I/O control units designed for obtaining messages from, and sending messages to remote devices. As regards remote message control, the I/O control handles the following functions: receipt of messages from remote terminals, sending of messages to remote terminals, automatic dial-up, and code conversion. The user supplies the system with line-control specifications and installation-oriented routines to analyze message headers.

Messages received can be stored in processing queues or output-terminal queues. Macro statements enable the installation program to obtain messages for processing and to send messages. A log of all message traffic may be stored in a secondary storage device.

remote polling technique—Refers to various systems that are controlled through constant polling of teller or other consoles on each line by the central terminal unit. Polling is a request to each console for a message or for readiness to receive a reply. Because the full-duplex line permits the remote terminal unit to respond instantly to polls (less than 1/10th of a second), as many as 16 teller consoles can be efficiently serviced on one line. The turn-around delay inherent in a half-duplex line greatly reduces the number of consoles which can be polled and serviced efficiently, thereby requiring more lines.

removable random access—Describes a feature of storage device like disk packs, tape strips or card strips which can be physically removed and replaced by another, thereby allowing for a theoretically unlimited storage capacity. Contrasted with both sequential storage and fixed media random access storage.

repeater—Refers to a specific device used to amplify and/or reshape signals.

repeater, regenerative—Concerns a specific repeater designed so that signals retransmitted are practically free from distortion.

repeater station—1. Relates to various stations with a repeater located for the purpose of building up and equalizing the strength of a telephone or telegraph signal in a long line. 2. Refers to an intermediate station in a microwave system which is arranged to receive a signal from an adjacent station and amplify and retransmit to another adjacent station. Usually performs the function in both directions simultaneously.

repertoire, instruction—Most instruction repertoires include fixed and floating point integers and fractional arithmetic. Provisions are made for partial word transfers, partial compares, repeated

search operations and masking. Special add and subtract instructions perform parallel addition or subtraction of two or three fields within a single data word. To provide fast programming of double precision arithmetic, special features have been incorporated into the arithmetic section. The basic function codes in the instruction repertoire of the system provide unlimited programming versatility. Much of the real programming power of the computer lies in the unique format of the instruction word. Of the 30 bit positions in the instruction word, nine serve as special purpose designators. When these designators are used in combination with the function codes, the computer can perform more than 25,000 individual programming operations. (UNIVAC)

report generator—Refers to various software programs designed to direct the production of output reports if the computer is provided with format and specifications, input file detail, sorted input data, input-output procedure rules and other information.

report program generator—A basic programming device, the report program generator develops a convenient programming method for producing a wide variety of reports. The generator may range from a listing of a card deck or magnetic-tape reel to precisely arranged, calculated, and edited tabulation of data from several input sources.

representation, analog—Refers to representations that do not have discrete values but are continuously variable.

representation, digital—A representation of variables as data, by means of digits or discrete quantities, as determined by their appearance or non-appearance.

reproducer—1. Used for duplicating cards and card data, or for punching cards in any format. 2. A device that will duplicate on one card, all or part of the information contained on another card.

reproducing punch—See reproducer.

request-repeat system—A system employing an error-detecting code and so arranged that a signal detected as being in error automatically initiates a request for retransmission of the signal that was detected as being in error.

rescue dump—To record on magnetic tape the entire contents of the memory, which includes the status of the computer system at the time the dump is made. R dumps are made so that in the event of power failure, etc., a run can be resumed from the last rescue point (R point) rather than rerunning the entire program (NCR).

rescue points—For many applications it is very desirable, indeed essential, to create rescue points (R points) from which it is known that the program can be resumed in a proper manner. If a processing mishap does occur after creating a rescue point, the operator can restart his run at any rescue point by use of the restart routine. For long runs, the liberal use of rescue points will mean that the run is, in essence, segmented. A mishap will affect only one segment and all the valid processing that preceded the establishing of the latest point is saved and need not be reprocessed (NCR).

reserved words—Refers to specific words which are set aside in the COBOL language which cannot be used as data names, files names, or procedure names and are of three types; connected, optional words, and key words.

reset—1. Procedures designed to return a device to zero or to an initial or arbitrarily selected condition. 2. Various processes designed to restore a storage device to a prescribed initial state, not necessarily that denoting zeros. 3. Zero state.

resident, core memory—In most systems the term resident is used to denote a part of the executive which resides in core memory at all times. Some specific examples of resident routines are the dispatcher, the real-time clock routine, and the internal-error processing routines. Nonresident routines are taken from the library.

respond-typeout key—Concerns a specific push button on a console inquiry key board which locks the typewriter keyboard and permits the automatic processing to continue.

response, frequency—Concerns various measures of the ability of various devices to take into account, follow, or act upon a varying condition; e.g., as applied to amplifiers, the frequencies at which the gain has fallen to the one-half power point or to 0.707 of the voltage gain, either at the high or low end of the frequency spectrum. When applied to a mechanical controller, the maximum rate at which changes in condition can be followed and acted upon, since it is implied that the controller can follow slow changes.

response operation, audio—In many systems the typical audio unit provides composed audio responses to digital inquiries sent from telephones linked to the computer system. Usually the calling party enters a request by dialing digits which are immediately transmitted to the unit and then forwarded to the processor. The computer processes the data, composes a coded response, and returns the message to the audio unit.

The unit interprets the coded reply, selects the proper words from its stored vocabulary, and tells the inquirer what he wants to know.

restart—1. Refers specifically to one of a set of preselected points located in a program such that if an error is detected between two points, the problem may be rerun by returning to the last such point instead of returning to the start of the problem. 2. A positional procedure to return to a previous point in a program and resume operation from that point.

restitution—Refers to a series of significant conditions resulting from decisions based on demodulated telegraph signals.

restore—1. A procedure designed to return a variable address or various other computer words to their initial or preselected value. 2. Procedures designed to return a register, trigger, error-condition signal, etc., to zero or to a specific initial condition.

retention period—Refers to a designated period of time during which records must be saved before they may be disposed of, usually stated in terms of months or years, but sometimes expressed as contingent upon the occurrence of an event — employee termination, contract closure, and the like.

reticle, font—An optical character recognition term referring to a system of lines forming various character outlines or dimensions, which are placed on the image of an input character and which determines whether that character conforms to the prescribed shape and range of dimensions. Other various outlines on the font reticle check for minimum space between lines and characters and also the maximum size of punctuation marks.

retrieval, data—A basic concept which refers generally to the retrieval or return of data by selecting, searching, or retransmission of information from a file, data bank, or storage device.

retrofit—An adjustment of existing systems or programs for the purpose of fitting in or accommodating a new part and performing all other changes necessary in related systems or programs.

return instructions—Concerns a specific group of instructions which are usually developed in subroutines at the end of a program to provide for the transfer of control from the return subroutine to the main routine.

reverse scan—A particular editing operation designed to suppress zeros, i.e., to replace them with blanks and eliminate the zero suppression word mark.

right justified—Concerns printing and refers to data which are right justified when the right-hand digit or character occupies its allotted right-hand position.

roll-back—Concerns a system designed to restart the running program after a system failure. Snapshots of data and programs are stored at periodic intervals and the system rolls back to restart at the last recorded snapshot.

roll-in—Generally concerns a return to a main or internal storage unit of data which had previously been transferred from main or internal memory units to various external or auxiliary units.

roll-out—A process designed for use in diagnostic routines, in which a register or counter is read out by the following process; add 1 to the digits in each column simultaneously; do this n times, where n is the radix of the number in the register; when the result in each column changes from n-1 to 0, issue a signal.

round-off—1. Refers to a process designed to change a more precise quantity to a less precise one, according to some rule. 2. An arbitrary but consistent rule designed for the limitation of cumulative errors arising from truncation through this lesser decrease of precision.

round-off error—Relates to a specific error resulting from rounding off a quantity by deleting the less significant digits and applying some rule of correction to the part retained; e.g., 0.2751 can be rounded to 0.275 with a rounding error of .0001. (Contrasted with truncation error.)

routine—1. A machine instruction sequence that carries out a well-defined function. 2. A set of coded instructions arranged in proper sequence to direct the computer to perform a desired operation or series of operations. Types: algorithmic, assembly, benchmark, compile, control, conversion, dating, executive, executive system, object and service.

routine, closed—Generally refers to various routines that are not inserted as a block of instructions within a main routine, but are entered by basic linkage from the main routine.

routine, compile—A specific computer group of instructions that are also called a compile, compiler, compiling routine, and a compilation. An executive routine that, before the desired computation is started, translates a program expressed in pseudocode into machine code (or into another pseudocode for further translation by an interpreter). In accomplishing the translation, the compiler may be required to adapt or to specialize the instructions.

routine, diagnostic—1. Refers to a basic routine used to locate a malfunction in a computer, or designed to aid in locating the mistakes in a computer program. Thus, in general any routine specifically designed to aid in debugging or troubleshooting. (Synonymous with malfunction routine, and related to debugging.) 2. A specific routine designed to locate either a malfunction in the computer or a mistake in coding.

routine, open—Concerns various types of routines that can be inserted directly into a larger routine without a linkage or calling sequence.

routine, post-mortem—1. Generally A standardized routine designed to either automatically or on demand print data concerning contents of registers and storage locations, after the routine stops, in order to assist in locating errors or mistakes in coding. 2. A service routine useful in analyzing the cause of a failure, such as a routine that dumps out the content of a store after a failure. (Related to post mortem.)

routine, relocatable—Refers to a specific routine designed and stored such a way that it may be moved quickly and conveniently to other locations.

routing—Relates to various assignments of communications paths for the delivery of messages.

routing, alternate—Concerns various assignments of a secondary communications paths to various destinations if the primary paths are unavailable.

row binary card—A Hollerith card in which the rows are contiguous components of a binary vector. (Contrast with column binary card.)

ruly English—An unique type of English in which every word has one and only one conceptual meaning, and each concept has only a single word to describe it. Used by the U.S. Patent Office to develop their index codes.

run diagram—Files, transactions, information and data in a graphic representation that is to be handled under program control to produce the newly updated files, list of changes, or specific reports.

* _ * _ *

sampling—1. Refers to various types of procedures designed to obtain a value of a variable at regular or intermittent intervals. 2. Also, procedure of systems analysis in which traffic volumes, file activity, and other transfers are estimated on the basis of representative samples taken. 3. Refers also to a method of communication line control in which messages on a circuit are sampled by a computer that selects only those for which computer processing is required. 4. Sampling provides a random method of checking and control. In using it, a transaction or item is selected and the processing that it undergoes checked in detail. This provides an indication of accurate and complete processing.

satellite computer, real-time—Satellite computers in various real-time systems relieve the larger systems of time consuming input and output functions as well as tasks for performing preprocessing and postprocessing functions, such as validity editing and formatting for print.

satellite processor—Refers generally to a small processor designed especially and primarily for off-line card-to-tape conversion, printing of tape contents, and other selected, high-volume operations; frequently used to support and add to the capacity of a large processor to

further increase its productivity.

scalar—A device that produces an output equal to the input multiplied by a constant, such as a linear amplifier, a set of pulleys or speed gears. See factor, scaling.

scale—1. In some instances this is a ruler-like drawing placed on the graph to aid in the determination of values within the plotting grid. 2. Often times refers to a range of values frequently dictated by the computer word-length or routine at hand. 3. A procedure used to alter the units in which the variables are expressed, in order to bring all quantities within a given range. 4. Also, a design to change the units in which a variable is expressed so as to bring it within the capacity of the machine or the program at hand.

scan—1. Refers to electromagnetic units designed to examine stored information for a specific purpose as for content or for arrangement. 2. To examine the status of communication lines or other input-output channels to determine whether data is being received or transmitted.

scanner—1. Refers to various instruments which automatically sample or interrogate the state of various processes, files, conditions, or physical states and initiates action in accordance with the information obtained. 2. Many scanner instruments sequentially check each of the sites on a particular leased line for traffic. Other scanners at the control center can sequentially check several lines to determine whether a message is present or not.

scanner, flying-spot—As regards optical character recognition (OCR), this is a device which employs a moving spot of light to scan a sample space, the intensity of the transmitted or reflected light being sensed by a photoelectric transducer.

scanner, interrupt—Refers to various external devices that are continuously scanned for interrupt requests. A scanner in the computer counts through the nonpriority external device addresses sequentially, each time asking if the addressed device is requesting an interrupt. When an interrupt request is found, the scanner will stop at that address and attempt to interrupt the computer program.

scanning limits—Concerns the action of comparing input variables against either prestored or calculated high and/or low limits to determine if an alarm condition is present.

scatter-read/gather-write—Gather-write is defined as the ability to place the information from several nonadjacent locations in core storage (for example, several logical records) into a single physical record such as a tape block. Scatter-read is regarded as the ability to place the information from a physical record into several nonadjacent locations in core storage.

scatter write operation—Refers to procedures for obtaining various data elements from one location and simultaneously transferring them to several output areas.

scheduled down time—Relates specifically to the measured or required idle time necessary for normal servicing of computer equipment during which such equipment is unavailable for operations. This is usually expressed as a percent of total available time. It is also known as preventive maintenance time.

scheduled maintenance time—Refers to a measurement of machine time which is specifically devoted to repairs, and usually on some regular pattern or schedule, during which time preventive maintenance activities are also performed.

scheduler—In many systems this is a special portion of the executive software section. The scheduler controls the time when the execution of the program will be performed.

scheduling algorithm—Refers to a set of mathematics rules that is included in the scheduling routine of the executive program. The scheduling algorithm determines the length of a user's quantum and the frequency with which this quantum is repeated.

scheduling, dynamic—Concerns specific scheduling that changes with the different demands that are made on the system rather than being fixed as in conventional applications.

Schneider front-end—Relates to a front-end train of amplifiers to interface gas chromatograph instruments to a real-time computer (IBM).

scientific notation—Quantities are expressed as a fractional part (mantissa) and a power of ten (characteristic).

scratchpad memory—A fundamental concept which refers to a high-speed memory device used to store the location of an interrupted program, and to retrieve the latter after the interrupting program has been completed.

SDA, (source-data automation)—Refers to the many methods of recording information in coded forms, such as on paper tapes, punched cards, or tags that can be used over and over again to produce many other records without rewriting.

SDI—Abbreviation for selective dissemination of information, i.e., a process which relates to a particular literature search notification and hard copy supply system and which thus serves clients with internal or external reports, articles, or other documents, i.e., any system for selectively distributing information in accordance with given profiles.

search—Concerns a type of systematic examination of the available information in a specific field of interest.

search, binary—Refers to various techniques designed for finding a particular item in an ordered set of items by repeatedly dividing in half the portion of the ordered set containing the sought-for item until only the sought-for item remains.

search, chain—A procedure in which a search key is used and is transformed to bring out an initial address. If the contents of the initial address contain the key matching the search key, the contents contain the sum or other information sought. If unsuccessful, another address is found in the contents, and the process is repeated until the item is found or the chain ends. Thus a chain search operates in a file of unordered but related or interconnected data.

search, conjunctive—Refers to a unique search defined in terms of a logical product, i.e., conjunctive form, in contrast to a disjunctive form, or logical sum.

search, dichotomizing—A specialized search designed so that the series of items is divided into two parts, one of which is rejected, and the process is repeated on the unrejected part until the item with the desired property is found. This process usually depends upon the presence of a known sequence in the series of items.

search, disjunctive—Refers to a unique search defined in terms of a logical sum, i.e., disjunctive form, in contrast to a conjunctive form or logical product.

search time—A measurement relating to the time required to locate a particular field of data in storage. Searching requires a comparison of each field with a predetermined standard until an identity is obtained. This is contrasted with access time that is based upon locating data by a means of the address of its storage location.

second generation computer—A name given to a group of computers often classified as the second era of technological development of computers when the transistor replaced vacuum tubes. Machines using transistors occupy much less space, operate faster, require less maintenance, and are more reliable. The second generation computer was prominent in the years 1959-1964 and included the IBM 1401, the Honeywell 800, the RCA 501, and the Remington Rand Solid State 80. The third generation of equipment featured microcircuits or miniaturization of components which reduced cost, increased reliability and were faster than transistors.

second-level address—The part of a computer instruction which indicates a location where the address of the referenced operand is to be found. In some computers the machine address indicated can itself be indirect. Such multiple levels of addressing are terminated either by prior control or by a termination symbol. Same as: indirect address.

sector—A concept similar to a binary word but which may include characters or bits not allotted to the programmer. Example: A word can be 27 bits, plus sign. However, the sector can contain 32 bits—the remaining 4 bits may be used by the logic in the computer for spacing, etc.

seek—1. A fundamental activity related to the process of obtaining specific records from a random-access file. The number of seeks is the number of file items inspected before the desired item is found. 2. Various procedures designed to look for data according to information given regarding that data; occasionally used interchangeably and erroneously for search, scan, and screen.

segment—1. Specifically applicable to multiprogramming, i.e., in a routine too long to fit into internal storage, a part short enough to be stored in the internal storage. These parts contain the addresses of succeeding parts of the routine. Routines that exceed internal storage capacity may be automatically divided into segments by a compiler. 2. A procedure or process designed to divide a routine into an integral number of subroutines with each part capable of being completely stored in the internal storage and containing the instructions to jump to other segments. 3. To store part of a program or routine separately, usually in external or intermediate storage areas and devices to be brought in as needed to high-speed storage.

segmentation—Refers to various types of programmer-defined and monitor-implemented procedures or techniques of dividing a program into essentially self-contained segments so that only certain parts need be in memory at any instant. Segmentation may be performed to allow several programs to be in memory at the same time or to allow a program to be operated that is too large for the available memory space.

segmentation and control, automatic—Related to multiprogramming, auto-matic segmentation and control permits the computer to efficiently handle programs that exceed the core-memory capacity of a particular system configuration. Without reprogramming, the computer in many larger systems automatically adapts its operational procedures to allow the processing of any program on any system configuration. Segments of all programs concurrently being executed are "fitted" into available memory space for execution. Thus, the user is not forced to install a system of maximum memory capacity to accommodate one long program; he need not purchase more equipment than he normally needs for efficient operation.

selective tracing—Relates to a specific tracing on particular and specific data most often related to some highly specific instructions such as, transfer instructions only, or for specified locations, registers, storage units or areas, etc.

selector channel—In many larger communication-oriented systems selector channels are used where high-speed devices are to be attached to a system. A single channel can operate only one I/O (input/output) device at a time. Two or more channels connected to, any computer system provide the ability to read, write, and compute from multiple input/output devices.

self-adapting—Refers to the ability of specially designed computer systems which can change performance characteristics in response to its environment.

self-checking code—A code designed so that errors produce forbidden combinations. A single-error detecting code produces a forbidden combination if a digit gains or loses a single bit. A double-error detecting code produces a forbidden combination if a digit gains or loses either one or two bits and so forth. (Related to self-checking number and error-detecting code.)

self-complementing code—A special machine language in which the code of the complement of a digit is the complement of the code of the digit.

self-organizing—Refers to various sytems which have the capability of classification or internal rearrangement, depending on the environment, in accordance with given instructions or a set of rules.

self-organizing machine—Refers to a class of machines that may be characterized loosely as cybernetic types containing a variable network in which the elements are organized by the machine itself, without external intervention, to meet the criteria of successful operation.

semantic errors—Refers to definite programmer errors concerned with the meaning or intent of the programmer and are definitely his responsibility. Consequently, he is provided with an extensive set of debugging aids for manipulating and referencing a program when in search of errors in the logic and analysis.

semantics—A particular study of the meanings of words, signs and symbols, and the relationships of the things they denote.

semantics, language theory—Relates to the meaning of words in a sentence as contrasted to syntax, which is the structure of a sentence.

semi-conductor—This term specifically refers to an electrical device which is composed of high conductive metals and low conductive insulators designed to change the nature or strength of electrical flows in various circuits. Latest semiconductors are metal-oxide or MOS.

semifixed length record—As permitted in many computers, this is a particular fixed-length record which has a length subject to change at the choice of the system analyst or programmer, although such lengths usually remain fixed for a given problem or run or specific operation or routine.

send-only service—Concerns transmission service in which the data-communication channel is capable of transmitting signals, but is not equipped to receive signals.

sense—Refers to various types of examination of data particularly relative to a set of criteria. 2. A process to determine the present arrangement of some element of hardware, especially a manually set switch. 3. Actions which detect special signals. 4. To read holes in paper or cards and magnetic spots on tape, drums, etc.

sensing, mark—Concerns a special reading technique for detecting special pencil marks entered in special places on a punch card, and automatically translating the marks into punched holes.

sensitivity ratio—1. A measurement of the degree of response of an instrument or control unit to change in the incoming signal. 2. A measured ratio of a change in output to the change in input which causes it, after steady-state has been reached, usually expressed as a numerical ratio with the units of measurement of the two quantities stated.

sentinel—A name for a common symbol to mark a unit of information, e.g., the end of an item, field, block, tape, file, etc.

separator—Refers to a specific flag that separates and organizes items of data.

separator, word—Refers to a character in

machine coding that is designated to segregate fields.

SEPOL—An acronym Soil-Engineering Problem-Oriented Language.

sequence, calling—1. Pertains to a basic set of instructions designed to be used to begin or initialize or to transfer control to a subroutine, but usually to complete the return of control after the execution of a subroutine is finished. 2. Refers to the instructions used for linking a closed routine with the main routine; i.e., basic linkage and a list of the parameters.

sequence checking—Refers to a sequence check designed to be used to prove that a set of data is arranged in either ascending or descending order before it is processed. It is generally a mechanized operation performed in a separate machine run or simultaneously with another operation run.

sequence, collation—Concerns an ordered sequence in which the characters are processed to be acceptable to a computer.

sequential control—Refers to a distinct mode of computer operation designed so that instructions are executed in consecutive order by ascending or descending addresses of storage locations, unless otherwise specified by a jump.

sequential file—A data file whose key-fields are arranged in a definite sequence. This is contrasted to a random file.

sequential data, set-indexed—A name for a particular data set organization designed to combine the efficiency of sequential organization with the ability to rapidly access records out of sequence but used only on direct-access devices.

serial arithmetic—Refers to specific operations designed so that each number is divided into digits to be operated upon singly usually in the adder-subtracter or a comparator. The same number of addition operations are required as there are binary digits in the operands; a simpler and slower operation than parallel arithmetic.

serial transmission—A standard method for moving data in sequence, one character at a time, as contrasted with parallel transmission.

shift, arithmetic—A process designed to multiply or divide a quantity by a power of the number base; e.g., if binary 1101, which represents decimal 13, is arithmetically shifted twice to the left, the result is 110100, which represents 52, which is also obtained by multiplying (13 by 2) twice; on the other hand, if the decimal 13 were to be shifted to the left twice, the result would be the same as multiplying by 10 twice, or 1300. (Related to shift and cyclic shift.)

sign bit—A binary digit designating the algebraic sign of a quantity, plus or minus.

significance, bit—Refers to the bit presence or absence in a specific location of an instruction word which distinguishes the instruction to be of certain type, for example, zero vs. one-address instruction.

significant digit—Designed to contribute to the precision of an accurate numeral. The number of significant digits is counted beginning with the digit contributing the most value, called the most significant digit, and ending with the one contributing the least value, called the least significant digit.

sign position—1. The left-hand digit position in a numeric field, or the left-hand character position in an alpha-numeric field, in which is stored the sign (minus symbol if negative) of the quantity stored in that field. 2. The position at which the sign of a number is located.

simplex channel—A communications channel that permits transmission in one direction only.

simulation—1. The experimental technique of an operating system by means of mathematical or physical models that operate on real world or specifically devised problems in a time-sequential method similar to the system itself. 2. A pseudoexperimental analysis of an operating system by means of mathematical or physical models that operate in a time-sequential manner similar to the system itself. 3. Many problems cannot be solved analytically, but adequate criteria for success can be deduced from trial-and-error processes in which the model of the system is dynamically studied. For example, to determine the best operating conditions for a pilot manufacturing plant, one could build a mathematical model of the plant to "try out" the multitude of variables, parameters, i.e., conditions and circumstances, by simulating dynamic operations—all this "before" deciding on size, structure, locations and variations of the plant. 4. The representation of physical systems and phenomena by computers, models or other equipment; e.g., an imitative type of data processing in which an automatic computer is used as a model of some entity, e.g., a chemical process. When information enters the computer to represent the factors of process, the computer produces information that represents the results of the process, and the processing done by the computer represents the process itself. 5. In a computer programming, the tech-

nique of setting up a routine for one computer to make it operative as nearly as possible like some other computer.

simulation, continuous—The type of simulation which may be represented by continuous variables. The system is therefore suitable for representation by a set of differential equations. These may be further classified as linear or nonlinear. Example: missile flights.

single cycle key—Refers to a specific push button on printers, which when depressed, causes an additional line to be printed despite an end-of-form indication.

single-step operation—Concerns a manual method of operating an automatic computer in which a single instruction or part of an instruction is performed in response to a single operation of a manual control. This method is generally used for detecting mistakes.

skew—In reference to facsimile transmission, skew is the deviation from a rectangular picture (frame) caused by the lack of time coincidence between the scanner and the recorder.

slave computer—1. A "fail-safe" or backup system (application) whereby a slave or second computer performs the same steps of the same programs so that if the master computer fails or malfunctions, the slave computer continues without a deterioration of operations. Various space or urgent missile computations require back-up or duplicate systems. 2. A computer that is used in a slave application.

slot—In reference to a magnetic drum, all the cells under a set of read-write heads at one instant in time.

slow memory—A measurement concept relating to those portions of the memory with a relatively slow-access rate from which information may be obtained automatically.

smoothing, exponential—Refers to a specific statistical technique for predicting future demands based on current and past demands activity without storing and saving masses of past history data.

snapshot program—Concerns an error control technique, i.e., when a trace program is an interpretive program, it is called an interpretive trace program, and when a trace program gives output only on selected instructions or for a selected set or single condition it is called a snapshot program.

software packages—The voluminous group of manufacturer-provided support, primary, or subroutine programs which are quite often supplied by the computer manufacturer with the purchase of equipment, or those which can be purchased from software companies, or individuals who have specialized in writing programs (software).

solid-logic technology (SLT)—An IBM-coined term these are microelectric circuits, the product of solid-logic technology, used as the basic components of the system. Called logic circuits because they carry and control the electrical impulses that represent information within a computer, these tiny devices operate at speeds ranging from 300 down to six billionths of a second. Transistors and diodes mounted on the circuits are as small as 28 thousandths of an inch square and are protected by a film of glass 60 millionths of an inch thick.

sort, external—Usually refers to the second phase of a multipass sort program, wherein strings of data are continually merged until one string of sequenced data is formed.

sorting, merge—A procedure designed to produce a single sequence of items, ordered according to some rule, from two or more previously unordered sequences, without changing the items in size, structure, or total number. Although more than one pass may be required for a complete sorting, items are selected during each pass on the basis of the entire key.

sort, internal—The process of two or more records within the central computer memory; the first phase of a multipass sort program.

sort/merge—Refers to various sets of routines designed to arrange random items in an ordered sequence. These routines can also be used to combine two or more ordered sequences into a single file.

source language—1. The basic language used to specify computer processing; translated into object language by an assembler or compiler. 2. Very often a compiler language such as FORTRAN from which machine-language instructions are developed by the use of translation routines or compilers. 3. The language in which the input to the FORTRAN processor is written.

source program—A program that must be translated into machine language before use.

SPA—Abbreviation for Systems and Procedures Association, an organization of management personnel.

special character—A character other than a digit or letter, e.g., *+–$=.

stack pointer—In larger systems this refers to nested storage types (push-down), i.e., the address of the location at the top of the column is often called the stack pointer and is held in a pre-

146

assigned register.

stack, push-down—A procedure which develops a reserved area of memory into which operands are pushed and from which operands are pulled on a last-in, first-out basis.

stand-alone capability—Generally refers to multiplexors designed to function independently of a host or master computer, either some of the time or all of the time.

start-stop system—Concerns various systems designed so that each group of code elements corresponding to an alphabetical signal is preceded by a start signal which serves to prepare the receiving mechanism for the reception and registration of a character, and is followed by a stop signal which serves to bring the receiving mechanism to rest in preparation for the reception of the next character.

staticizer—1. A specific type of storage device for converting time-sequential information into static time parallel information. 2. A type of buffer.

storage, core-rope—A unique memory device invented by Olsen of the Lincoln laboratory of the Massachusetts Institute of Technology. Information is stored in the form of an array of cores and wires, the wires being wound in one direction or the other through the core. The pattern which results resembles a rope and permits a selection of a single core for a given pattern or pulse. The information is stored in the wiring rather than in the core itself, the core acting much as a switch. Same as core-rope memory, linear selection switch rope memory, rope storage, and Olsen memory.

storage, external—1. Storage from which the data to be operated on are normally obtained. It may be under the control of the computer, but data to be operated on must be transferred to secondary or internal storage before operations commence, and are returned to external storage only after operations are completed. External storage devices usually have larger capacities and lower access speeds than internal and secondary storage. 2. A storage device outside the computer that can store information in a form acceptable to the computer, e.g., cards, tapes.

storage, magnetic-film—1. The magnetic film storage of the computer provides highspeed internal storage. By using this thin-film storage area as an auxiliary temporary storage medium, faster computation can be obtained. In a typical installation, any one of the addresses in control store can be accessed in 167 nanoseconds and have a complete cycle time of 667 nanoseconds. Because of this high speed, thin-film is the most frequently used portion of the computer's internal storage area; it may be referenced three times in the same time that it takes to make one reference to the core-storage area. The high access and internal switching times of thin-film store make it ideal for use as temporary storage of operands while the actual computation of data is taking place.

storage, matrix—Refers to a sophisticated storage unit whose elements are arranged in a matrix so that access to any location requires the use of two or more coordinates, i.e., a cathode ray tube store and a core store using coincident-current selection.

storage, nonvolatile—Refers to standard storage media that retains information in the absence of power and which may be made available upon restoration of power, e.g., magnetic tapes, drums, or cores.

storage, permanent—1. Refers to a method or to a device designed to retain intermediate or final results outside of the machine, usually in the form of punched cards or magnetic tape. 2. That particular storage which is non-volatile, i.e., retains its content when the power is switched off normally, but also, perhaps, when power failure occurs.

storage protection—1. Especially in time-shared systems, continued existence of a stored program requires protection from all contemporary programs and, in particular, that each stored program have inviolate storage areas. This is accomplished by independently establishing reserved areas in each storage module and inhibiting a program of reading, writing, or transferring to a location that is not within its reserved areas. Every instruction that references the central store has the final address checked to insure that it falls within a permissible area. 2. Various procedures allow several programs to reside in core storage at the same time while one is being executed. They also allow transfer of data from peripheral equipment to memory while other programs already are in memory. Storage protection eliminates danger that one program would inadvertently be placed over, and thereby destroy, another program.

storage, push-down—In larger systems this is a storage designed to work as though it comprised a number of registers arranged in a column, with only the register at the top of the column connected to the rest of the storage. Each word in turn, enters the top register and is then "pushed down" the column from register to register to make room for the next words to arrive. As the words are transferred out of the storage units (out of the top register), other data in storage moves back up the column from register to register to fill the top register.

storage registers, associative—Same as associative storage. Refers specifically to those registers which are not identified by their name or position but which are known and addressed by their content.

stylus printer—Used to form characters by forcing a set of selected styli or wires against the ribbon or paper. The specific wires of a 5 x 7 array are selected to form a character. Very closely examined characters appear as patterns of dots. Same as wire printer.

supervisory control, processor controller (P-C)—In some specific large systems the P-C communicates the messages and the commands to the operator and, if desired, directly to the process equipment and instrumentation. The sensors that measure process conditions are continuously monitored by the P-C. The P-C program analyzes this information and then generates the required output information. Messages from the P-C to the operator may be displayed by several methods in the operator's working area. These messages guide the operator in adjusting the status of instruments located at the point of control.

suppression, zero—A process to cause the elimination of insignificant zeros (those to the left of a quantity in a field or word) during a printing operation.

switched-message network—Refers to a communications service offered by the common carrier in which a customer may communicate with any other customer receiving the same service. Examples are TELEX and TWX.

switching center—A communications location in which incoming data from one circuit is transferred to the proper outgoing circuit.

switching theory—A particular branch of theory which relates to combinational logic, its operation, behavior and consequences, i.e., concerning such devices as computers, Turing machines, logic elements, and switch networks.

symbolic addressing—Refers to a fundamental procedure or method of addressing using an address (symbolic address) chosen for convenience in programming or of the programmer in which translation of the symbolic address (by the input program) into an absolute address is required before it can be used in the computer.

symbolic assembler—A sub-language program designed to let the programmer code instructions in a symbolic language. The assembler allows mnemonic symbols to be used for instruction codes and addresses. Constant and variable storage registers can be automatically assigned. The assembler produces a binary object tape and lists a symbol table with memory allocations and useful diagnostic messages.

symbolic language—The various procedures that treat formal logic by means of a formalized artificial language or symbolic calculus whose purpose is to avoid the ambiguities and logical inadequacies of natural languages. Advantages of the symbolic method are greater exactness of formulation, and power to deal with complex material.

symbolic logic—1. Refers to the study of formal logic and mathematics by means of a special written language that seeks to avoid the ambiguity and inadequacy of ordinary language. 2. The mathe-

matical concepts, techniques and languages as used in the foregoing definition, whatever their particular application or context. (Synonymous with mathematical logic, and related to logic.)

symbolic notation—A method of representing a storage location by one or more figures.

symbolic programming—Concerns the use of arbitrary symbols to represent addresses in order to facilitate programming.

symbol string—A concatenation of items or characters, i.e., a one dimensional array of such items ordered only by reference to the relations between adjacent members.

synergic—The combination using every organ of a system, e.g., a coordinated system.

syntax—Refers to the rules governing sentence structure in a language, or statement structure in a language such as that of a compiler program.

syntax-directed compiler—A compiler based on the syntactal relationships of the character string.

syntax recognizer—Refers to a unique subroutine which recognizes the phase class in an artificial language, normally expressed in Backus normal form (BNF), formal language theory.

system check—An overall performance check on the system, usually not made by built-in computer check circuits, e.g., control totals, hash totals, and record counts.

system control panel—In most systems manual control operations are held to a minimum by the system design and operating system. The result is fewer operator errors. The system control panel is divided into three major sections: operator control section—contains only those controls required by the operator when the processor is operating under full supervisory control; operator intervention section—contains additional controls required for the operator to intervene in normal programming operation; customer engineering section—contains controls intended only for customer engineering use in diagnostics and maintenance.

system diagnostics—A program resembling the operational program rather than a systematic logical pattern program which will detect overall system malfunctions rather than isolate or locate faulty components.

system, information-retrieval—A standard version of system for locating and selecting, on demand, certain documents or other graphic records relevant to a given information requirement from a file of such material. Examples of information-retrieval systems are classification, indexing, and machine searching systems.

system loader—It functions as a part of the monitor (control) system by loading system routines, object programs, and library subroutines. System routines are programs such as the FORTRAN II compiler or the ASIST assembler and utility programs. Each of these routines is uniquely defined with a name and entry. An object program is a binary main program with subprograms. Object programs are the compiler and assembler output of source-language programs. Library routines are those subroutines and input/output drivers that may be called by an object program or system routine. The loader has the ability to load an object program in parts (primary, secondary and library) from a

possible three separate devices. In this case the three parts combine to form a complete object program. The loader may be called on at any time during the system operation to load a system routine or object program. The loader is an absolute binary program in the master file (ASI).

systems analysis—1. The business activity analysis to determine precisely what must be accomplished and how to accomplish it. 2. The organized, step-by-step study and analysis of the detailed procedure for collection, manipulation, and evaluation of information about an organization with the goal of improving control over its total operation or segments of it. 3. The examination of an activity, procedure, method, technique, or a business to determine what must be accomplished and the best method of accomplishing the necessary operations.

systems generation—In some computers, a systems disk must be generated by the user who specifies the configuration, file protected area, error handling, etc.

systems programmer—The individual primarily concerned with writing either "operating systems" (computer internal control programs) or languages for computers. Systems programmers produce those control programs and/or monitors that operate central processors and peripheral equipment. They write test programs that detect errors and malfunctions. They design utility programs to control formats of output and do sorting and merging of files. It is they who are primarily responsible for efficiency of many computer systems.

* – * – *

table, decision—Refers to tabulation

150

matrix or array of possible courses of action, selections, or alternatives which can be possible and thus considered in the analysis of various problems, i.e., a graphic aid to problem description, flow and potential results, much as the purpose of a flowchart.

table look-up (TLU)—1. A specific process or method of extracting from a table the additional information associated with a particular field in the table. 2. To obtain a function value corresponding to an argument, stated or implied, from a table of function values stored in the computer. Also, the operation of obtaining a value from a table.

table, symbol—Refers most often to mapping for a set of symbols to another set of symbols or numbers. In programming, the assembler builds a table of labels used in an assembler language program and assigns to those labels a set of relative or absolute core locations.

table, truth—A tabular representation of a switching function, or truth function related to Boolean algebra, in which every possible configuration of argument values 0-1, or true-false is listed, and beside each is given the associated function value 0-1 or true-false. The number of configurations is 2^n, where "n" is the number of arguments, unless the function is incompletely specified, i.e., don't care conditions. An example of a truth table for the AND-function and the OR-function (inclusive) is:

Variable		AND Function	OR
A	B	AB	A+B
0	0	0	0
0	1	0	1
1	0	0	1
1	1	1	1

tag—1. An information unit whose composition differs from that of other members of the set so that it can be used as a marker or label. A tag bit is an instruction word that is also called a sentinel or a flag. 2. A specific identifier such as a label, an index, etc.

tape, certified—Refers to computer tape that is machine-checked on all tracks throughout each and every roll and is certified by the supplier to have less than a specific total number of errors or, to have zero errors.

teleprocessing—A term registered by IBM denoting systems that transmit data from one point to another in the course of processing.

teletype—A Teletype Corporation trademark. A system for transmitting messages over a distance. This system employs keyboard or paper-tape transmitting devices and print-out receiving units.

teletype code—The standard five-channel teletypewriter code made up of a start impulse and five character impulses, all of equal length, and a stop impulse whose length is 1.42 times all of the start impulse. Also known as the 1.42 unit code. The teletype code has been used by the telegraph industry for about 100 years.

teletype exchange (TELEX)—An automatic teleprinter exchange service developed and sold by Western Union.

teletype grade—In transmission this represents the lowest type communication circuit in terms of speed, cost, and accuracy.

teletypewriter—Trade name used by AT&T to refer to the telegraph-terminal equipment.

TELEX (TEX)—A Western Union automatic teletype exchange service extending into Canada via Canadian Pacific railroad facilities. Subscribers can dial each other for direct two-way telemeter communications.

telpak—1. An AT&T name used to designate its service for leasing wide band channels. 2. Broad-band communication channels for transmitting data from magnetic tape to magnetic tape or directly between computers at rates greater than 60,000 characters a second.

tens complement—The radix complement of a numeral whose radix is ten. The tens complement is obtained by subtracting each digit of a number from 9, and adding 1 to the least significant of the resultant number. For example, the tens complement of 2456 is 7544.

terminal devices (console)—The terminal device or console capable of supplying input to and receiving output from the central computer is a critical component in a remote computer system. Most initial time-sharing systems have chosen some form of electric typewriter as a terminal device. The principal choices have been Teletypes Models 33 and 35, Western Union TELEX units, and modified IBM Selectric typewriters.

terminating symbol—Refers to a symbol on various tapes indicating the end of a block of information. (Related to gap.)

test conditions-overflow (underflow)—Often tests are made for underflow and overflow conditions which occur when a result too large or too small for the arithmetic register has been generated, i.e., once an underflow or an overflow occurs, the appropriate indicator can remain "set" until it is tested. After the test, it is conventional for the overflow or underflow condition to be restored to normal.

testing, program—Refers to a procedure completed to discover whether the program is successful in meeting the defined systems requirements.

text—Concerns the bulk of a message that contains the information to be conveyed.

text editing, time sharing—See: Time sharing, text editing and modification.

thin film (control store)—In some larger newer systems the magnetic-film storage of the computer provides high-speed internal storage. By using this thin-film storage area as an auxiliary, temporary storage medium, faster computation can be obtained. Thin film permits whole circuits (many of them) to be etched on chips as small as 1/20 of an inch square. This saves space and increases reliability.

Any one of the addresses in control store can be accessed in 167 nanoseconds and have a complete cycle time of 667 nanoseconds. Because of this high speed, the film is the most frequently used portion of the computer's internal storage area; it may be referenced three times in the same time that it takes to make one reference to the core storage area. The high access and internal switching times of thin-film store make it ideal for use as temporary storage of operands while the actual computation of data is taking place. Special address assignments for arithmetic registers, index registers and other purposes are provided. These special addresses have dual accessibility in most instructions, that is, it can be referenced directly by the base and address of an instruction word by a special designator within the word.

thin-film memory—1. Refers to a design of computer storage that utilizes a film (only a few millionths of an inch thick) of metallic vapor that has been deposited on a thin glass plate. The film can be polarized in a billionth of a second (a nanosecond) for fast-memory access. 2. A storage device made of thin disks of magnetic material deposited on a nonmagnetic base. Its operation is similar to the core memory.

three address—Refers to a coding method of specifying the location of operands and instructions in which the storage location of the two operands and the storage location of the results of the operations are cited; e.g., addend, augend, and sum addresses all specified in one instruction word.

threshold—A logical operator that has the property that if P is a statement, Q is a statement, R is a statement . . . ., then the threshold of P, Q, R, ..., is true if and only if at least N statements are true, false if less than N statements are true, where N is a specified nonnegative integer called the threshold condition.

throughput—That productivity based on all facets of an operation, e.g., a computer with a capability of simultaneous operations of read/write/compute would have a high-throughput rating.

time constant, first order—As related to a first-order system, this refers to a specific time required for the output to complete 63.2% of the total rise or decay as a result to step change of the input.

time, cycle—Concerns the measured interval between the call for, and the delivery of, information from a storage unit or device.

time delay—Refers to the measured amount of elapsed time between the end of one event and the beginning of the next sequential event.

time division—A process of communication in which several messages time-share a single transmission channel.

time-division multiplex—Relates specifically to a sequential switching system that connects the terminal equipment to a common channel. Outside the times during which these connections are established, the section of the common channel between the multiplex distributors can be utilized to establish other terminal connections.

time, out of service—A measurement of such time periods as fault time, awaiting repair time, repair delay time, repair time, machine spoiled work-time, but not generally debatable time, external delays or unused time.

timer, clock—This clock device cycles a value contained in a full word of the main storage location. It can be used for job accounting by measuring the duration of time for each job, for an interrupt to prevent a runaway job from gaining control of the system, for time-of-day recording, and for polling a communication network on a regular basis—for example, every minute, every half hour, etc. The full cycle of a typical timer is 15.5 hours.

time, real—Concerns the performance of computing during the specific time in which the related process, event, problem, or communication is taking place, i.e., the computing must be fast enough, during the process of the happening of the event for the results of this computing to influence the related process or result.

timer, interval—In many systems with the interval timer, the control program provides the facility to keep track of the time of day, and to interrupt periodically as required. More than one interval can be controlled at once. For example, a five-second interval between successive polling of a teleprocessing line can be specified, and at the same time a two-minute limit on the duration of a new program undergoing test can be in effect.

timer, watchdog—Concerns a specific timer set by the program to prevent the system from looping endlessly or becoming idle because of program errors or equipment faults.

time-sharing—1. Generally, the apportionment of intervals of time availability of various items of equipment to complete the performance of several tasks by interlacing. (Contrasted with multiprogramming.) 2. Refers to the use of a device for two or more purposes during the same overall time interval, accomplished by interspersing the computer component actions in time. 3. In some instances, a multiple communications control unit (MCCU) attached to the computer allows many consoles to "time-share" the central processing unit simultaneously during transmission and receiving periods. Time sharing is a computing technique in which numerous terminal devices can utilize a central computer concurrently for input, processing and output functions.

time-sharing, analytic aid to research—In many large systems, besides the calculation capabilities aiding research workers, interactive computer systems allow the research scientist to experiment and arrive at a solution to a problem by cut-and-try techniques. The insight provided by direct interaction in the carrying out of solution steps furnishes clues to the next steps to try. These techniques have been applied to research in bio-medicine, linguistics, physics, and mathematics.

time-sharing, console to console consulting—In many systems even though a remote system may be well documented, may have excellent diagnostic messages, and even may have a question-answering program, there will still be times when a user cannot resolve a problem without consulting with an expert on the system. It is helpful at such times if the system permits message exchange between consoles and provides a system control officer to answer questions and provide advice to users with special problems. Console discussions are also desirable.

time-sharing, conversational compilers—General purpose systems usually provide languages and procedures by means of which a user may construct a program, modify it, test it, and, in some cases, add it to the file of system subcomponents. Most of the program preparation languages developed for time-sharing systems are dialects of existing languages. Processors for the languages vary from those borrowed with only slight modification from batch mode processing to conversational mode compilers designed especially for on-line use.

time-sharing, error diagnostics—It is highly desirable in a remote system that a user's actions be closely monitored by the system, with errors in procedure or entry called to the user's attention as soon after commission as possible. The error message sent to an offending user should be provided whenever possible.

time-sharing executive—A typical executive processes all users' requests (executive commands) and allows users to call for, operate, and modify object programs using all available system services. It provides complete bookkeeping facilities for file storage in, and retrieval from, secondary memory. It includes facilities for collecting accounting data.

time-sharing, fail soft—Refers to various

concepts that have been proposed for remote computer systems but that thus far have not been widely implemented in the principle of "graceful degradation" or "fail-soft". This concept implies a system which can reorganize itself to isolate and cut off the offending equipment while continuing to operate. The capacity and efficiency of the system decreases, but service to users continues in the best manner with the remaining equipment.

time-sharing, HELP program—HELP is a question-answering program that accepts queries in natural language and responds with appropriate answers from one of several data bases associated with the system components of the SDS Time Sharing System. When a user does not know how to employ a particular service or if he runs into difficulties while using a service program, he merely types the word HELP to invoke the question-answering program. HELP places very few constraints on the user. (1) No rigid structure is imposed. (2) Unrestricted grammer and phrasing are accepted. (3) Character and the line delete (similar to strike-overs facilitate input. (4) Reasonable misspelling is understood.

time-sharing, log-out—Generally a user with a task in the ready or running modes has only limited console actions which he may take. These are certain reserved functions, such as "cancel the last task," "interrupt the last task," and "log-out."

time-sharing monitor system—In various types of large systems the monitor system is a collection of programs remaining permanently in memory to provide overall coordination and control of the total operating system. It performs several functions. First, it permits several users' programs to be loaded into core memory simultaneously. The monitor makes use of the time-sharing hardware to prevent one user's program from interferring with other users' programs. Each program is run for a certain length of time; then the monitor switches control to another program in a rotating sequence. Switching is frequent enough so that all programs appear to run simultaneously. Another function of the time-sharing monitor is to process input/output commands. The input/output service routines preprocess data so that all devices appear identical to the user's program, thus simplifying coding. The monitor makes use of the program interrupt system to overlap input/output operations with computation. If a user's program must wait for completion of an input or output operation, the monitor automatically switches to another user's program. A program may be terminated temporarily by user intervention, or it may suspend its own operation. Temporary termination does not remove the program from memory. A program may be dumped on backing storage and discontinued under user control.

time-sharing, multiplexor channel—In larger communications-oriented systems the channel permits simultaneous operation of attached low-speed devices through a time-sharing (byte-interleaved mode) principle. Each device sends an identifier to the channel each time it requests service. The multiplexor channel, using this identifier, updates the correct control counts, etc., and stores the data in the correct location. The multiplexor channel has the effect of subdividing the data path into many subchannels. To the programmer, each subchannel is a separate channel, and can be programmed as such. A different device may be started on each subchannel and controlled by its own list of channel commands. Card readers, punches, printers, terminals, etc., are examples of devices that can operate in the multiplexing mode. The polling of terminals is initiated by the processor, but continues independently of the processor under control of the multiplexor channel. (IBM)

time-sharing, paging—Refers to various types of techniques used in third generation computers to solve storage management problems in "paging." A page is a fixed size segment of storage, usually 512 or 1024 addressable units. When the central processor is in paging mode, it treats each address as a two-part item. One portion (the least significant 9 or 10 bits) is an absolute address relative to a page boundary. This portion is usually called the displacement. The other portion (the remaining bits of the address) is considered to be a page number or identifier. A table of identifiers vs. current page locations is searched and the location corresponding to the matched page identifier is added to the displacement to form an absolute address. The problem of relocatability is reduced since all addresses are stated relative to page boundaries. Pages of data and programs may be loaded or moved into physical pages and relocation accomplished simply by adjusting the page table.

time-sharing, periodic dumping—Generally provisions are included in a time shared system for periodic dumping of system and user files onto a back-up medium, such as a magnetic tape. This function, which can be carried out during off-peak hours, guards against catastrophic system failures which destroy current working files.

time-sharing, real time—Refers to a process which is providing data on a critical real-time basis and requires that immediate processing and response be made if the process is to continue.

time-sharing, scientific and engineering calculation—Generally speaking most time-shared systems provide conversational calculation facilities allowing research scientists, engineers, and technicians to use the computer as a large slide-rule.

time-sharing, software requirements—In larger systems, software in a time-shared system may be divided into three categories: 1. The system proper. This is a collection of programs which controls the time-shared system, provides general services to the user, and fulfills user requests. The programs include the executive package, which is not directly callable by a user, and a utility package which is directly usable. 2. The system subcomponents. These are application packages not necessarily vital to the system's operations. These programs provide specific services to the user. An example of a system subcomponent is a FORTRAN compiler. 3. The user program. These are programs prepared by the user for his private purposes or in some cases for availability to some or all other users.

time-sharing system (IBM-TSS/360)—An operating system for large-scale 360 configurations having time-sharing features.

time-sharing, text editing and modification—Many large scale time-shared systems provide a text handling component. Such a facility is used by authors composing reports, by production groups preparing manuals, by secretaries handling correspondence, and in one large system in the preparation of land title reports. Experiments are being conducted coupling this capability with direct typesetting and computer-controlled document reproduction.

time-sharing, time-quantum method— Because scheduling rules are highly dependent upon the objectives, constraints, and usage of the system, usually a time-quantum or interval is alloted to a running task. If the task does not terminate or otherwise relinquish control prior to the expiration of this time-quantum, the executive regains control, suspends the task and places it on the ready queue usually at the bottom. If the only functions which can be requested by a user are system functions (that is, no user prepared programs are permitted), the time-quantum method may not be necessary since the system functions can be constructed to relinquish control at or before specified time intervals.

time-sharing, user—Over a period of time the experience of many of the operational time-shared systems has been that special consideration must be given to the current level of experience of the user with the system in proving conversation and guidance to him. The first time a user makes a mistake and the system responds with a lengthy explanation of the error and suggestions on how to correct it, the user is impressed. Several occurrences of the same long-winded message start to annoy him. When it occurs the tenth or twentieth time, he is insulted and frustrated and feels that the computer is insensitive to the fact that by now he is aware of all the details of the error message.

time slices, time-sharing—In large systems time quanta of a few hundred milliseconds are usually chosen. It has been shown in second time shared systems that the smaller the time quantum the better average response time if all user tasks are highly interactive. However, very small time slices badly penalize programs requiring a large amount of computation between console interactions. To work out of this dilemma, some systems have two ready queues; one with a small time interval for highly interactive programs, another with a large time interval for lone computation problems. This compromise technique reduces the amount of swapping and overhead on the longer running programs caused by frequent interruptions but provides rapid response for highly interactive programs.

time slicing—Same as time sharing.

time, swap—Relates to the measurement of the time required to transfer a program from external memory to high-speed internal memory and vice versa.

time, turn-around—Refers to the measured time required to reverse the direction of a transmission in a communication channel.

TLU (table look up)—Obtaining of a function value corresponding to an argument, stated or implied, from a table of function values stored in the computer.

top-down method—A compiling technique using a template-matching method; prototypes for a statement of unknown nature are assumed one-by-one, until one prototype is found which matches.

touchtone—An input achievement of great significance to the data communications industry, developed by the

American Telegraph and Telephone Company. With this service, the conventional telephone dial is replaced by a panel of buttons, which when pushed generate a tone which operates switching equipment at the telephone exchange. These tones can be used to provide input to a computer, and it is hoped that touchtone equipment will soon be able to incorporate a full alphabet in addition to the ten digits.

total, hash—1. The development of a summation for purposes of verification of one or more corresponding fields of a file that would usually not be totalled. 2. A control developed from a specific number in each record processed that has no significance other than as a control. 3. A sum of numbers in specified fields of a record or of a batch of records used for checking purposes. No attention is paid to the significance of the total. Examples of such numbers are customer numbers or part numbers.

trace—An diagnostic technique interpretive in nature that provides an analysis of each executed instruction and writes it on an output device as each instruction is executed.

track—1. A location or sequence of binary cells arranged so that data may be read or written from one cell at a time in serial fashion; for example, a track on a magnetic drum is a path one-bit wide around the circumference of the drum. 2. The portion of a moving-storage medium, such as a drum, tape, disc, that is accessible to a given reading station.

tracks, density—The measurement of the number of bits which may be written in a single position across the width of the tape, including parity bits.

transceiver—1. A unit of equipment for card-to-card transmission by way of telephone or telegraph wires. 2. A device that transmits and receives data from a punched card to a punched card. It is essentially a conversion device which at the sending end reads the card and transmits the data over the wire. At the receiving end it punches the data into a card.

transducer—A specific device which is used to convert energy from one form to another; e.g., a quartz crystal imbedded in mercury can change electrical energy to sound energy as is done in sonic delay lines in computer-storage systems.

transfer, block—Refers to the conveyance of a group of consecutive words from one place to another.

transfer check—A type of check related to the accuracy of a data transfer.

transfer function—1. A specific mathematical expression, frequently used by control engineers, that expresses the relationship between the outgoing and the incoming signals of a process or control element. The transfer function is useful in studies of control problems. 2. Also a mathematical expression or expressions that describe(s) the relationship between physical conditions at two different points in time or space in a given system, and also describes the role played by the intervening time or space.

transfer instruction, conditional—See branch, conditional.

transfer instruction, unconditional—See branch, unconditional.

transfer rate, peak—Refers to a particular rate at which data is transmitted through its channel, but measured during the time data is actually being transmitted, i.e., tape transfer rates are measured in terms of characters per second, discounting gaps between blocks, words, etc.

transfer table—Generally a table designed to contain a list of transfer instructions of all the programs that are in core, which enables transfers of control to be made from one to another program.

transient—1. In communications systems a physical disturbance intermediate to two steady-state conditions. 2. Pertaining to rapid change. 3. A build-up or breakdown in the intensity of a phenomenon until a steady-state condition is reached. The time rate of change of energy is finite and some form of energy storage is usually involved.

transistor—1. A basic component which is a nonlinear semiconductor device capable of signal amplification. 2. A small, solid-state semiconducting device, ordinarily using germanium or silicon, that performs nearly all functions of an electron tube, especially amplification. 3. Tiny elements in an electronic circuit that do much the same job as a vacuum tube. They are light weight, reliable, practically unbreakable, and highly efficient. 4. An electronic device utilizing semiconductor properties to control the flow of currents from another circuit, e.g., a triode transistor that permits the control of a current in one circuit by the use of a smaller current in another circuit. 5. Transistors operate in a circuit like an electronic valve. By sending a pulse on a third line the valve opens to let current pass. If a pulse is not sent, the valve stays closed. Transistors are used for certain logical decisions, but mostly as amplifier to maintain the proper voltage and current levels after pulses have moved through other components. 6. A three-element semiconductor device consisting of emitter, base, and collector.

transistor, metal-oxide—MOS is a part of the acronym MOSFET, the FET meaning Field Effect Transistor. Thus MOS-LSI are types of transistors for Large Scale Integrated (LSI) metal-oxide semiconductor components for computer memory units.

translation, one-for-one—Refers to the specific process in which each programming instruction is equal to one machine language instruction.

transmission adapter—In some systems the transmission adapter (XA) provides for the connection of remote and local devices to the data adapter as well as the necessary controls to move data to or from the processing unit via the XIC (transmission interface connector). A number of data adapters are available to allow attachment of various remote devices through their communication facility as well as the attachment of various local devices.

transmission, asynchronous—Refers to the transmission process such that between any two significant instants in the same group (block or character), there is always an integral number of unit intervals. Between two significant instants located in different groups, there is not always an integral number.

transmission codes, fixed ratio—Concerns various error detection codes that use a fixed ratio of one bit to the total number of bits.

transmission codes, recurrent—Refers to codes in which check symbols are used to detect against the burst type of error.

transmission codes, spiral parity checking—Generally a method used to detect single bit errors. Each check character is obtained by shifting the level for each successive checking character.

transmission, parallel—A type of system for sending all bits of a particular character simultaneously.

transmission rate, instantaneous—A particular rate at which data is transmitted through its channel, but measured during the time data is actually being transmitted, i.e., tape transfer rates are measured in terms of characters per second, discounting gaps between blocks, words, etc.

transmission, serial—To move data in sequence, one character at a time as contrasted with parallel transmission.

trap—1. Considered to be a special form of a conditional breakpoint that is activated by the hardware itself, by conditions imposed by the operating system, or by a combination of the two. Traps are an outgrowth of the old idea of switch-controlled halts or jumps. Frequently, a number of internal triggers or traps exist in a computer. Since these traps are usually set only by unexpected or unpredictable occurrences, and since the execution time and number of instructions for testing them can be burdensome, it is usual for these triggers to cause an automatic transfer of control, or jump to a known location. The location from which the transfer occurred, and the cause of the transfer are recorded in other standard locations. Some trapping features can also be enabled or inhibited under program control, e.g., an overflow trap. (Related to tracing routine.) 2. Specifically a routine to determine indirectly the setting of internal triggers in the computer.

traps, interrupt—In larger systems, for each type of interrupt there is a program-controlled trap that may prevent or allow the corresponding interrupts. If a trap is in the "1" condition, the corresponding interrupt is allowed. If it is a "0," the corresponding interrupt is prevented. The following is a list of traps and their corresponding interrupt events: programmed I/O (input/output) trap—programmed I/O interrupt; operator trap—operator interrupt; add-overflow trap—add-overflow interrupt; power-fail trap—power-fail interrupt; external-device trap—nonpriority external-device interrupts; priority external-device trap—priority external-device interrupts; and memory-parity fail trap—memory-parity fail interrupt. If the ED (external device) trap is a "1," standard external-device interrupts are allowed. Priority interrupts are prevented if the priority trap is a 0. Setting a trap to that 1 condition is sometimes referred to as arming the trap. Conversely, clearing a trap to the 0 condition may be called disarming the trap.

tree—A specific term often used for some types of decoders because their diagrammatic representation can resemble the branches and trunk of a tree, i.e., a decision tree.

trigger—Concerns bistable electronic device used to store information, to generate gates, and to condition AND and OR circuits, etc.

triple precision—An error protection procedure for the retention of three times as many digits of a quantity as the computer normally handles; e.g., a computer whose basic word consists of 10-decimal digits is called upon to handle 30-decimal digit quantities.

truncate—1. A procedure which causes the reduction of precision by dropping one or several of the least significant digits; in contrast with rounding off. 2. To drop digits of a number of terms of a series, thus lessening precision; e.g., the number 3.14159265 is truncated to five figures in 3.1415, whereas one may round off to 3.1416. 3. To terminate a computational process in accordance with some rule.

truth table—A Boolean representation of a switching function, or truth function, in which every possible configuration of argument values 0-1, or true-false is listed, and beside each is given the associated function value 0-1 or true-false. The number of configurations is 2^n, where "n" is the number of arguments, unless the function is incompletely specified, i.e., don't care conditions. An example of a Boolean truth table for the AND-function and the OR-function (inclusive) is:

Variable		AND Function	OR
A	B	AB	A+B
0	0	0	0
0	1	0	1
1	0	0	1
1	1	1	1

TTY—Abbreviation for Teletypewriter equipment.

Turing machine—A unique and useful mathematical abstraction of a device that operates to read from, write on, and move an infinite tape, thereby providing a model for computerlike procedures. The behavior of a Turing machine is specified by listing an alphabet; i.e., collection of symbols read and written, a set of internal states, and a mapping of an alphabet and internal states which determines what the symbol written and tape motion will be, and also what internal state will follow when the machine is in a given internal state and reads a given symbol.

twelve edge—The upper most edge of an 80 column Hollerith card. Interpreting equipment requires a twelve edge feed first.

twelve (12) punch—A punch in position 12 of a column. It is often used for additional control or selection, or to indicate a positive number as if it were a plus sign.

two-pass assembler—An assembler designed to require scanning of the source program twice. The first pass constructs a symbol table. The second pass does the translation.

two's complement—In binary, a radix complement with the radix equal to 2.

two-, three- or four-address instruction—Refers to instructions consisting of an operation and 2, 3, or 4 addresses respectively. The addresses may specify the location of operands, results or other instructions.

TWX—A Bell system which provides subscribers with two-way communications via teleprinter equipment connected to the general-switched telephone network. TWX offers both 60 wpm and 100 wpm source.

type statements—A series of statements in FORTRAN used to override the normal mode of assigning variable names and also to reserve arrays.

typewriter, console monitor—The primary function of this specific typewriter is to monitor system and program operations. Such system conditions as ADD OVERFLOW, EXPONENT OVERFLOW, etc., and program conditions as SYNTAX ERROR, SYMBOL LENGTH, INTEGER SIZE, etc., are brought to the operator's attention via the typewriter. The typewriter also may be programmed to request information from the operator. The typewriter also may be used to enter programs and data into the central processor and to type out the results in lieu of other peripheral equipment specifically designed for these functions.

* – * – *

unconditional branch—A specific operational instruction of basic importance that develops a deviation from the program-execution sequence despite existing conditions.

unconditional jump—A basic operational instruction that switches the sequence of control to a specified location (Synonymous with unconditional branch and unconditional transfer of control).

unconditional transfer—An instruction jump which is made to occur under all possible conditions.

underflow—1. In an arithmetical operation, this term relates to the generation of a quantity too small to be stored by the register or location that is to receive the result. 2. The generation of a quantity smaller than the accepted minimum, e.g., floating-point underflow.

unit, central processing (CPU)—The central processor or main component of the computer system. It contains the main storage, arithmetic unit and special register groups.

unit position—Refers to the furthermost right position or the low order location. In the number 1054, the 4 is in the units position.

universal Turing machine—A Turing machine that can simulate any other Turing machine.

unpack—1. A procedure to decompose packed information into a sequence of separate words or elements. 2. A procedure to recover the original data from packed data. 3. A method to separate combined items of information each into a separate machine word.

user area (UA)—Relates to a specific area on a magnetic disk where semipermanent data is stored. This area is often used to store programs, subprograms and subroutines. This area is contrasted with reserved areas that contain compilers, track and sector information, etc., which may not be written into.

user file, time sharing—Refers to time-shared system subcomponents which are different from user files only in their availability. System subcomponents may be used by all users but may not be modified by any except those specifically designated as system users. The executive merely maintains records on the location and attributes of the files of data and programs, stores and retrieves these as requested, and if the file is executable binary code, loads, relocates as required, and executes the file as requested.

user-oriented languages, time sharing—In larger systems the design of languages to be used at remote terminals is more critical than in batch-mode systems. One of the aims of time sharing is to increase the accessibility of computers to non programming problem solvers. One would therefore expect to have a higher percentage of lay users in a time-shared system. Language forms, syntax, and special words should be tailored to these users lacking in computer expertise. While this seems to have been done in the numeric calculation languages so far developed, it is not always the case in other non-numeric areas. An example is the DDT language used in the SDS 940 Time Sharing System. For convenience to the developers of DDT, verbs in DDT are stated in one or two characater forms. The result is that virtually no mnemonic value can be attached to the verbs. The user is forced to remember the codes assigned to the approximate 50 verbs.

utility program—Refers to standard routines used to assist in the operation of the computer, e.g., a conversion routine, a sorting routine, a printout routine, or a tracing routine.

utility routine—1. Refers to standard routines usually a service or housekeeping routine. 2. Various subroutines for controlling machine functions or machine-produced conditions that have little relation to the actual processing of data.

* — * — *

VAB (voice answer back)—This refers to an audio response unit which can link a computer system to a telephone network to provide voice responses to inquiries made from telephone-type terminals. The audio response is composed from a vocabulary prerecorded in a digital-coded voice or a disk-storage device.

validity check—1. Very important checks for accuracy of character representation. 2. A checking technique based on known reasonable limits on data or computed results. For instance: a man cannot work 400 hours in one week, a month does not have 32 days, an hourly classified man very seldom has a net pay greater than $250.00 per week, etc. Also called a reasonableness check.

variable-length instructions—A feature designed to increase core efficiency by using only the amount necessary for the application and increases speed because the machine interprets only the fields relevant to the application. Halfword (2 byte), two-halfword (4 bytes), or three-

halfword (6 bytes) instructions are used.

variable length word—A computer word designed so that the number of characters is not fixed but is variable and subject to the discretion of the programmer, i.e., storage locations, registers, parallel logic wiring, and gating are arranged in such a way as to handle a character or digit singly, but in storage each character is addressable and thus may be considered a word.

variable word length computer—A computer designed so that the number of characters addressed is not a fixed number but is varied by the data or instruction.

vertical parity check—See: parity check.

virtual address, effective—In newer systems, the virtual address value after only indirect addressing and/or indexing modifications have been accomplished, but before memory mapping is performed.

virtual memory—See: memory, virtual.

visual supervisory control—A specific example follows: The P-C (processor-controller) communicates messages and commands to the operator and, if desired, directly to the process equipment and instrumentation. The sensors that measure process conditions are continuously monitored by the P-C. The P-C program analyzes this information and then generates the required output information. Messages from the P-C to the operator may be displayed by several methods in the operator's working area. These messages guide the operator in adjusting the status of instruments located at the point of control. Data messages based upon visual observation of the process and its instrumentation are sent back to the P-C or the process operator. These messages are evaluated by the P-C to provide additional output, if required, for continued process-operator guidance. Communication between the control-room operator and the process is maintained through the P-C. When the P-C supervisory program computes new set point values, it may—at the discretion of the operator—automatically adjust the set points of the controlling instrumentation to the new values.

voice-grade channel—Refers to a channel which is suitable for transmission of speech, digital or analog data, or facsimile.

volatile storage—Concerns a common storage device in which stored data are lost when the applied power is removed, e.g., an acoustic delay line.

*_*_*

waiting lines (queuing theory)—When a flow of goods (or customers) is bottlenecked at a particular servicing point, losses accumulate in the form of lost business, idle equipment, and unused labor. Attempts at minimizing such costs involved in waiting lines, or queues, is the object of queuing theory, an O/R (operations research) technique for the most efficient handling of a waiting line at a particular service point.

watchdog timer—A specific timer set by the program to prevent the system from looping endlessly or becoming idle because of program errors or equipment faults.

WATS (Wide Area Telephone Service)— 1. A popular telephone service that provides a special line allowing the customer to call a certain zone (or band), on a direct-distance dialing basis, for a flat monthly charge. The continental United States is divided into six bands for the purpose of rates. 2. A service provided by AT&T that provides a special tie line allowing the subscriber to make unlimited calls to any location in a specific zone on a direct-distance dialing basis for a flat monthly charge.

word, external-interrupt status—Generally a status word is accompanied by an external-interrupt signal. This signal informs the computer that the word on the data lines is a status word; the computer, interpreting this signal, automatically loads this word in a reserved address in core memory. If the programmer or operator desires a visual indication of the status word, it must be programmed.

word-mark—An indicator to signal the beginning or end of a word.

words, mask—The mask word is designed to modify both the identifier word and the input word which is called up for a search comparison in a logical operation.

words, reserved—Refers to the words which are set aside in COBOL language which cannot be used as data names, file names, or procedure names, and are of three types: connected, optional, and key words.

working space—Concerns that specific portion of the internal storage reserved for the data upon which operations are being performed. (Synonymous with temporary storage, and contrasted with program storage.)

work-in-process queue—Refers to items that have had some processing and are queued by and for the computer to complete the needed processing.

WPM—The abbreviation for words per minute. A common measure of speed in telegraph systems.

wrap-around storage—Concerns an arrangement of core storage in which the lowest numbered storage location is the successor of the highest numbered one.

write, memory lock—Refers to a 2-bit write-protect field optionally provided for each 512-word page of core memory addresses. (Some computers.)

write-only—The operation of transferring information from logic units or files.

write-read head—Concerns a small electro-magnet used for reading, recording, or erasing polarized spots that represent information on magnetic tape, disk, or drum.

——*

X punch—1. A standard punch in the X or 11 row of an 80-column card. 2. A punch in position 11 of a column. The X punch is often used to control or select, or to indicate a negative number as if it were a minus sign.

——*

Y punch—1. A standard punch in the Y or 12 row of an 80-column card, i.e., the top row of the card. 2. A punch in position 12 of a column. It is often used for additional control or selection, or to indicate a positive number as if it were a plus sign. (Synonymous with twelve (12) punch.)

——*

zero-address instruction—Refers to a particular instruction which does not refer to any memory location, e.g., a shifting instruction.

zero, binary—Refers to one of the two possible binary states or digits, and that one which has a zero assigned to it as a matter of conventions or rules, it can be represented by the presence or absence of a voltage, current, or hole at a given point. The other state is 1.

zero suppression—A process to cause the elimination of insignificant zeros (those to the left of a quantity in a field or word) during a printing operation.

zone bits—Concerns various bits other than the four used to represent the digits in a dense binary code.

APPENDIX A

IMPACT OF THE COMPUTER ON SCIENCE AND ENGINEERING

IMPACT OF THE COMPUTER ON SCIENCE AND ENGINEERING

During the past decade, the world has witnessed an amazing growth in computer technology. Some of the new developments and applications are well known to scientists and engineers — some are not. Many are still in the early stages of research. There is no doubt, however, that the sum total of these new developments and applications is dramatically affecting the traditional ways of thinking in the scientific and engineering communities.

The most important developments in scientific and engineering applications, not necessarily in order of importance or chronology, include the following: (1) Greater Speed and Lower Cost, (2) Software and Application packages, (3) Time-sharing and Remote Terminals, (4) Real-time Applications, (5) Graphics, (6) Minicomputers, (7) Microprogramming, (8) Virtual Memory and Virtual Machines, and (9) Associative Memories. Following is a brief description of these developments:

Speed and Cost

Computing speed has increased almost exponentially during the past decade, with a corresponding reduction in computing cost. For example, the recently announced CDC STAR computer is capable of performing 10 million arithmetical and logical operations per second, yet it costs no more than the largest second-generation computers more than a thousandfold slower. One microsecond (10^{-6} second) memory access time has become commonplace. At microprogramming level (to be discussed later), some simple operations (instructions) take only 20 to 40 nanoseconds (10^{-9} second). With such operational speeds already attained, it has become quite evident that the modern computer is rapidly approaching the ultimate speed barrier. Laser speeds applied to computing are very close to the speed of light, experimentally.

Costs have also been greatly reduced. Core memory formerly was an expensive part of a computer. Now, core memory prices are quoted at a penny per bit and are still falling substantially.

The increase in operating speeds and reduction in costs have been accompanied by an amazing shrinkage in component size. With the combined effectiveness of high performance and per bit cost and microminiaturized size reduction, engineering and scientific applications hitherto considered impossible are now being reconsidered. A word of warning is now in order, however. With the amazing advancement of computer technology, one may be led to the delusion that nothing is unsolvable on the computer. A simple example will disprove this belief. In the field of Operations Research, there is the famous traveling salesman's problem. Suppose a salesman, starting anywhere within the Continental United States, must visit all 48 state capitols. What route should he take in order to minimize the total distance traveled? There are approximate solutions to this problem, but a rigorous solution has yet to be found. There are 48! permutations or 1.24×10^{61} different routes. At modern computing speeds, it would take approximately 10^{49} years to evaluate all possible routes in order to arrive at an exact solution. It is obvious that a brute-force attack would be senseless. To solve such problems, human intelligence and ingenuity are still necessary.

Software and Application Packages

Trends in these fields have led to much easier and more widespread user programming. For example, an average person can learn to write simple programs in the BASIC language in two hours. Languages are also becoming more powerful and more permissive. Simple programmer errors can sometimes be discovered, edited, and corrected automatically by the computer. In a conversational mode, almost any error in programming can be instantly detected by the system and corrected by the user.

More languages are now available for handling non-numerical data. These languages extend computer capability far beyond the conventional numerical computation and accounting applications which previously dominated computer usage. New application packages (similar to COGO, STRESS, ECAP, etc., but covering a much wider range) are being made available at a rapid rate. On the other hand, due to time-sharing, multiprogramming, virtual memory, etc., the systems programs (operating systems, compilers, supervisors, etc.) are becoming more and more complicated and sophisticated. As a result, computer science has evolved into a true profession in its own right.

Time-sharing and Remote Terminals

Years ago, when batch processing was the only mode of operation in computer centers, scientists and engineers often found it quite frustrating to use the computer. After walking to the keypunch room, waiting for an available keypunch machine, keypunching and submitting their program deck, they were often forced to wait several hours for the results. Many scientists and engineers decided it was much simpler to perform calculations manually and refused to use the computer. The reduced need for programming experience and the new use of easily accessible time-shared terminals have changed the situation entirely. Scientists and engineers no longer make excuses to

170

avoid using the computer. In one scientific computer center, the number of computer users increased by at least a factor of three upon arrival of a few terminals with a BASIC compiler. Besides easy accessibility and fast turn-around, time-shared remote terminals have other important advantages. One such advantage is the availability to the user of access to large data banks. As the terminal networks grow, more and more data banks have become available, and sharing of common program libraries and data banks among scientists is equally as important as sharing a central computer processor unit (CPU). Another important advantage is the ease of user communication which enables one user to "talk" to the CPU and with another user within the same terminal network. This capability can be very useful in solving certain types of common base problems.

Time-shared remote terminals also have some disadvantages, however. A minor one is that the computer is quite often inefficiently under-utilized as it also is even in a well-managed batch processing (one-at-a-time user) shop. The major disadvantage, however, relates to the isolation of the users, who are mostly amateurs, from the professionals. Some users may never have the opportunity to learn more efficient and less error-prone programming methods or numerical procedures because of lack of contact with professionals in these fields. In one specific case, a user continued to use triple-precision matrix inversion when a simple pre-conditioning operation would have rendered this procedure unnecessary.

Real-time Applications

Real-time applications have flourished as a result of time-shared operating systems, fast response, and minicomputers. They are especially helpful to engineers in process control and scientific experimentation. Laboratory and hospital automation and direct digital control are some of the fast growing areas of real-time applications. The efficiency of large-scale, real-time systems such as airline reservation systems, distant early warning systems, etc., is greatly enhanced by the availability of standardized but sophisticated system software at costs which are no longer prohibitive. Improvements in hardware reliability have also made real-time systems more attractive, and computer networks have helped to solve the problems arising from individual computer failure.

Graphics

The introduction of graphical input/output devices such as Cathode-Ray Tubes (CRT's) has rendered incalculable assistance to scientists and engineers. This assistance has been further enhanced by rapid advances in photography, photogrammetry, holography, laser technology, and the growing field of pattern recognition. These innovations have not only increased

171

the speed of performing graphical tasks, but have also enabled the achievement of previously impossible tasks. A good example is the degree of resolution required in miniaturized circuitry diagrams. Humans are incapable of developing the necessary ultra fine precision required. Yet, with a good automated plotter, the task is quite simple. The list of graphical applications is almost endless: map drawing, engineering drafting, information storage and retrieval, computer-aided-design, highway design, architecture, meteorology, aerospace, etc.

Minicomputers

Quite recently minicomputers were introduced by the Digital Equipment Company with their PDP series. Since then, almost every computer manufacturer has entered this prodigious market. The competition has become so fierce that a bare minimum CPU can now be purchased for as little as $2000, and soon even less. The "mini", as the name implies, is a stripped-down general-purpose digital computer. Although the memory cycle time is often as fast as many third-generation computers, a large number of functions, normally supported by hardware in standard computers, may have to be implemented by software. The number of registers and data paths is a bare minimum. Thus, the reduction in cost is offset by a lower overall performance. However, starting with a minimum system, a firm may add (at extra cost, of course) many optional components such as expanded core memory, floating-point hardware, read-only memory, and various peripherals. Thus, the minis are highly modular. The buyer may choose a configuration which meets his specific requirements at minimum cost. The modularity and the cost-effectiveness combine to make these machines especially suitable for special-purpose applications such as traffic control, typesetting, process control, etc. They can also serve as communications terminals, data concentrations, and slave computers to larger systems. Some of the systems are microprogrammable which adds to their versatility. Modern scientists and engineers thus have the availability of an extremely wide spectrum of computer systems, both in cost and in complexity, at their command. Yet at higher language levels, such as FORTRAN, they are all compatible (with very minor variations) with larger systems. With this wide variety of choices available, scientists and engineers are no longer at the mercy of the accountants, who are usually the administrators of computer centers. And with multi-computer multi-terminal networks, downtime has also ceased to be a significant problem.

Microprogramming

The concept of microprogramming was conceived as early as the 1940's by the British engineer M. V. Wilkes. But the large-scale commercial implementation of this concept was not begun until the introduction of the IBM 360 series of computers. Today, every major computing system is capable of being microprogrammed. Microinstructions are usually stored in a read-only memory (ROM or ROS). These instructions take over many of the control functions (e.g., gating, branching) hitherto performed by hardware. They are semi-permanent (i.e., not easily altered) and act as an intermediate language between software, as machine languages, assembler languages, or even higher languages. One of the major impacts of microprogramming is that new machines are now able to eliminate the so-called machine or assembly language. Higher language instructions are accepted, interpreted, and executed directly.

The two most outstanding advantages of microprogramming to scientists and engineers are emulation and performance improvement. One computer can be microprogrammed to emulate almost any other machine. The advantage here is obvious and tremendous. Suppose a user has a large repertoire of assembler-written 7094 computer programs. These programs may be used directly on a machine operating in the 7094 emulator mode, thus avoiding costly code conversion. Today, there are microprogrammed machines which can emulate most of the major second-generation computers. Microprogramming also improves performance in both mathematical and non-mathematical operations, the most dramatic improvement being in non-mathematical operations. These improvements have had a great impact on optimum algorithm design and have also promoted a wider application of non-mathematical programs (e.g., pattern recognition, information retrieval, and file operations). Microprogramming is still in an early stage of development. Many people are not yet familiar with its concepts. But its impact will certainly continue to grow in the future.

Virtual Memory and Virtual Machines

Nearly every serious programmer complains about his computer memory capacity, no matter how large it may be. In order to run large programs, various ad hoc techniques of segmentation and overlay schemes have been in use for years. Virtual memory denotes a formalized, efficient, and sophisticated algorithm which gives the user virtually unlimited memory. This is accomplished by paging and disk-core swapping, but it is transparent to the user. The concept of virtual memory is not new, but it has been commercially implemented only recently. Its advantages to scientific and engineering applications are obvious.

Similar to virtual memory is the virtual machine, whereby one machine can be commanded to behave like another machine, even with a specified operating system. Today, virtual memory and virtual machines are mostly implemented by software and simulation. Wider use of emulation by micro-programming and associative memory will undoubtedly reduce the cost and improve the performance of such systems in the future.

Associative Memory

Conventional core memory is addressed by location. Associative memory is a radical departure from this conventional concept. Associative memory is addressed by its contents or its partial contents. Initially, all associative memory locations are cleared to zeros. When a "memory write" instruction is given, the instruction specifies no memory address — only what is to be written into it. The hardware device stores this information into any location which has not been previously used (i.e., a cleared location). When a "memory read" instruction is given, again no address is specified — only the information contents or partial contents. Imagine how effective such a device would be in an operation such as table look-up! As yet, associative memory is still too costly to be of general use. As it becomes less expensive it will have a far greater impact than just to speed the table look-up operation. Effectively, it makes every memory location an arithmetic logic unit. Other advantages of associative memories are: more effective interrupt and more efficient virtual memory algorithms.

APPENDIX B

**CLASSIFICATION INDEX OF COMPUTER
APPLICATIONS IN SCIENCE AND ENGINEERING**

CLASSIFICATION INDEX OF COMPUTER APPLICATIONS IN
SCIENCE AND ENGINEERING

Introduction

This appendix contains consolidated and edited references selectively gathered from recent issues (1968-1970) of *Computing Reviews*, a monthly periodical published by the Association for Computing Machinery. These references have been classified according to the system used by *Computing Reviews* and arranged in alphabetical order within each discipline according to carefully selected keywords.

The purpose of this classification index is two-fold. First, it displays the myriad of diversified computer applications currently active in the fields of science and engineering. Second, it is designed to serve as a quick reference to current literature regarding these applications. Each reference entry includes the subject title (with the keyword(s) in boldface type) and review number(s). The location of referenced literature can easily be determined by locating the proper review number in the Bibliography Section of *Computing Reviews Comprehensive Bibliography of Computing Literature.*

General Applications

Before beginning the classification index, several of the general computer applications and methodologies in science and engineering are worth noting. These applications have been arranged under seven general headings.

STATISTICAL PACKAGES — Variance and covariance analysis; regression analysis; polynomial regression; principal components; factor analysis; error propagation; non-linear estimation; time series analysis; power spectrum analysis.

MATRIX MANIPULATIONS — Arithmetical operations on matrices such as transposition, inversion, addition, eigenvalues, and eigenvectors.

MATHEMATICAL PACKAGES — Integration; differentiation; interpolation; Fourier transform; solution of linear differential equations; Bessel, Gamma, Mathieu and other functions; special integrals; real and complex roots; wave functions.

INFORMATION CODING AND RETRIEVAL — File organization and retrieval; patent search; KWIC and abstracts; indexing; coding methods; classification.

ARTIFICIAL INTELLIGENCE — Pattern recognition; theorem proving; formal, ordinary, and partial differentiation; interactive systems.

SIMULATION — Monte Carlo methods; discrete and continuous systems simulation; mathematical models; random number generation.

REAL-TIME — On-line and remote terminals; laboratory process monitoring; automatic digital control; common data bank sharing; telemetry; graphical input/output.

Classification Index of Computer Applications

3.10 NATURAL SCIENCES — GENERAL

INFORMATION MEASURE FOR **CLASSIFICATION**   16064

CONSTRUCTION OF HIERARCHIC AND NON-HIERARCHIC **CLASSIFICATIONS**   16664

NUMERIC SEMANTIC **CODE** SYSTEMS FOR UNIVERSAL MACHINE USE 14644

SIMULATION OF STATISTICALLY **COMPOSITE SYSTEMS**   14173

ECONOMIC METHODS OF PLOTTING **CONTOURS**   20066

DEVELOPMENT AND OPERATION OF A SPECIALIZED TECHNICAL **INFORMATION** AND DATA CENTER (CRYOGENIC)   16456

AUTONOTE: A PERSONAL **INFORMATION** STORAGE AND RETRIEVAL SYSTEM   18247

TWO-DIMENSIONAL **INTERPOLATION** FUNCTION FOR IRREGULARLY SPACED DATA   16254

A COMPUTER SYSTEM FOR AUTOMATION OF A **LABORATORY**   16664

HOW CAN **MACHINES** DO WHAT THEIR MAKERS CAN'T?   19709

AUTOMATIC SCANNING FOR ANALYSIS OF **MICROGRAPHS**   17174

NON-DETERMINISTIC **PROGRAMMING**   16456

ROBOT DATA SCREENING, AN AUTOMATIC **SEARCHING** TECHNIQUE 19340

3.11 NATURAL SCIENCES — ASTRONOMY, SPACE

FORMAL LANGUAGE AND **CELESTIAL MECHANICS**   15294

SIMULATION OF THE TRANSFER OF VISIBLE RADIATION IN **CLOUDS** 14399

THE REMOTE RECONNAISSANCE OF **EXTRA-TERRESTRIAL** ENVIRON-MENTS   17228

LITERAL DEVELOPMENTS OF THE **LUNAR** THEORY   15104

PICTURE ENHANCEMENT FOR THE **MOON, MARS,** AND MAN   18449

STABILIZATION OF COWELL'S METHOD FOR **ORBITAL MECHANICS** 18093

CHANDRASEKHAR'S **PLANETARY** PROBLEM   14400

FAMILY I: SOFTWARE FOR NASA-AMES **SIMULATION** SYSTEMS   17366

NUMERICAL METHODS FOR **SPACECRAFT** GUIDANCE AND CONTROL 17393

DISTRIBUTED PROCESSOR FOR MANNED **SPACE FLIGHT**   17352

MATHEMATICAL IMPLEMENTATION OF THE OVERLAP PLATE REDUC-TION TECHNIQUES (DETERMINATION OF **STELLAR POSITIONS**)   15104

3.12 NATURAL SCIENCES — BIOLOGY

MODEL OF **ADRENOCORTICAL** SYSTEM   15303, 15304

ALGEBRAIC PRINCIPLES FOR **ANALYSIS** OF BIOCHEMICAL SYSTEMS 14403

CONSTRUCTION OF **BIOCHEMICAL** MODELS   20069

BMD, **BIOMEDICAL** PROGRAMS   15105

ON-LINE ANALYSIS OF **BIOMEDICAL** IMAGES   20076

SIMULATION OF THE KREBS CYCLE OF A NONLINEAR **BLOOD** FLOW MODEL   17175, 17176

KINETIC PARAMETERS OF RED **BLOOD** CELL SURVIVAL   17177

SIMULATION OF **BLOOD**-GLUCOSE REGULATION   16506, 16507, 16511, 16512

ANALYSIS OF **BONE** AUTORADIOGRAPHS   16952

BRAIN STEM CORE   15308

CELL RECOGNITION FROM EQUIPROBABLE EXTINCTION RANGE CONTOURS   15933

CELLULAR AUTOMATA   16744

CONIC SECTIONS IN **CHROMOSOME** ANALYSIS   20067

CHROMOSOME ANALYSIS   15107

AN INTERACTIVE PROGRAM FOR **CHROMOSOME** ANALYSIS   17026

AUTOMATIC ANALYSIS OF **CHROMOSOMES**   16805

TOUCHING AND OVERLAPPING **CHROMOSOMES**   17394

LINEAR SKELETONS FROM SQUARE CUPBOARDS **(CHROMOSOMES)** 17968

MIXED DATA **CLASSIFICATORY** PROGRAM: AGGLOMERATIVE, DIVISIVE SYSTEMS   15690, 15691

APPLICABILITY OF FOURIER TRANSFORM ANALYSIS TO BIOLOGICAL **COMPARTMENTAL** MODELS   13947

SIMULATION OF CONCEALED **CONDUCTION**   19711

COMPUTER **DIAGNOSIS:** STATISTICAL ASPECTS   17814

GENERATING **DIAGNOSTIC** KEYS   19873

DIFFERENTIATION IN THE CELLULAR SLIME MOLD   15301

SCANDINAVIAN **EEG** SOCIETY, FREQUENCY ANALYSIS OF EEG   19191, 19192

ANALOG INKED-TRACE READER **(EEG)**   19190

STEADY-STATE OF MULTI-**ENZYME** NETWORKS AND THEIR PROPERTIES 20071

ENZYME SIMULATION   19710

PROGRAMS TO ESTIMATE THE PARAMETERS OF **ENZYME KINETICS** 20072

WEIGHTED LEAST SQUARES FOR DETERMINATION OF MICHAELIS CONSTANTS AND MAXIMUM VELOCITY OF **ENZYME REACTION**   14641

BIOLOGICAL **EVOLUTION** AND INFORMATION   17613

GLOBAL PROPERTIES OF **EVOLUTION** PROCESSES   13732

SIMULATION OF **GENERIC** POPULATIONS   13568

FUTURE **GOALS** OF ENGINEERING IN BIOLOGY AND MEDICINE   13734

BIOLOGICAL INVESTIGATION BY **INFORMATION** PROCESSING SIMULA-TION   13948

INPUT-OUTPUT MODELS OF BIOLOGICAL SYSTEMS   19188

CLINICAL BIOCHEMISTRY **LABORATORY**   20075

PHYSICAL THEORIES, AUTOMATA, AND ORIGIN OF **LIFE**   13733

LUNG MODEL FOR SIMULATING THE AERODYNAMICS OF THE BRON-CHIAL TREE   16665

A CELLULAR MODEL OF ELECTRICAL CONDUCTION IN THE **MAMMALIAN** ATRIOVENTRICULAR NODE   13735

EVALUATING **MEMBRANE** POTENTIAL AND SPIKE PATTERNS   19193

TRANSFORMATIONS, SEMIGROUPS, AND **METABOLISM**   15302

AUTOMATED MICROBIAL **METABOLISM** LABORATORY   15311

SIMULATION OF INTERACTING **MICROBIAL CULTURES**   14402

AUTOMATIC DETERMINATION OF **MITOTIC INDEX**   16953

SIMULATION OF STOCHASTIC PROCESSES THROUGH **MODEL-SAMPLING** TECHNIQUES   20070

MACRO-**MOLECULE**-LIGAND BINDING STUDY DATA ANALYSIS   16804

DISSECTION OF **NERVE** BUNDLE ACTIVITY   19189

TROPHIC ROLE OF THE **NERVE** CELL   15307

SIMULATION OF **NEURAL** NETS   15511

AUTOMATION ANALYSIS OF **NEURAL** SETS   13327

NEUROLOGICAL DIAGNOSTICS   16161

HYBRID COMPUTERS, APPLICATION TO **OPTIMIZATION**   20074

APPLICATION OF GRAPH THEORY IN **PATTERN RECOGNITION**   15931

SIMULATION OF **PHOTOSYNTHESIS** WITH PLANT CANOPES   18390

PHYSIOLOGICAL SIMULATION   13945, 14847

KINETIC MODELING IN **PHYSIOLOGY**   20073

SIMULATION IN **PLANT ECOLOGY**   15106

SIMULATION OF **REGULATORY MECHANISMS** OF CELLULAR PROLIFERA-TION   16163

PAS(150), A DIGITAL ANALOG SIMULATOR FOR BIOLOGICAL **RESEARCH** 16346

NEW **RESEARCH** TECHNIQUES FOR THE LIFE SCIENCES   18987

COMPUTERS IN BIOMEDICAL **RESEARCH**   18770

REGULATION OF **RESPIRATION** — RESPONSE TO SINUSOIDALLY VARY-
ING CO_2 INHALATION   19531

SIMULATION OF THE PHYSIOLOGY OF **RESPIRATION**   16505

THEORY OF **RETICULAR** FORMATION   15309

PHYSIOLOGY OF THE **RETINA**   18986

MACHINE-INDEPENDENT LANGUAGE FOR **SIMULATION** OF COMPLEX
CHEMICAL AND BIOCHEMICAL SYSTEMS   16576

SYSTEMS THEORY AND BIOLOGY   15296, 15297, 15298, 15299

TAXONOMIC INTRA-CELLULAR ANALYTIC SYSTEM (TICAS) FOR CELL
IDENTIFICATION   12532

CODING AND PROCESSING OF PHYSICAL SIGNS IN **TOXICITY** TESTS
15108

3.13   NATURAL SCIENCES — CHEMISTRY

COMPUTERS IN **ANALYTICAL CHEMISTRY**   20236

ARTIFICIAL INTELLIGENCE IN THE CONTEXT OF ORGANIC CHEMISTRY
19874

PROCEEDINGS, IBM SCIENTIFIC COMPUTING SYMPOSIUM ON COMPUTERS
IN **CHEMISTRY** (1969)   18989

ENZYME CHEMISTRY   16509, 16510

COMPUTATION OF CHEMICAL **EQUILIBRIA**   19341

THE RAND CHEMICAL **EQUILIBRIUM** PROGRAM   17615

INTERPRETATION OF ORGANIC CHEMICAL **FORMULAS**   18391

GENERATING EXPLANATORY HYPOTHESIS IN ORGANIC CHEMISTRY,
HEURISTIC DENDRAL   16121

MECHANIZATION OF **INDUCTIVE INFERENCE** IN ORGANIC CHEMISTRY
17616

THE ARCS (PFIZER **INFORMATION** SYSTEM) RINGDOC USED WITH COM-
PUTER   15312

INFORMATION STORAGE AND RETRIEVAL SYSTEM I, STORAGE AND
VERIFICATION OF STRUCTURAL INFORMATION   15313

FUTURE DESIGN OF COMPUTERIZED **INSTRUMENTS**   19342

ON-LINE FAR-INFRARED MICHELSON **INTERFEROMETRY**   18996

SOLUTION OF CHEMICAL **KINETIC** PARAMETER ESTIMATION   18772

CHEMICAL **KINETICS** PROBLEM IN NUMERICAL ANALYSIS OF NONEQUI-
LIBRIUM FLOWS   14642

ROLE OF COMPUTER IN **LABORATORY**   18990

LABORATORY AUTOMATION   18991

LIQUID SCINTILLATION, COUNTING, AND GAS CHROMATOGRAPHY
20077

SIMULATION OF A **MASS SPECTROMETER**   18713

MECHANICAL TRANSLATION FROM WISWESSER LINE NOTATION TO
CONNECTION TABLE   16667,16668

COMPILATION OF **MOLECULAR WEIGHTS** AND PERCENTAGE COMPOSI-
TION OF ORGANIC COMPOUNDS   18988

USE OF NON-UNIQUE **NOTATION** IN A LARGE CHEMICAL INFORMATION
SYSTEM   15110

A MODIFIED IUPAC-DYSON **NOTATION** SYSTEM   15111

CHEMICAL **NOTATION** AND CODE FOR COMPUTER MANIPULATION   15109

DOCUMENTATION OF **REACTIONS** BY ANALYSIS OF STRUCTURAL
CHANGES   14643

MACHINE INDEPENDENT LANGUAGE FOR **SIMULATION** OF COMPLEX
CHEMICAL AND BIOCHEMICAL SYSTEMS   16576

REMOTE ANALYSIS OF **SPECTRAL** DATA   18997

DATA ACQUISITION FOR STOPPED-FLOW **SPECTROPHOTOMETRY**   18774

COMPUTER ASSISTED **SPECTROSCOPY**   19532

HIGH RESOLUTION MASS **SPECTROSCOPY**   19533

CHEMICAL **STANDARDS** AND THEIR RETRIEVAL   18992

GENERATING CONFIGURATIONS DESCRIPTORS FOR **STEREOISOMERIC**
SQUARE-PLANAR AND OCTAHEDRAL COMPLEXES   17799

GENERATING UNIQUE REPRESENTATIONS OF **STEREOISOMERS**   13949

AUTOMATION OF **STRUCTURAL GROUP CONTRIBUTION** METHODS IN
ESTIMATION OF PHYSICAL PROPERTIES   15514

PARTIAL ISOMORPHISMS IN GRAPHS AND **STRUCTURAL SIMILARITIES** IN TREE-LIKE ORGANIC MOLECULES   15515

X-RAY DIFFRACTOMETER   17084

X-RAY ANALYSIS   18994

3.14   NATURAL SCIENCES — EARTH SCIENCES

OBJECTIVE **CONTOUR** CONSTRUCTION   17800

CONCEPTS OF USE IN **CONTOUR** MAP PROCESSING   17179

MATHEMATICAL MODELS FOR ANALYSIS OF **CONTOUR** LINE DATA 15103

PLOTTING **CONTOURS**   20066

GEOPHYSICAL **DATA** MANAGEMENT   17395

PROGRAMS FOR **GEOGRAPHICAL** RESEARCH   13329

ELECTRONIC DATA PROCESSING IN **GEOGRAPHY**   20237

AUTOMATED PHOTO-IDENTIFICATION OF RURAL **LAND USE** TYPES 20238

MAGNETIC FIELD PRODUCED BY A MOVING LIQUID   13330

STUDY OF EARTH'S **NORMAL MODES**   17178

NUMERICAL METHODS TO STUDY CIRCULATION OF THE WORLD **OCEAN** 19534

USING COMPUTERS IN THE **OIL** INDUSTRY   16806

NUMERICAL SURFACE TECHNIQUES IN **PETROLEUM** EXPLORATION 18513

PULSE-TRAIN ANALYSIS   16347

PROCESSING OF **SEISMIC** SIGNALS   16572

STRATIGRAPHIC ANALYSIS   15315

EARTH **TIDES**   16122

TREND SURFACE ANALYSIS   16514

3.15   NATURAL SCIENCES — MATHEMATICS, NUMBER THEORY

COMPUTATIONAL PROBLEMS IN **ABSTRACT ALGEBRA**   19343

COMPUTER PROGRAMS IN **ABSTRACT ALGEBRA**   19343

REDUCE: A USER-ORIENTED INTERACTIVE SYSTEM FOR **ALGEBRAIC** SIMPLIFICATION   17508

ANALYTIC ALGEBRAIC MANIPULATIONS   13736

IMPLEMENTATION OF INTERVAL NUMBERS AND **ALGORITHMS** IN ALGOL 60   17180

ANALYST ASSISTANCE PROGRAM (AAP)   18188

FINITE-REVERSAL PUSHDOWN **AUTOMATA**   17328

REAL ROOT **CALCULUS**   19535

A SIEVE METHOD FOR CLASSIFYING **COMPOSITE NUMBERS**   14645

OPTIMAL STOCHASTIC **CONTROL** WITH SMOOTHED INFORMATION 17452

IN-AND-OUT **CONVERSIONS**   14174

CURVE FITTING INTERACTIVE SYSTEM   18186, 18187

COMMON PRIME FACTORS OF **FERMAT NUMBERS**   19194

TABLES OF ARITHMETIC FUNCTIONS RELATED TO **FIBONACCI** NUMBERS 17321

THE SECOND **GOLDBACH CONJECTURE** REVISITED   17618

COMPUTERS IN **GROUP** THEORY   17617

AUTOMORPHISM **GROUP** OF A FINITE GROUP   16807

CHARACTERS OF WEYL **GROUP**   19712

CONSTRUCTION OF THE CHARACTER OF A FINITE **GROUP** FROM GENERATIONS OF RELATIONS   19344

SOME APPLICATIONS OF **GROUP**-THEORETICAL PROGRAMS TO THE DERIVATION OF CRYSTAL CLASSES OF R_4 19345

SEARCH FOR SIMPLE **GROUPS** OF ORDER LESS THAN ONE MILLION 19713

NON-EQUIVALENT FINITE SEMI**GROUPS**   19714

COMPUTATION OF SEMI**GROUPS** AND GROUPOIDS   19715

SOLUTION TO **HARRISON'S PROBLEM**   18999

SOME EXAMPLES OF **MAN-MACHINE INTERACTION** IN THE SOLUTION OF MATHEMATICAL PROBLEMS   19347

RESEARCH IN **NON-ASSOCIATIVE ALGEBRA**   19716

OPTIMUM SUCCESSIVE **OVER-RELAXATION** FACTOR   18997

A NUMBER SYSTEM FOR THE **PERMUTATIONS**   19998

UNIQUE REPRESENTATION OF **PRIME FACTOR** $2^n - 1$, n ODD, IN QUAD-RATIC FORMS   17969

RECURSIVE TECHNIQUES IN PROGRAMMING   17273

ALGEBRAIC **TOPOLOGY** OF SOME COMPLEX MANIFOLDS   20078

3.16   NATURAL SCIENCES – METEOROLOGY

CIRCULATION OF THE EARTH'S **ATMOSPHERE**   16955

NUMERICAL HYDRODYNAMICS OF THE **ATMOSPHERE**   16670

SIMULATION OF EARTH'S **ATMOSPHERE**   16954

THEORY OF MEAN **ATMOSPHERE** WAVES   15316

MODELING OF ATMOSPHERE'S GENERAL **CIRCULATION**   13950

AUTOMATIC **CONTOUR MAP**   17693

ECONOMICAL METHOD OF PLOTTING **CONTOURS**   20066

DISPLAY SYSTEMS IN NUMERICAL METEOROLOGICAL EXPERIMENTS   16955

MULTILEVEL MODEL OF SHORTRANGE WEATHER **FORECAST**   14404

SOME COMPUTER ASPECTS OF **METEOROLOGY**   15112

PARALLEL PROCESSING OF WEATHER **PREDICTION**   16348, 17181

AN OPERATIONAL **SIX-LAYER** PRIMITIVE EQUATION MODEL   15693

3.17   NATURAL SCIENCES – PHYSICS, NUCLEAR SCIENCES

COMPUTER-BASED PHYSICS, AN **ANTHOLOGY**   18777

SIMULATION OF AN **ATOM** USING PSEUDOCORE POTENTIAL   15519

BALLISTICS   19349

GEOMETRY PROGRAM THRESH FOR EVALUATING **BUBBLE-CHAMBER** PICTURE   16956

CRYSTAL DATA EDITOR   15517

THE **CRYSTALLOGRAPHER'S** FRIEND   13332

ALGORITHMS FOR **DIRAC ALGEBRA**   18591

FEYNMAN PATH INTEGRALS IN IMAGINARY TIME AND SPHERICAL POLAR COORDINATES   18782

FOWLER-NORDHEIM **FIELD EMISSION** FUNCTIONS   14406

INCLUDING ARBITRARY EXTERNAL BOUNDARIES IN THE MAC INCOMPRESSIBLE **FLUID** COMPUTING   18783

FOUR-GIMBAL SYSTEMS FOR SIMULATION DISPLAY   17397

GROPE-1 SYSTEM ANALYSIS OF **FRICTION** AND BACKLASH PROBLEMS   19538

DESIGN OF MAGNET SYSTEMS TO TRANSPORT **HIGH ENERGY** BEAMS   15516

HIGH ENERGY PHYSICS APPLICATIONS   17970

ANALYSIS OF EULERIAN METHODS FOR ONE-DIMENSIONAL INVISCID COMPRESSIBLE **HYDRODYNAMICS**   19536

PHYSICS AND **INFORMATION**   17619

MONTE CARLO ANALYSIS OF **KNUDSEN FLOW**   19002

PROCESSING **MAGNETIC FIELD** DATA   15694

ELECTRONIC STRUCTURE IN LARGE **MOLECULAR** SYSTEMS   14407

MUONIC-MOLECULE CALCULATION   18780

MONTE CARLO PRINCIPLES AND **NEUTRON** TRANSPORT   18590

NEUTRON KINETICS WITH KNOWN APPROXIMATE ERROR   20239

ON-LINE MULTIPLE-PARAMETER ANALYZER FOR **NEUTRON SPECTROMETER**   16808

SIMULATION IN CONTROL SYSTEMS DESIGN OF THE GENTILLY **NUCLEAR** GENERATION STATION   18394

THE YALE-IBM **NUCLEAR** PHYSICS DATA ACQUISITION SYSTEM   15317

NUCLEAR EXPERIMENTATION   15518

INTERNATIONAL **NUCLEAR** INFORMATION SYSTEM   19348

OPTIMIZATION OF **PARTICLE** CALCULATION   19000

MODEL CALCULATIONS OF **PHASE** TRANSACTIONS   18781

COMPUTER-BASED **PHYSICS**   18777

SIMULATION OF ANANOLOUS **PLASMA** DIFFUSIONS   13951

SOLUTION OF THE FOKKER-PLANK EQUATION FOR A HYDROGEN **PLASMA** FORMED BY NEUTRON INJECTIONS   14848

ALGEBRAIC PROCEDURES IN **QUANTUM** FIELD THEORY   13331

SCATTERING OF ELECTROMAGNETIC **RADIATION**   17801

PROCESSING OF **RADIATION** SENSOR   19393

MODULAR **REACTOR** CALCULATIONS   17802

STOCHASTIC PROCESSES IN NUCLEAR **REACTOR** THEORY — BIBLIO-GRAPHY   13333

OPTIMUM CONTROL OF NUCLEAR **REACTOR** SYSTEMS   13737

NUCLEAR **REACTOR** STABILITY ANALYSIS BY CSMP   18189

SIMULATION OF TRIGA **REACTOR** PULSES   16515

OPTIMAL CONTROL COMPUTATIONS FOR NUCLEAR **REACTORS**   18776

NUCLEAR **REACTORS** AND THEIR VARIATIONAL AND OPTIMIZATION PROBLEMS   18775

RELATIVISTIC TWO-BODY COLLISION   19001

SYMBOLIC COMPUTATION OF **RIEMANN TENSOR**   19195

SPARK CHAMBER DATA REDUCTION   19537

APPLICATION OF GENERAL-PURPOSE **SPECTROPHOTOMETER** SYSTEM 16672

COMPUTER-ASSISTED **SPECTROSCOPY**   16673

SPATIAL DIFFERENCING OF THE **TRANSPORT EQUATION**   18784

KINOFORM: A NEW **WAVEFRONT** RECONSTRUCTION DEVICE   17396

TWO-DIMENSIONAL **WAVE PROPAGATION** THROUGH NONLINEAR MEDIA 19351

COMPUTATION OF SATURATION PARAMETERS IN A MULTILEVEL **ZEEMAN** SYSTEM   18395

3.19   NATURAL SCIENCES — MISCELLANEOUS

INFORMATION, THERMODYNAMICS, LIFE, AND THOUGHT   17614

EVALUATING FOREST MANAGEMENT BY PARAMETRIC **LINEAR PROGRAMMING**   17551

GPS: A CASE STUDY IN GENERALITY AND **PROBLEM** SOLVING   18236

EXPERIMENTAL INVESTIGATION OF **VIDEO PATTERN RECOGNITION** 18006

3.20 ENGINEERING — GENERAL

COMPUTER-**AIDED** (CAD) DESIGNS   16678

COMPUTER **APPLICATIONS** IN ARCHITECTURE AND ENGINEERING   16959

ENGINEERING **APPLICATIONS** OF COMPUTERS   15520

APPLICATION OF FACET **CLASSIFICATION**   16207

DESIGN AND PLANNING   13952

THE POTENTIAL OF COMPUTERS IN **DESIGN** PRACTICE   15521

DIGITAL **FILTERS**   13954

INTERACTIVE SYSTEM USING **GRAPHICAL** FLOWCHART INPUT   19197

BASIC **GRAPHICS**   18190

ICES (CIVIL ENGINEERING SYSTEM)   14175, 13953

SYSTEM OVERVIEW, **ICES**   14176

ICES STRUDL-1 STRUCTURAL DESIGN LANGUAGE   14646, 14647, 14648, 14649

ICETRAN PROGRAMMING LANGUAGE   14178

DETECTING **INTERSECTIONS** OF THREE DIMENSIONAL OBJECTS   15696

MAN-MACHINE SIMULATION   14184

COMPUTER AIDS TO ENGINEERING **MANAGEMENT AND DESIGN**   13738

EQUATIONS OF **MOTION** USING TENSOR NOTATION   13335

DETERMINATION OF DIGITAL SIMULATION **MODELS** BY DIRECT-SEARCH MINIMIZATION   16958

DIGITAL MODELING OF **NONLINEAR** SYSTEMS   16957

NONLINEAR SYSTEM ANALYSIS   13334

THE **PERSPECTIVE** REPRESENTATION OF FUNCTIONS OF TWO VARIABLES   15115

PLANNING NETWORK FOR RESOURCE ALLOCATION, COST PLANNING AND PROFITABILITY ASSESSMENT   14185

GENERATION OF **PROBLEM-ORIENTED LANGUAGES**   14177

PRODUCTION CONTROL SYSTEM SIMULATOR   17398

RELIABILITY OF SYSTEMS   16349

SIMULATION USING DIGITAL COMPUTERS   15113

ON DEFINING THE **SIMULATION** PROCESS   18785

ALGOL-LIKE LANGUAGE FOR **SOLID MECHANICS**   13739

MATRIX ANALYSIS OF **STRUCTURES**   18191

THEORY OF HIERARCHICAL, MULTILEVEL **SYSTEMS**   20240

COMPUTER-AIDED DESIGN OF DIGITAL SYSTEM **TRANSFER FUNCTIONS**
16350

CONSTRUCTION OF A MNEMONIC DICTIONARY FOR COMPUTER-AIDED
ENGINEERING **WRITING**   15114

3.21   ENGINEERING — AEROSPACE

SIMULATION IN DYNAMIC **AEROELASTICITY**   14186

AIRCRAFT SYNTHESIS   13740

AIRCRAFT DESIGN BY MAN-COMPUTER GRAPHIC SYSTEM   14849

SURFACES FOR COMPUTER-AIDED **AIRCRAFT** DESIGN   15117

SHOCK-FREE TRANSONIC FLOWS FOR **AIRFOIL** DESIGN   19539

SPECIAL COMPUTER FOR SIMPLIFIED HIGH PERFORMANCE GROUND
ANTENNA STEERING   13336

SURVEY OF OPTIMUM **CONTROL** THEORY   14851, 14852, 14853

SIMULATION FOR **EXTRAVEHICULAR** ACTIVITIES   14187

SIMULATION OF LOW-ALTITUDE CLEAR AIR TURBULENCE FOR AUTO-
MATIC **FLIGHT CONTROL** DESIGN   13571

INTERACTIVE SATURN **FLIGHT** PROGRAM SIMULATOR   19539

BOADICEA **FLIGHT** PLANNING   15878

HIGHBRID FREQUENCY RESPONSE TECHNIQUE APPLIED TO AIRCRAFT
FLUTTER TESTING   18593

HELICOPTER FUSELAGE VIBRATION ANALYSIS IN THREE-DIMENSIONS
19540

SIMULATION OF **HELICOPTER** MOTOR   19875

AIRCRAFT **LANDING** GEAR BRAKE SQUEAL AND STRUT CHATTER
SIMULATION   20080

INTERACTIVE GRAPHICS IN AIRCRAFT **LANDING** AND TAKEOFF   18396

AIR **NAVIGATION** CONTROL SYSTEM   14651

AN ALGORITHM FOR CONVEX **PROTOTYPES**   19003

MULTIPLE **RADAR** METHODS   17399

EXPLICIT FORMS OF THE **ROTATIONAL** EQUATION OF MOTION   17184

GEOSTATIONARY OPERATIONAL ENVIRONMENTAL **SATELLITE** (GOES) DATA COLLECTION SYSTEM   16123

OPTIMAL CONTROL OF **SATELLITE ALTITUDE ACQUISITION**   16351

DESIGN OF LOW COST GROUND STATION FOR **SATELLITE COMMUNICA-TIONS**   13337

WEIGHTED **SCHEDULING** WITH MULTIPLE CONSTRAINTS   15320

SIX-DEGREE OF FREEDOM FLIGHT EQUATIONS   16352

SIMULATION OF **SPACE MISSIONS**   16760

SPACE MISSION ANALYSIS   16674

STABILITY DERIVATIVES FROM FLIGHT DATA   18592

AREAS OF EXPECTATION FOR AUTOMATIC **TRACKING** OF FLIGHT OB-JECTS   17186

MULTI-RADAR, AUTOMATED AIR **TRAFFIC** CONTROL   17185

AIR **TRAFFIC** CONTROL   14652, 15116

INITIAL VALUE METHOD FOR **TRAJECTORY** OPTIMIZATION   16809

3.22   ENGINEERING — CHEMICAL

DATA PROCESSING **ANALOG TO DIGITAL** CONVERSION   14409

MATERIAL AND HEAT **BALANCE** COMPUTATIONS   17187

BOOLEAN FORMATION OF CHEMICAL RECIPES AND AUTOMATIC **CON-TROL** OF CHEMICAL BATCH PROCESSING   16124

SELECTING **DAMPING** MATERIALS   13574

AUTOMATION IN THE DETAILED **DESIGN** OF A CHEMICAL PLANT   14650

LANGUAGE FOR CHEMICAL PLANT **DESIGN** AND SIMULATION   17620

MULTICOMPONENT BATCH **DISTILLATION** SIMULATION   19541

THEORETICAL STUDY OF **FILTER CAKE** WASHING   17401

SIMULATION OF TURBULENT **FLOW**   13574

HEAT EXCHANGE BETWEEN GAS AND CERAMIC PLATES IN A TUNNEL FURNACE   16125

191

STRUCTURE MATCHING IN **INFORMATION** PROCESSING   13741

SIMULATION OF **MICROMIXING** IN REACTORS WITH ARBITRARY RESIDENCE TIME DISTRIBUTIONS   13572

MATHEMATICAL **MODELING** IN CHEMICAL ENGINEERING   17400

COMPUTER PROGRAMS FOR **PLASTICS** ENGINEERS   16516

SIMULATION MODEL OF THE MOTION OF RANDOM-COIL **POLYMER** CHAINS   18192

OPTIMIZATION OF **SULFURIC ACID** SYNTHESIS   14854

3.23   ENGINEERING — CIVIL

MODEL FOR OPTIMIZATION OF **ARCHITECTURAL** PLANNING   16126

COMPUTER APPLICATIONS IN **ARCHITECTURE** AND ENGINEERING   16961

ICES **BRIDGE** I DESIGN SYSTEM   15524

BOP: AN APPROACH TO **BUILDING** OPTIMIZATION   16128

REPRESENTATION OF SPATIAL RELATIONSHIPS FOR **BUILDING** DESIGN 15120

DYNAMIC PROGRAMMING IN PLANNING OF A **CONDUIT**   14653

AN OPTIMAL METHOD FOR PROCESSING VARYING CONSTRAINTS IN PLANNING PROBLEMS, APPLIED TO **DAM** CONSTRUCTION   14188

ARCH **DAMS**, SUAD PROGRAM FOR STATIC ANALYSIS OF ARCH DAMS 17402, 17403

ESTUARY PROBLEMS AND NETWORK PROGRAMS   14190

ICES SYSTEM CIVIL ENGINEERING LANGUAGE, MIT   15118, 15119

ICETRAN: FORTRAN FOR ICES   14178

MAPPING JERUSALEM BY COMPUTER   19717

AN INTEGRATED METHOD FOR FACIES AND **RESERVOIR** ANALYSIS 16518

SAFETY IN CAR FOLLOWING   16525

MULTI-STORY PORTICOS, SIMPLIFIED HARMONIC ANALYSIS FOR ANTI-**SEISMIC** DESIGN   18194

ICES STRUDL-1, **STRUCTURAL** DESIGN LANGUAGE   14646, 14647, 14648, 14649

STRUCTURAL DYNAMICS ANALYSIS (HABEAS)   18193

AUTOMATIC ANALYSIS OF LARGE STRUCTURES   15697

STRUCTURES   15698

A TERRAIN MODEL FOR LINE OF SIGHT   19004

ICES TRANSET-1, TRANSPORTATION NETWORK ANALYSIS   15118, 15119

COMPUTER APPLICATIONS TO URBAN PLANNING AND ANALYSIS   16353

SIMULATION OF A COMPUTER-CONTROLLED WAREHOUSE   15319

3.24   ENGINEERING – ELECTRICAL, ELECTRONIC

ADAPTIVE CONTROL AND OPTIMIZATION   14412

THE NON-UNIFORM DIPOLE ANTENNA   19355

AN ERROR BOUND FOR CAPACITANCE CALCULATIONS   19354

COMPILER FOR AUTOMATIC CHECK-OUT EQUIPMENT (PLACE)   16354

LINEAR CIRCUIT ANALYSIS BY SYMBOLIC ALGEBRA (SYMCIR)   18195

CIRCUIT THEORY: AN INTRODUCTION TO THE STATE VARIABLE AP-PROACH   19352

TRENDS IN COMPUTER-AIDED CIRCUIT DESIGN (CACD)   19198

COMPUTER-ORIENTED CIRCUIT DESIGN   19718

SWITCHING CIRCUITS FOR ENGINEERS   13338

ESTIMATION OF TERMINAL CAPACITY IN PROBABILISTIC COMMUNICA-TION NETS   17406

COMPUTER PROGRAMS FOR COMPUTATIONAL ASSISTANCE   19543

COMPUTER DESIGN   19545

CONTROL SYSTEM PERFORMANCE MEASUREMENT   17803

SIMULATION OF HIGH VOLTAGE DC SYSTEM IN AC LOAD FLOW   14415

FM DISTORTION IN LINEAR NETWORKS FOR BAND LIMITED PERIODIC SIGNALS   16132

ANALYSIS OF DISTRIBUTED PARAMETER SYSTEMS WITH NONLINEAR BOUNDARY CONDITIONS   16138

NUMERICAL SOLUTION OF ELECTROMAGNETIC PROBLEMS   13743

ELECTRO-OPTICAL RINGBEAM ELECTRON GUN   13578

APPLICATION OF COOLEY-TUKEY ALGORITHM TO **EQUALIZATION**   15701

EQUIPOTENTIAL LINES FOR CYLINDRICAL GEOMETRY   17804

CALCULATION OF ARMATURE SLOT **FIELD** DISTRIBUTIONS   18400

FIELD COMPUTATION BY MOMENT METHODS   15527

DIGITAL **FILTER** AUTOMATIC CONTROL   16358

SIMULATION OF A SAMPLE-AVERAGE **FILTER**   18401

FILTER SYSTEMS AND DESIGN, ELECTRICAL, MICROWAVE, AND DIGITAL   19542

OPTIMAL NONLINEAR **FILTERING**   13742

ACTIVE RC **FILTERS** EMPLOYING A SINGLE OPERATIONAL AMPLIFIER   16141

ELECTRONIC DESIGN USING **GRAPHICS**   17623

HYDRO SYSTEM OPTIMIZATION   14191

INTEGRATED ELECTRONICS   19719

COMPUTER-AIDED **INTEGRATED CIRCUIT** DESIGN   16130

INTEGRATED CIRCUIT STRUCTURE, PHYSICS, AND MODELS   16360

UNIVERSAL DATA EQUIPMENT **INTERFACE** FROM THE ADSAF STANDARDIZATION EFFORT   19544

CALCULATING THE STEP RESPONSE OF **LUMPED OR DISTRIBUTED** PARAMETERS   18398

TIME DOMAIN SYNTHESIS OF FINITE **MEMORY**   16359

MAGNETIC SECOND-HARMONIC **MEMORY**   16361

SIMULATION OF STEPPING **MOTOR** PERFORMANCE   13576

NASAP — **NETWORK** ANALYSIS FOR SYSTEM APPLICATION   13575

SCEPTRE: AUTOMATIC **NETWORK** ANALYSIS   14416

NETWORK ANALYSIS   18397

LOCATION PROGRAMMING APPLICATION TO **NETWORKS**   16180, 17190

APPROXIMATION AND SYNTHESIS OF LINEAR **NETWORKS**   17621

SOME ADVANCES IN DISTRIBUTED **NETWORKS**   19196

OPTIMAL STAGE ESTIMATION OF HIGH **NOISE**   17404

194

STABILITY STUDY OF RANDOMLY SAMPLED **NONLINEAR** CONTROL SYSTEMS   18399

BOUNDS OF THE RESPONSE OF **NONLINEAR** SYSTEMS   15321

OPERATIONAL CALCULUS IN ELECTROTECHNOLOGY   14411

OPTIMUM **PHASE-SHIFT** NETWORK   16142

S-PLANE: MANIPULATION OF **POLE-ZERO PATTERNS**   17191

POWER SYSTEM ANALYSIS   14654

MULTILAYER BOARDS (**PRINTED CIRCUITRY**)   13577

SIMULATION OF MULTIPATH **PROPAGATION** EFFECT ON FM SYSTEMS 14413

OPTIMAL ALLOCATION OF **REDUNDANCY**   15879

STATE VARIABLES IN **SAMPLED DATA** SYSTEMS   14855, 14856, 14857, 14858, 14859, 15332

CALCULATING **SHORT CIRCUITS** IN NETWORKS   17405

FREQUENCY MODULATED **SPECTRA**   14414

SUBCARRIER **TRACKING** METHODS   16136

NUMERICAL METHODS FOR THE **TRANSIENT** RESPONSE OF LINEAR NET-WORKS WITH LUMPED, DISTRIBUTED, OR MIXED PARAMETERS   19356

DESIGN AND APPLICATION OF **TRANSISTOR** SWITCHING CIRCUITS 14655

SWITCHING PARAMETERS OF **TRANSISTORS** AND THEIR MEASUREMENTS 15321

SYSTEM PLANNING VIA SECOND ORDER SENSITIVITY METHOD WITH APPLICATION TO HIGH VOLTAGE **TRANSMISSION** LINES   16135

SYNTHESIS OF MULTIVARIABLE CASCADED **TRANSMISSION** NETWORK 16137

3.25   ENGINEERING — ENGINEERING SCIENCE

SIMULATION OF AUTOMOBILE **ACCIDENTS**   16362

FEEDBACK **CONTROL** WHICH PRESERVES OPTIMALITY FOR SYSTEMS WITH UNKNOWN PARAMETERS   16225

LEARNING NONLINEAR **CONTROL** SYSTEMS   14860

PROBLEMS IN **CONTROL** SYSTEMS WITH SOLUTIONS   14861

GENERALIZATION OF **CONTROL** SYSTEM THEORY   15121

A **SEARCH** TECHNIQUE FOR MULTIMODAL SURFACES   17407

DIRECTED LIBRARY **SEARCH** TO MINIMIZE COST   18786

REALTIME **SPECTRAL** ANALYSIS   13744

SYSTEMS ANALYSIS   19546

SOLUTION OF CONFINED **VORTEX** PROBLEMS   18786

3.26   ENGINEERING — MECHANICAL

AN EVENING DESIGNING WITH A COMPUTER (**COMPUTER-AIDED DESIGN**) 17622

FINITE-DIFFERENCE COMPUTATION OF NATURAL **CONVECTION**   17320

ENGINEERING **DESIGN**: THE CHOICE OF FAVORABLE SYSTEMS   18402

DESIGN AND ANALYSIS OF MECHANICAL COMPONENTS   14417, 14418

MECHANICAL DESIGN USING **GRAPHICS**   17622

ANALOG SIMULATION FOR PARALLEL-FLOW **HEAT EXCHANGERS**   17361

THE FUTURE OF **MACHINE TOOL** AUTOMATION   17485

MASS TRANSFER TO FLUIDS IN LAMINAR PIPE FLOW   19720

KINEMATIC SYNTHESIS OF A GENERAL **PLANAR MECHANISM**   14192, 14193, 15702

NUMERICAL DETERMINATION OF **SHIP** LINES   14419

STEAM TURBINES   15703

3.29   ENGINEERING — MISCELLANEOUS

COMPUTER GRAPHICS USED FOR **ARCHITECTURAL** DESIGN AND COSTING   17367, 17408

NETWORK SIMULATION IN **ARCHITECTURAL** PLANNING   18596

COMPUTERS IN **ARCHITECTURE** DESIGN   16679

COMPUTER-AIDED **BUILDING LAYOUT**   16680

COMPUTER **GRAPHICS**   15881

CONTROL OF **HALL EFFECT** EXPERIMENT   19199

SYNTHESIS OF **HOLOGRAMS**   16813

ON-LINE **IMAGE PROCESSING** SYSTEM   16814

IMAGES FROM COMPUTERS   16964

CORELAP – COMPUTERIZED RELATIONSHIP **LAYOUT** PLANNING   17972

DYNAMIC PROGRAMMING FOR **LOCATING INSPECTION STATIONS**   17192

MAPPING MULTIDIMENSIONAL SPACE TO ONE DIMENSION FOR OUTPUT DISPLAY   16815

PROCESS CONTROL IN **NATURAL GAS** TRANSMISSION   16571

DUAL COMPUTER CONTROL FOR THE GENTILLY **NUCLEAR POWER** STATION   16861

PIPING ISOMETRIC DRAWINGS   13339

REPRESENTATIONS FOR SPACE PLANNING   16814

SIMULATION OF **STEAM** PRESSURE SYSTEMS   18594

AUTOMATION OF A **STEEL MILL**   16570

TECHNIQUES OF **SYSTEMS ENGINEERING**   14194

SIMULATION AND OPTIMIZATION OF AN ELECTRO-MECHANICAL **TRANS-DUCER**   18403

APPENDIX C

BASIC PRINCIPLES OF COMPUTER SYSTEMS

Basic Principles of Computer Systems

As technology progresses and the mountain of resulting data grows higher, more and more people are forced to acknowledge the incalculable value of this strange machine which has the power to store and retrieve information, make decisions, and control inventories, machines, or even the operations of whole plants. The list of applications seems almost endless and yet grows longer day by day. Not only must people acknowledge the value of the computer, but they are now finding themselves compelled to gain a much better understanding of it.

How does the computer solve problems? How does it store and retrieve information? How does it follow instructions, perform checks on itself, and correct its own errors? Fundamentally, it performs these processes much the same as a human being does. The digital computer has five basic functions: (1) input, (2) storage, (3) control, (4) processing, and (5) output. These functions of the computer (Figure 1) may be compared quite closely to the functions of the human brain as it processes information. Let us examine these analogies.

(1) INPUT. This is the process of obtaining and assembling the facts so they can be accessed. The brain receives basic information through its senses. This is accomplished on a computer by feeding in data punched into cards, tapes, etc., or relayed from remote terminals, through a direct manual keyboard, etc.

(2) STORAGE. After input, the pertinent data must be kept readily available for use in working a problem. Like the human brain, the computer also possesses a memory capability for storing information. It is similar to the human memory in that it may be randomly and immediately accessible. Computer storage devices include such items as tapes, discs, drums, cores, and punched cards.

(3) CONTROL. In order to solve a problem, a step-by-step procedure must be followed. These steps must be executed in the proper sequence to arrive at a valid solution, and the control function is the means by which this is accomplished. A human goes through this same process many times each day, although the sequencing of the steps may be carried out subconsciously so that he is unaware of its step-wise occurrence. The control function on a computer is

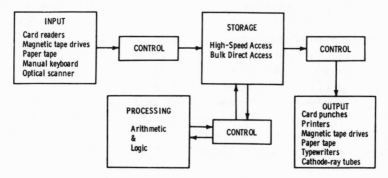

Figure 1. Computer sequence.

accomplished through the use of control programs which direct the CPU, or Central Processing Unit, in sequencing the various operations of the computer.

(4) PROCESSING. Processing is the actual calculating, or arithmetic manipulation, performed to arrive at a solution. Once a person is taught how to add numbers together, he performs calculations quite easily. The same is true of a computer, where the CPU is the switching device which performs the processing function, using an "on-off" or binary number code manipulation.

(5) OUTPUT. After the necessary facts are gathered and stored and the necessary calculations are performed, a solution is obtained. The output function is the delivery of this solution in one of many different forms. Human output may take the form of a spoken or written answer, an overt action, or merely a facial expression. The output of a computer can be in many media types. Generally, it will be printed, punched on cards or tape, stored in memory, displayed on a Cathode-Ray Tube (CRT), or communicated to other remote devices, such as Voice Answer Back (VAB).

PROGRAMMING

A computer is completely helpless in solving any kind of problem until it has been given a detailed set of instructions. The computer is incapable of any reasoning to solve a problem. All it can do is subserviently follow directions step-by-step until the job is completed. This applies to any problem in which the computer is used to attempt its solution, whether it's the simple addition of two numbers or the complex equations involved in guiding a missile through space. These detailed instructions are called the computer program.

In order to write a program, the problem to be solved must be carefully defined and understood. Next, it must be analyzed and broken down into its basic components and sequence steps.

The most common method of accomplishing this is to construct a flowchart of the problem. The flowchart is a diagram, using lines and symbols, which depicts each problem-solving step in its logical sequence from start to solution of the problem. And it shows how all the parts of the problem fit together to form the whole. A sample flowchart is shown in Figure 2.

Once the flowchart is completed, it must be converted into short, distinct instructions which are usable by the specific computer used. This, in essence, is the computer program. Each part of the flowchart must be broken down into simple instructions, and one part of the flowchart must require 20 or more individual steps in the computer.

The basic concept behind the computer's decision-making ability is illustrated in the sample flowchart (Figure 2). It is based upon the idea of using a question which can be answered with a simple "yes" or "no." By this method the computer can be directed either to skip or to execute a specific set of instructions. This action of skipping part of the program, or of choosing which of two sets of instructions to follow, is called branching. In branching, the computer decides which of two sets of instructions to follow simply by making a "yes-no" decision.

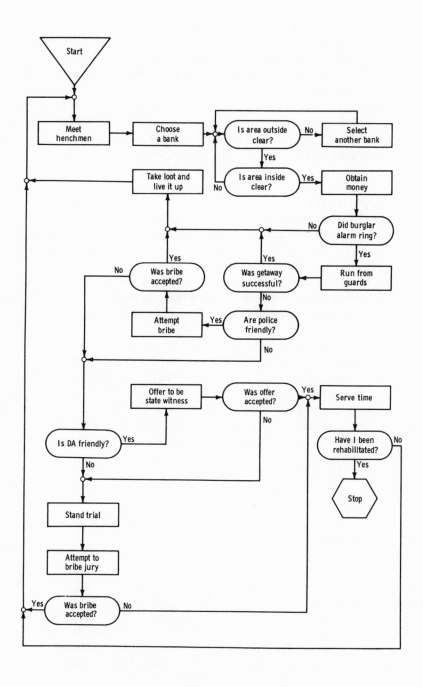

Figure 2. A sample flowchart.

203

The computer is said to have a logical capability because it can make decisions. But, in doing so, it simply follows instructions. It is the person writing the program who decides when a decision is needed, and what factors will determine which choice is taken.

After the problem has been diagrammed in a flowchart and broken down into individual simple operations, the actual program, or instructions which tell the computer how to handle each operation, must be written. But the computer doesn't understand English. So, the instructions must be written in a language, or code, that the computer understands.

SYMBOLIC LANGUAGES

Binary code is the computer's language, and one must understand binary before he can learn how a computer really works. However, thanks to short-cut methods, known as symbolic languages and other modern computer languages, binary coding is completed by the computer itself.

A symbolic language is simply an artificial language which is, in many cases, very similar to common English. The symbolic languages, however, have been formalized to avoid the ambiguities and logical inadequacies of the natural languages such as English.

Through the use of symbolic languages, almost anyone can quickly learn to write programs for a computer. Languages, such as FORTRAN, COBOL, ALGOL, and BASIC, make it easy for businessmen, scientists, and engineers to write programs using words and symbols already familiar to them. The program written in symbolic language is automatically translated into binary code, or "machine language," by computer techniques. The computer has this capability because somebody previously had written a special program, called an "assembler," or a compiler that converts other people's symbolic programs into machine language. Once the symbolic program or source program has been converted to binary, it can move as "flip-flop" electronic impulses into the computer's CPU and memory.

COMPUTER MEMORY

When information has been translated by the computer into binary language, the computer is ready to store it in its memory. There are many kinds of memory devices used in computers, but most of today's high-speed machines use magnetic or semiconductor cores. Magnetic cores are tiny little "doughnuts" the size of pinheads which are made of a special ferromagnetic ceramic material. Each core can be magnetized at any time in either of two directions. One direction stands for a binary 0, the other direction for a binary 1.

By arranging these cores in a column, any binary number can be stored. Each one of the columns is assigned an address and can store either one fact or one instruction. If the computer is told to read the contents of address 105, it will read each of the cores in the column designated 105, moving the bits of information in the form of electronic pulses to whatever location designated, such as to the arithmetic unit.

Thousands of these tiny ferrite doughnuts are strung on criss-crossed wires inside a frame. The frames are stacked one on top of the other to make a basic memory unit, and one unit can store over 150,000 bits of information. Other types of memory devices can store billions of bits in very small areas.

COMPUTER INPUT DEVICES

PUNCHED CARDS. Punched cards have many uses, such as college registration cards, electricity bills, and payroll data. They are low-cost and versatile. The standard punched card is called a Hollerith card after Dr. Herman Hollerith who, as head of the U.S. Census Bureau's tabulating section, invented punched cards to help with the 1890 census. The 1880 census had taken seven years to complete and Dr. Hollerith feared that, due to the growing population, the 1890 census might not be finished in time to start the next census in 1900. Because of his work and designs of punched cards and card tabulating machines (not computers), the 1890 census was completed in less than three years.

The familiar and standard punched card has 80 vertical columns and can hold 80 characters of information (letters, numbers, or punctuation). Using the Hollerith punching system, one punch in a single column (number row) can represent any number from 0 to 9. Above the nine number rows are three zone rows: 0, 11 and 12. By making two punches in a single column—one in a zone row and the other in a number row, it is possible to represent any letter of the alphabet or various other symbols. Certain special characters can be represented by three punches in a single column. A period is represented by a 12 punch, a 3 punch and an 8 punch. A dollar sign is represented by an 11 punch, a 3 punch and an 8 punch. The typical card contains punches for the alphabet followed by punches for numbers 0 through 9. The Hollerith symbolic language must be translated (it's done automatically) into binary to be used by a computer.

PUNCHED PAPER TAPE. Punched tape is low-cost and easily stored in rolls. Some kinds of business machines, including typewriters and cash registers, can be equipped to automatically punch paper tape as they are used in normal business. The resulting records can be easily fed into computers for further processing.

MAGNETIC TAPE. Two major advantages make magnetic tape the principal recording medium for computer data. Tape can hold huge quantities of data—a single 10-1/2 inch reel of tape can hold the contents of 250,000 punched cards, and magnetic tape can be read with very great speed. Some computers can read up to 240,000 characters a second from magnetic tape, compared with only 1,200 characters a second from punched cards.

Rolls of magnetic tape serve as one type of a computer's external memory, just as books serve as a person's external memory. Both provide information as needed. In working many problems, computers require both fresh data and stored data. In doing a payroll, for example, the fresh information probably would be fed into the computer from punched cards or paper tape. In addition, the computer would need certain basic facts, such as employee's rate of pay, income tax deductions and so forth. This information would be stored on magnetic tape or a magnetic disc to be fed into the computer's internal memory as needed.

The magnetic tape used in a computer system is similar to the kind used in a home recorder. It is a plastic ribbon with an iron oxide coating that can be magnetized. A tiny area of oxide is magnetized to indicate a 1 in binary code; a blank area in the pattern stands for zero. A pattern of symbols is arranged in vertical columns on the tape, just as holes are punched on a paper tape. One advantage of magnetic tape is that its pattern of symbols almost always is in "pure binary" and can be read directly by the computer. The code punched into paper tape may be punched in binary. But, it may also use a special code of its own, as is the case with some telegraph punching equipment. Like tape used on a home recorder, computer magnetic tape can be easily erased and reused.

MAGNETIC DISCS. An alternative to external memory units which use magnetic tape, or sequential storage, some computer systems use magnetic discs, or random access units. The discs, which look something like big phonograph records, can make information available to the computer substantially faster than tape, because there is usually a read-write head positioned immediately above each track on the disc.

MAGNETIC INK. Documents printed with magnetic ink are "read" in much the same way magnetic tape is read. The additional advantage of magnetic ink characters, which were developed by General Electric, is that they can be read by people, as well as by computers. Today, every bank makes wide use of magnetic ink characters, particularly on checks.

OPTICAL SCANNERS. If all numbers and words, not just those printed in magnetic ink, could be read by computers, it would save much of the bother of translating information into special codes for computer input. The computer industry has now achieved this kind of versatility. An optical scanner or reader (OCR) has a set of electronic patterns in its memory and a photoelectric cell that scans material to be read, converting characters into electronic pulses. The scanner can "read" any character that matches the patterns stored in its memory, including hand-written documents, sketches and diagrams.

HIGH-SPEED PRINTING. This is the most important medium for getting information out of the computer. A high-speed printer whips out information at as much as 6000 lines a single minute. An individual typing 6000 lines at a speed of 60 words a minute on a fast, electric typewriter, would take forty hours. Types of information turned out by these fast printers include accounting forms, checks, and department store bills.

TYPEWRITER. As part of their input-output or terminal units, most computers use electric teletypewriters. Human operators can conveniently enter information directly into the computer. Also, operators can receive short answers to problems worked by the computer through the typewriter terminal.

If there is a programming error, the computer may diagnose it and type out information that will enable the human operator to make a correction immediately.

DISPLAY LIGHTS. Some computers have sections of lights on the control console that can instantly show what information is in the control, memory and the arithmetic sections. The display often is in binary; if a light is on, it is a 1; if it is off, it is a 0.

CATHODE-RAY TUBE. Some types of scientific problems completed by computers have answers that are in curves, patterns, or other lines. While these answers can be printed, it is sometimes more convenient to translate the information into an image that is flashed on a cathode-ray tube, similar to a TV screen. The human operator may learn what he needs for alteration or further development by simply looking at the image. Or, for future reference, he may photograph the pattern. CRTs also have input typewriters, "light pens" and function selector keys for data and information manipulation on-line (direct) to the computer.

BATCH PROCESSING

Before the development of direct communications to a central computer (on-line communications), the majority of computer operations were performed by bulk processing, or the grouping of data into batches. These data were collected in volumes to match or calculate the amount of computer time required for processing. Data was forwarded for processing in the form of original documents or copies, or punched into cards or paper tape. Once at the processing center, additional handling was necessary to convert source data into cards or tape, as well as to add supplementary data to the pre-punched cards. Further off-line sorting was also necessary to arrange the file data in the required order for processing. The cut-off dates for processing were controlled by setting them on a regular basis, such as weekly or monthly.

The cumulative process associated with the establishment of each batch, in conjunction with the fixed cut-off, resulted in peak load requirements. This often resulted in around-the-clock operations to obtain the necessary results and special reports. These peak processing periods frequently lead to the installation of oversized systems to absorb the peak volume at costs far in excess of the overall productivity realized.

As the utilization of electronic data processing was expanded for multi-plant or multi-office operations, data collection problems grew more complex. Attempts to deal with this problem led to the multi-system approach, where systems of different sizes and capabilities were located in the various departments, divisions, and offices. Output data from these systems were then sent to the main processing center for organization-wide processing and analysis. This method was worked in some instances, but serious data collection problems still persisted.

By now it was obvious that the physical collection and transfer of data by mail or similar means slowed down the computer operations considerably. The logical solution seemed to be the use of public telephone and telegraph facilities. The combination of semi-automatic electrical data communication with the multi-system approach yielded a partial solution to the problem of data collection and processing. However, the actual processing of data continued to be performed on a batch basis, which meant that transactions were transmitted only periodically. This resulted in historic reports for management rather than current ones. The solution lay in the ability to operate upon transactions immediately.

To more fully understand the problem created by batch processing, assume that a remotely located sales office receives an order from a customer. As the initial step, the clerk consults the inventory listings. If the listings indicate that the required items are available, the order is taken, and the customer is informed when delivery will be made. This arrangement, however, contains one important flaw. The inventory listings used by the sales office may not reflect the current inventory status at the time the order is placed. This situation results from the fact that the inventory listings are updated on a periodic basis and are, therefore, correct only on the date they are processed. Between updatings, orders may be placed for items that are not actually available. These items later have to be back-ordered and the promised delivery date cannot be met.

PROGRESS TO ON-LINE, REAL-TIME (OLRT)

To close this time gap between actual transactions and master file updating, UNIVAC and other manufacturers pioneered the concept of real-time processing. The real-time system combines data processing with communications. This unique method of operation involves direct communication of transaction data between remote office locations and the central computer, thus allowing the data to be processed almost simultaneously with transmission.

In order to gain a better appreciation of the capabilities and implications of a real-time system, let us refer to the previously mentioned sales application. The remote sales office would be equipped with an inquiry-response device capable of communicating directly with the computer itself. To place an order, the necessary information is entered into the system through the input device. Since the device has a direct connection with the computer, complete information concerning the inventory status of the items ordered is confirmed in seconds. If the items are available, the invoice is printed automatically, along with associated shipping information, at the sales office. This indicates to the salesman that the order has been filled as requested. If any particular item of the order depleted the inventory to the reorder point, the computer automatically sends a message to the reorder source, warehouse, or factory directly connected to the computer, requesting an updating inventory. All of these operations are executed in a matter of seconds.

The phenomenal success of real-time systems can be directly attributed to the total systems concept. This concept is found not only in the equipment, but in the software and operating programs as well. The success of OLRT is a result of the skill with which these elements have been combined into a total system.

Real-time systems place remote inquiry-response devices in offices, plants, laboratories, and warehouses—all connected through communications lines or microwave relays to the central computer. These units allow simple and instant input of data, and answers can be returned almost immediately. Thus, hundreds of people have access to live storage by being on-line to a large, sophisticated computer for random access "real-time" information.

REAL-TIME APPLICATIONS

Since real-time generally pertains to a technique of processing data so fast that there is virtually no passage of time between inquiry and result, each of many varying inquiries may be communicated to the system separately and the results received immediately. Batch processing could be improved by immediate collection of data at the source, but processing would still be deferred until batches have been accumulated. Real-time is a mode of operation in which data, necessary to the control and/or execution of a transaction, can be processed in time for that specific transaction to be affected by the results of the processing. Thus, time is of the essence . . . great speed, concurrency, simultaneity.

Real-time is basically the refinement of integrating data processing with communications. It eliminates the slow information-gathering discussed above which resulted in dated reporting techniques and lax communications. It insures that data within the system are as current as the decisions which they must support. Answers are provided when needed; data is delivered instantly; incoming information is edited, updated, and made available on demand. Imminent problems are automatically detected by "exception principle" reporting, and management is notified in time for corrective action. The split-second input-reply principle was pioneered for military real-time systems which were employed to guide and track missiles in flight. And computer manufacturers soon realized that many types of businesses, laboratories, and colleges also needed constant control, updating, and reporting.

Airline real-time systems must be capable of simultaneously receiving inputs from agents, sending output messages to the remote terminals, receiving and sending urgent teletype messages and initiating requests. This eliminates underbooking and overbooking in reservations, lost profits, and disgruntled customers.

Real-time computing is vital for certain types of production automation. In industrial process-control applications many rapidly changing variables must be monitored, analyzed, and controlled continuously to make corrective actions and instigate exception report programming for continuous operation and optimum results.

Real-time processing for decision-making based on requirements for immediate information retrieval are examples of complex, rapidly changing systems. Some cases might be "flash" credit-approval requests, or decisions on orders based on exact current inventory and its location. Other examples of necessity for fast analysis of completely current information are banks, libraries, hospitals, automobile-traffic control, police-information networks, etc.

Even in medium-sized businesses, real-time permits rapid fill-ins and reorders or warnings to buyers and section managers about imminent stock shortages. Information is immediate concerning stock location, quantities on hand at remote warehouses, instant price changes, and delivery priorities. This instant knowledge provides for improved service, more satisfied customers, and lower operating costs through more efficient use of time, space, and personnel.

For manufacturers, the quantity of raw materials available in stock or from teletype-tied suppliers, or the status of finished or semi-finished products might be all-important to deliveries and profits. Costly management decisions for multiplant manufacturers would no longer be affected by delayed action or guesswork since reserve and forward stocks are always known exactly, and delivery schedules can be adjusted to fit actual conditions in the plants, warehouses, or schedules—with no loss in time, efficiency, or customer satisfaction.

Thus, the speed and sophistication of real-time hardware and software enables the military, business, industry, scientific research, etc., to make rapid responses to unanticipated fluctuations in process variables far better than is possible by simple human supervision. The real-time computer can instantly correlate the behavior of numerous production factors. It can integrate the relationships among similar, diverse, or remote data for better quality control, increased safety, and lowered costs for greater efficiency and competence of managers of all types. The combination of real-time and time-sharing provides for the most optimum use of real-time systems. From the point of real-time, each terminal in the multiconsole system may be using different programs and may actually share the central processor sequentially. Inquiries, however, are measured in seconds, while the CPU computes hundreds of thousands of times faster, i.e., in microseconds and nanoseconds (millionths and billionths of seconds). Thus, the high speed of the machine and the slowness of human reactions give each user the equivalent of an entire computer at his immediate command. Even medium-sized time-sharing systems have the capability of computing in microseconds and transmitting data back (to a bank teller, for example) at rates of thousands of numbers or characters per second. The answers achieved by the computer must be buffered (temporarily held) because the communications are too slow relative to computer processing speeds. Yet, the human would have great difficulty accepting information as fast as communications devices can furnish it despite their sluggishness compared to the CPU computing speeds.

The reader is warned, however, that the apparent magic of real-time is not without difficulties in at least three primary areas: (1) the regimentation, organization, and maintenance of records and data; (2) the background systems necessary to properly develop and use the information which must be made available in proper form, format, and content; and (3) the software or programming necessary for storage and retrieval including addressing, segmenting, and memory protection. The observer who watches the valuable and timely information appear on the video display or on the sheets of the teletypewriter is usually unaware of its complexity.

Of basic importance at the outset is the segmenting of information between noncritical general activity, which is to be more economically batch processed, and the segregated activity, which pertains to information which is more dynamic and of immediate need to operate the business on an hour-to-hour basis. Most often the general activity (batch or background) systems are employed at night or in between the time-shared real-time processing.

Generally the systems use controlling programs called monitors, executives, operating systems (OS), allocators, etc., as supervisory communicating controllers such that each inquiry request from remote stations is assigned priority as originally designed and/or subsequently altered as business conditions and requirements dictate.

APPENDIX D

SUMMARY OF MODERN COMPUTER LANGUAGES

SUMMARY OF MODERN COMPUTER LANGUAGES

Introduction

Two basic functions must be performed by a computer program: data "handling" and data "processing." The function of processing includes calculating, changing recorded entries, and creating information for new file records or report items. The function of handling—the lion's share of the programming effort—includes all the time-consuming detail of editing and selecting pertinent information, sorting records, arranging information in files, positioning information for reports, providing for beginning and ending procedures, providing continuity between processing operations, etc. The details of "handling" normally comprise more than 75% of business programming tasks. Usually manufacturers offer software packages or compilers which aid immeasurably in reducing this "handling" chore. They are especially important when changes are necessary in programs for some modifications which would require hundreds or even thousands of coded instructions—a task perhaps too time-consuming to be feasible. Operating on newer more economical equipment, the necessary modifications of programs usually require complete rewriting of most of the programs in the libraries. Using "emulators" or special software packages prevent these costly reprogramming tasks—or keep them down to economic workability (e.g., GE's GECOM, Honeywell's FACT, etc.). Documentation is vital to insure understandability among experts (specialists) of equal capability. If a programmer leaves or is reassigned, his programs cannot be understood without adequate documentation.

The detailed sequence of instructions (algorithm) used in solving a problem requires strict attention to the individuality of each instruction to attain the correct answer. Nonmathematical problems, with little or no algebra, are now quite often expressed as algorithms such as commercial and scheduling (PERT) problems in order to prepare them for computer input. Algorithms are the basis for procedure-oriented languages or are at least segments of these programs to be examined element by element. ALGOL and COBOL are examples of algorithmic languages—ALGOL for mathematical problems, COBOL for English-language commercial problems. These programs written in these and other compiler languages (FORTRAN, QUIKTRAN, PL/1, MAD, JOVIAL, ETC.) may contain hundreds of instructions, and these hundreds actually represent thousands or hundreds of thousands, even millions, of steps that will be executed by the computer in carrying out the instructions.

215

Types of Languages—Criteria for Selection

Only a few of the many languages available are discussed in this appendix. The general classes are as follows: machine or binary languages; symbolic assembly or mnemonic languages; algebraic compiler languages (as FORTRAN, ALGOL, etc.); report program generator languages; business-oriented compiler languages (as COBOL); or communications languages as QUIKTRAN, BASIC. There are also hundreds of specialized languages as "Prudential" (Insurance Co.) COBOL. These types are subsets designed for unique applications and for limited objectives. Emphasis is put on those characteristics which are important to the individual user. Many users thus have become increasingly interested in developing their own support software which can be more easily and quickly learned by their employees than the software furnished by suppliers. They can also be uniquely designed to use less memory and consume less computer time. Software companies are more than anxious to provide such services.

However, the determination of which language to use is sometimes quite a difficult decision. Criteria can include: knowledge of staff; number and type of jobs expected in the future; ease and speed of operating; costs as related to speed of operation and compilation; availability of other software packages; debugging aids; meshing of equipment on hand or contemplated purchase of new units. Other aspects of planning should include: decisions as to the rules and methods (and enforcement) for use of special symbols, input/output routines, registers, and standard routines. To avoid confusion, special programming tricks are usually not allowed. Complete documentation by a programmer is considered by most data processing managers as the most important elements of his work.

Comparisons of programming languages cannot be justified nor accurate because there are no standards for languages, compilers, operating systems or user's requirements. For example, various non-programmer scientific users prefer algebraic types as ALGOL, JOVIAL, FORTRAN, etc. Others prefer subsets of specific definition and operation. The design of the program usually will aid in determining the most efficient or easiest language to use.

Fundamental Algorithmic and Procedural Languages

FORTRAN. FORTRAN was developed by IBM as an aid to programming scientific problems and processes. The name was derived from FORmula TRANslator and is widely accepted as a convenient and practical language. FORTRAN IV has superseded FORTRAN II and contains many more powerful features which include greater versatility in input-output statements and specific functions. It is fundamentally a language and a processor (compiler) designed to be written in a mathematics-type language format. It is machine independent and procedure oriented. Because FORTRAN is based on mathematical concepts, instructions must explicitly and exactly follow the rules of grammar, symbols, and syntax. FORTRAN instructions relate to five function areas: input-output, arithmetic, control, looping (recursive or repeated execution of program steps or segments), and specifications. After a problem has been defined, analyzed, and flowcharted, it is programmed, frequently on special FORTRAN 72-column code paper, and then tested and debugged on the computer. On-line debugging can be accomplished using a time-sharing mode directly at the terminal.

FORTRAN is designed to permit expressions, algebraic operations (including three levels of subscripts, exponents, and Boolean operations), hierarchies, subroutines, and extensive input-output capability. All FORTRAN-type languages provide for commands that evaluate expressions and substitute results representing current values of variables. In most FORTRAN languages variable names begin with: I, J, K, L, M, or N for integer values, while all other variables are considered floating point or real variables and may take on any value—specifically, fractional values.

One basic logical decision command concerns the IF statement which causes expressions to be evaluated and control to be transferred to one of three statements, the branching depending upon the result of a calculation being either less than, equal to, or greater than zero. The more extensive FORTRAN compilers permit the use of overlay techniques called "chaining" for greater operation efficiency. Contrasted to several other languages, since every program in a job does not necessarily communicate with every other program, complete jobs need not reside in the same memory at the same time. Jobs may be divided into independent segments which may occupy various memory segments at different times.

COBOL. COBOL was developed by the Conference Of DAta SYstems Languages (CODASYL) in 1959. COBOL has been expanded, revised, and improved many times since then. COBOL 65, for example, has added many new streamlined capabilities and reduced many burdensome attributes of the former COBOL system. Since the word COBOL is an acronym for COmmon Business Oriented Language, the COBOL compiler is a processor specifically designed in sentences and structure for commercial use and application. The object program, after being compiled, can run on digital computers because it has been reduced to binary instructions and routines. The translation procedure (compiling) is accomplished by and within the computer itself. The compiler program (processor) reads, analyzes, and translates the source program which is then defined as the object program. The object program then processes data and instructions, the results of which are transferred to some external medium as:

cards, tapes, disks, drums, or Cathode-Ray Tube (CRT) terminals.

The COBOL language has specific key words, symbols and rules for its use. Generally, each key word and symbol specifies a definite set of machine operations, i.e., many series of prefabricated portions of object programs readily available. The COBOL language program brings together these groups of machine instructions. The rules for writing COBOL are considerably simpler than those for writing machine code or machine language. The programmer can use English words and conventional arithmetic symbols to complete the instructions required for his particular desired result.

COBOL programs are precise, distinct, and readily understood by non-technical people. They can be run on practically all types of computers with simplified testing procedures. COBOL documentation is quite standardized, complete, and easily understood by programmers and many business managers.

The programmer generally requires: the length of each kind of data; the location of the decimal point; name or names of data requiring identification; the organization of each type of data with respect to other data (groupings and relationship among groups); and the value of constants, specifically the actual value of names, numbers, special characters, etc. to be stored in the computer for future processing. Each type of data or information must be described in accordance with clearly defined rules and constraints. The Data Division is the part of the program reserved for this purpose and certain portions of it are related to specific machine characteristics.

COBOL has four structural divisions. The Identification Division identifies the program and states the various ways computers may accept and handle alphabetical information. The Environment Division states which equipment is to be used. The Data Division relegates the formats of input-output data by defining the manner in which input-output information appears. The Procedure Division defines the actual operations to be performed. COBOL also contains many important file organization features and can deal conveniently with variable data lengths. The strong points of COBOL are variability of input-output procedures and development of report generators.

PROGRAMMING LANGUAGE/1 (PL/1). PL/1 is a multipurpose programming language developed by IBM for the Models 360 and 370 Systems. The language is designed to be suitable for solving business and scientific problems and contains many of the advantages of both COBOL and FORTRAN. The language statements are as simple and concise as FORTRAN statements, and the flexibility in manipulation of input-output records or files is similar to to the advantages of COBOL.

All PL/1 statements are separated only by semicolons. Large sets of reserved words are available and comments can be of any length and inserted at practically any point in the program. Prior to using the program, various declarations can be made concerning arithmetic, strings, number characteristics, and quantities of digits and characters. Character strings can be joined to form longer strings by the use of a special linking operator. Data can be handled during input-output operations either as records, separate data, or items, and can be interrupted by higher priority or special conditions. Also, flexible procedures are available which identify items in arrays, for subscripting and sequencing. PL/1 is, therefore, very convenient for time-sharing and real-time operations. The primary advantage of PL/1 is that statements may be written as blocks and brought into storage only as needed, thus providing economic utilization of storage capacity. The overall effect of the versatility of PL/1 is that beginning programmers can turn out productive work quite quickly. The use of "labels" represents procedures in which the language adapts to various levels of detail and readability.

ALGOL. ALGOL stands for ALGOrithmic Language. It resulted from international cooperation to obtain a standardized algorithmic language, and IAL, International Algebraic Language, is the forerunner of ALGOL. ALGOL was devised in 1958 and revised in 1960. It is a strong language, used more widely in Europe than in the United States and is most often used in the programming of scientific problems or as a reference and publication language. It is also used as a guide for the development of new artificial languages or mathematical structures. It has become internationally accepted for designing mathematical, engineering and scientific problems. Briefly, ALGOL provides (1) precise in instructional statements, (2) a problem-solving procedure, (3) a translator or compiler. In many ways it is very similar to FORTRAN and COBOL. It has rules of grammar, syntax, format, and special characteristics. None of the three languages can be executed directly without first being compiled (processed, translated) into machine language.

After the formulation of the problem, it has to be structured for solution. The allocation of storage and the selection for the incorporation of the various library, housekeeping, or special mathematical routines must be made. The last step is the machine coding, and the run.

The ALGOL program closely resembles the detailed problem definition required for machine language, but the language and the problem definition format have been standardized. Not only does the computer itself produce the machine language program and the processing, but the program definition must be complete, unambiguous and expressed in an acceptable form with adherence to the rules and terminology.

The ALGOL language incorporates (1) arithmetical expressions, (2) Boolean expressions, (3) standard functions, (4) operational statements, (5) blocks and declarations (switch and array), (6) coding sections (procedure headings) and (7) loops. Almost all ALGOL manuals of various computer manufacturers state their specific lists of standard functions, limitations, and restrictions as well as reserved words. ALGOL 60 is currently most popular, and a time-sharing version called "Dartmouth ALGOL" is available.

JOVIAL. JOVIAL is an acronym for Jules Own Version of the International Algorithmic Language developed by Jules Schwartz of the Systems Development Corporation, Santa Monica, California. It is mostly used in programmed command and control procedures. The JOVIAL language is translated (compiled) by a program called a compiler. The compiler interprets, analyzes, and translates the program statements and the inputs and outputs from the source program to an object program on which the particular computer can operate. The major deviation from ALGOL is that jovial supplies the power the control data on the "byte" and even the "bit" level when desired. JOVIAL has extensive capabilities for developing software applications, utility and compiling-type programs. JOVIAL was apparently created quite specifically for government agency applications. It is used in real-time programs, commercial time-sharing applications and software design for other computers.

JOVIAL has extensive command and retrieve language rules but the basic structure of the program is relatively simple. The JOVIAL program fundamentally consists of procedure definitions and language statements. There are language statements which define and initialize data while others manipulate and test data.

CAL. CAL is an acronym for Conversational Algebraic Language. CAL, like BASIC, JOSS, QUIKTRAN, etc., is a time-sharing, real-time language for use by many remote simultaneous terminals. The CAL language is designed for higher-level time-sharing purposes and was developed at the University of California, Berkeley. It has been adopted quite widely throughout the United States for medium-sized time-sharing systems.

CAL programs consist of a series of steps; the programs can be saved or destroyed, errors are identified and error messages provide examples to illustrate the correct format required. CAL also provides for all types of arithmetic operations, editing capabilities, manipulation of data files, conditional expressions, etc. Numbers are expressed as integers or scientific notation or floating-point form and variables can be subscripted on an unlimited number of levels. CAL also allows statements to be deleted or added, thus making debugging a relatively simple task at the console.

Programming in CAL requires each step to have a statement number and the beginning statement to be indicated. CAL can handle programs of complexity as regards to arithmetic, but programmers are advised to use FORTRAN or ALGOL for major and large scientific programs.

JOSS. JOSS is an acronym for Jonniac Open Shop System. The Rand Corporation developed it for quick calculations too complex for calculators. It can serve more than 100 consoles simultaneously and can handle concurrent use by hundreds of people, each accessing the computer through his own console typewriter. Although many people seem to be using the computer simultaneously, the computer actually handles each user in sequence. It solves each problem or basic part of each problem so quickly that it "only appears" to the user that he alone has full use and control of the computer. Thus JOSS is a real-time language and is productive for solving many types of immediate calculations and problems. JOSS was designed for small and medium sized programs. It is not considered a general-purpose language in interactive environments. Even though it is similar to other languages, it has distinct and powerful features usually not found elsewhere. Arithmetic in JOSS is performed on numbers inputted in scientific notation using integer magnitudes and decimal exponents.

Time-Sharing Languages

When terminals function as computer consoles the user is concerned with the various subsets of FORTRAN (or other languages) which can be QUIKTRAN, CAL, BASIC, JOSS, etc. Users may solve problems immediately or may compose partial or complete programs. Diagnostic and debugging information are expressed entirely in the source language. Interpretive execution permits retention of all information contained in the user's original source statements. The combination of interpretive execution and multiprogramming makes the conversational mode a real-time, man-machine communication system highly efficient and feasible. Programs are constructed, tested and debugged statement by statement and on-line because of easy, direct, and sustained access to the computer. Large programs can be segmented; the user is unaware of other time-sharers; human errors are reduced due to immediacy of diagnostics and thought-continuity; exploratory, experimental and simulation efforts are enhanced, permitting users to exercise rapid judgment and evaluation in the formulation and testing of programs.

QUIKTRAN. QUIKTRAN is a language, compiler, and a data processing system. Checks or execution of each statement according to instructions from the sending location are done by the compiler. QUIKTRAN is a FORTRAN-like time-sharing language which handles lengthy jobs that must be processed in their entirety rather than statement by statement, by placing them temporarily in disk storage until the computer is free to do them. QUIKTRAN continuously monitors all incoming time-shared programming statements from each line to the computer. The communication system which has a typewriter keyboard is used as the terminal device at the user's location, and each terminal, together with its various peripheral equipment, is linked by telephone lines to a communications control system at the computer center or main computer.

QUIKTRAN uses FORTRAN-like language and includes built-in functions augmented by powerful and versatile operating statements permitting the user to operate upon and maintain complete control over his program. For easy parameter insertion and changes special codes are used, such as assigning new values to variables. The language has the facility of starting execution at any point and provides for easy insertion, deletion, or replacement of program statements. Other capabilities are cross-reference listing of program statement names and labels, detection of incomplete executions, and selective output. More than thirty control statements are used for programming.

QUIKTRAN subsystems—The computer system is divided into subsystems as follows: The scheduler controls operations maintaining consistent response times at all terminals; the translator is designed to transform the source language into an efficient equivalent internal form; the interpreter is designed to perform the execution; the process control program coordinates the translator and interpreter activities; the input/output control system performs all I/O functions; the exchange program controls the communications control system. A disk storage is available for user-library storage; a drum storage acts as a temporary working storage for the user's programs, and a magnetic-tape unit is used for logging transactions and for maintaining normal computer capabilities.

BASIC. BASIC is an acronym for Beginners Algebraic Symbol Interpreter Compiler. It was originally developed by Professors J. G. Kemeny and T. E. Kurtz at Dartmouth College under a grant by the National Science Foundation. BASIC is a language and a compiler that was originally designed for the GE-234 computer and the GE Datanet 30, a stored program data communications processor. It is very similar to CAL. Each line of BASIC begins with a line number which identifies it and specifies the order in which the statements are performed. The computer sorts out the program before running it and, therefore, statements need not be input in any specific order. It is not as powerful or versatile as ALGOL or FORTRAN but is considered more than adequate for most of the commercial and business problems that can be processed in a time-sharing mode.

Various conventions at specific computer centers or time-sharing installations allow the initial command to be either "HELLO" or "HOW DO YOU DO." BASIC permits conversational statements, free-style input (72 characters per line), segmenting of complex statements, accuracy of six significant digits, easy and safe program modification, editing functions allowing combinations of two or more programs into one, and it permits selection from a library of stored program or functions, such as procedures for solving simultaneous equations, curve fitting and statistical analysis. BASIC responds rapidly enough for debugging at the keyboard. In one pass it compiles computer instructions in fractions of seconds.

List-Processing Languages

These languages are designed for digital computers for the convenience and manipulation of data, especially non-numerical data whose length and structure change considerably during the calculation of a problem solution. They are referred to as symbol manipulation and non-numerical data processing languages. IPL (Information Process Language) was developed in 1957 by Newell, Shaw, and Simon. Others are LISP, SLIP, COMIT, FORMAC, FLPL and DYSTAL. Most list-processing languages are used as research tools rather than production-line programs. The basic research areas which have gained from the use of list processing are (a) pattern recognition, (b) algebraic manipulation, (c) simulation of human problem solving, (d) information retrieval, (e) machine translation of numerical languages. List-processing routines are oriented more toward techniques of programming rather than toward particular applications, except perhaps in the areas of information retrieval, algebraic manipulation, and language translation.

Some characteristics of lists are (a) variable length, subject principally to gross machine limitations, (b) different types of items may appear on lists including numbers, alphanumeric symbols and sublists, (c) items can be added at the beginning, end or middle, (d) any number of distinct lists can be created, (e) reference ability of lists by the program. The process used when elements of lists may themselves be lists is recursion. There are many levels of subsidiary lists, or sublists. Recursion is ordinarily mechanized through the use of a push-down stack, in which the temporary storage contents required by a subroutine are stored as the subroutine is entered. As the execution of the subroutine is completed, the temporary storage is restored from the stack and the space that is occupied is again made available. The ability to vary storage allocation during run time is called dynamic storage allocation. Recursion and dynamic storage allocation are useful program requirements and both are requirements of list-processing languages.

LISP. LISP stands for LISt Processing. It is radically different from traditional gramming. The instructions of an IPL-V routine pertain to: (1) the name, (2) the sequence of characters formed according to distinct rules, or internally as a set of computer words interlinked in a specific way. Atomic symbols may be either numeric or non-numeric, and the external representation of a non-numeric atomic symbol is a string of letters and digits starting with a letter, such as AB5Y, or a Greek letter. LISP also allows the use of special characters such as asterisks, minus signs, etc. Numeric atoms or atomic symbols can be decimal, octal or floating-point numbers.

IPL-V. IPL-V was developed by Newell, Simon and Shaw. The language is more machine-oriented than LISP and a program in IPL-V consists of sequences of instructions quite like the ordinary machine instructions. Generally, however, the programmer has more control over the calculations. Some programmers prefer IPL-V over LISP due to the similarity of IPL-V to normal machine programming. The instructions of an IPL routine pertain to: (1) the name, (2) the symbol, (3) the prefixes and (4) the length. The name part labels the entire routine and specific label points for transfer of control internally. The IPL-V data are in the form of a symbol list; each symbol can itself stand for a list. The prefixes are 3-bit numbers indicating the meaning of the symbol part, as well as the levels of indirect addressing. Thus, an instruction can be used in storing an input, recovering an output, performing an additional transfer, or calling a routine. The specific choice depends upon the first prefix. Routines may be either standard IPL-V processes or ones which the programmer himself defines. IPL-V differs from LISP because the programmer must communicate his arguments to routine explicitly. The communication cell is the procedure used and is actually a special-purpose push-down stack. Various prefixes cause a data unit to be either removed from or replaced into the communication cell. The erasure method is used in IPL-V to maintain storage for lists.

SLIP. SLIP is an extension to FORTRAN and not really a stand-alone system. SLIP increases the freedom for manipulating lists and also increases the amount of storage required for them. SLIP is a form of a set of special list processing FORTRAN functions. These functions are used to accomplish the operations a programmer normally does in list processing: (1) the creation and erasure of lists, (2) traversal of lists, (3) specific recursive communication of arguments, (4) translation of list structures between internal and external representations. SLIP programs are FORTRAN programs which use SLIP functions. SLIP programs resemble LISP programs because they consist of nestings of function calls. FORTRAN IF statements are used instead of conditional expressions and a special "VISIT" function aids automatic recursion and must be called explicitly by the programmer.

Two words, rather than one, are necessary for each element of a list; the first contains a two-address field called the right and left lengths (the left length points to the previous word on the list and the right length to the following word). This makes it easy to traverse a list backward and forward, a procedure different from LISP and IPL-V. The second word holds the list element itself. Each list has a header with pointers to both the beginning and end of a list; the list name is a pointer with its header. Readers are available to make the traversal of lists quick and easy. The mathematics of SLIP is the same as that of FORTRAN, though more efficient. In dealing with problems which involve large amount of numerical calculations and list processing, SLIP has a major advantage. BALGOL is the SLIP version of ALGOL.

COMIT. COMIT is basically used in studies of mechanical translation of human language. It is oriented and designed for lists in which the list elements are not lists themselves but are closer to strings. The manipulation of strings in COMIT is quite easy but somewhat awkward for both trees and recursion. COMIT programs operate by manipulation of a data depository called "work space." The work space holds a string composed of a sequence of constituents; the string could be a sentence and the constituents would represent words of the sentence, or even individual characters including spaces and punctuation marks. String constituents might also be subscripts and subscript values attached to them. COMIT provides sequences of shelves for temporary storage which may be replaced in their entirety by new data. Adding of new data can be done at the head of the shelf while preserving the rest in a manner similar to the LISP function append. A COMIT program is formed by sequence of rules. Each rule specifies a string transformation and has a right half and a left half. From left to right the work space is searched until a sequence of constituents matching the last half is found. Such a sequence is then replaced by the sequence of constituents corresponding to the right half. In the execution of a rule, no sequence of constituents in the work space may match the left half. Rules can be used to move data and the work space and to modify and test subscripts and their values.

SNOBOL. SNOBOL is an acronym for StriNg-Oriented symBOLic language. It was developed by D. J. Farber, R. E. Griswold, and I. P. Polonsky at the Bell Telephone Laboratories. In program compilation and generation of symbolic equations it has significant applications. It provides complete facilities for the manipulation of strings of characters. SNOBOL is especially applicable for programs dealing with text editing, linguistics, compiling, and symbolic manipulation of algebraic expressions. SNOBOL statements consist of a rule which operates on symbolically-named strings. The fundamental operations are: string manipulation, pattern matching, and replacement. There are procedures for integer arithmetic, indirect referencing, and input-output. The SNOBOL basic concepts begin with strings and string names and may be numbers or characters, while the strings may be any symbol.

FLPL and **DYSTAL** Other list-processing languages include FLPL, an acronym for FORTRAN List Processing Language. It was developed for use in a program for proving theorems in geometry. It is much like LISP but has no provision for recursion. Another FORTRAN-based system is DYSTAL, which stands for DYnamic STorage ALlocation. Constructive storage locations are used to keep the elements of a list when using DYSTAL so they can be integer-indexed. Programmers can then find the "nth" item of a list by simple table lookup. Programmers are freed from some of the constraints of FORTRAN by DYSTAL but it lacks the extensive flexibility in construction of a list which other list-processing languages contain. The integer-indexing ability, however, is unique.

Simulation and Simulation Languages

Simulation is defined as follows: (1) The representation of physical systems and phenomena by computers, models or other equipment; e.g., an imitative type of data processing in which an automatic computer is used as a model of some entity. When information enters the computer to represent the factors of process, the computer produces information that represents the results of the process, and the processing done by the computer represents the process itself. (2) In computer programming, a model of the technique of setting up a routine for one computer to make it operative as nearly as possible like some other computer.

A model is a system representation in which the processes or transactions bear a close resemblance or relationship to those of the specific system being simulated or studied. Therefore, models that are used in simulation are seldom highly abstract or strictly mathematical. Manipulation of a simulation system concerns the acceptance of inputs and the generation of outputs similar or analogous to those of the system represented.

In a simulation system the activity is dependent on the time framework and can be stable or unstable. It can be studied as a static or steady-in-state system or as regards the transient behavior of a dynamic system. The components are processes of a physical entity, such as hardware, which are precisely defined in physical simulation. The process which includes physiological or sociological behavior of individuals or groups is called behavioral simulation. Operational simulation incorporates processes which include human beings, such as when they are involved in automobile traffic, highway analyses, etc.

There are several specific languages well suited for simulation applications and to make simulation systems easier to manipulate, more accurate in results, and more universal in acceptance. The analog computer is used for simulation of continuous systems, but the special languages relate to general simulation which provides a variety of services and eases the job of translating a conceptual model of a system to develop useful statistical outputs. These languages contain status descriptors, which define the essential elements of a system or model. They also have procedures which modify models for controlling the dynamic performance or observations of model behavior. Most simulation languages develop data structures, transformations, sequencing of transformations, and output routines. Extensive error checking is available for preventing misuse of the language or in hand coding or key punching mistakes. Routines for debugging models and locating logical errors are most useful.

SIMSCRIPT. SIMSCRIPT, a general-purpose digital simulation system is based on the idea that the system can be described in terms of "entities," which are the specific objects or things of which a system is composed, "attributes," which are those properties associated with the entities, and "sets," which are which are groups of entities. The major prerequisites in the development of a simulation model are a complete list of explicit entities, their attributes, and the possible set memberships. The state of a system once described is changed by the occurrence of an event which is a user-defined subroutine written with either SIMSCRIPT or FORTRAN statements. Entities can be created or destroyed; set memberships of individual entities can be altered, and numeral values of attirbutes can be changed. Because entities and attributes must be individually located, much of the SIMSCRIPT language is devoted to providing convenient and flexible methods for performing storage and retrieval functions. Input to the SIMSCRIPT translator usually is developed on sets of cards containing definition, initialization, and subprograms.

General-Purpose System Simulator (GPSS)

GPSS has three basic components: blocks, transactions and equipment. By using the terms in block diagrams it develops simulation models. Block diagrams are graphic devices which delineate the logical and physical flow of transactions and moved from one block to another. There are eight parameters simulation block diagram are very specific from which models are built.

Punched cards or other entry program segments define the properties of each block in the model. Within the model, temporary GPSS elements are formed into transactions and moved from one block to another. There are eight parameters which are associated with each transaction and also eight possible priority levels (all Priority 3 transactions are serviced before Priority 2, etc.). As transactions enter blocks, various subroutines associated with those particular block types are interpretively executed causing a modification of one or more status descriptors.

Equipment elements are provided in GPSS with a fixed number of each of three types: storages, facilities, and logic switches. Equipment or logical concepts are represented by them. Transactions are processed by the equipment on a first-come, first-served basis within each priority class. There are ten types of elements in GPSS, each referenced by one or more of the block types. Blocks and transactions are what make up block elements. Equipment elements include facilities, storage and logic switches. Statistical elements are queues and distribution tables. Reference elements are savexes—for data storage. Arithmetic variables and functions are computational elements. A subset of fifteen attributes are associated with these types and are called standard system variables. Their values can be addressed by name and index number in a simulation model.

A GPSS model is made up of a set of definition cards and each card defines a block, function, table, arithmetic variable, or storage capacity. The GPSS program operates upon the model definition in essentially an interpretive fashion, providing considerable flexibility for handling multiple runs on the same or similar models.

DYNAMO. DYNAMO is used for continuous closed-loop information feed-back systems. Linearity or stability is not required in the system concerned. Therefore, a very broad class of systems can be developed or represented by the DYNAMO language. The definition of a continuous system is one in which all basic variables are continuous and possess a first derivative with respect to time; i.e., the state of the system is given by the levels of continuous variables at any point in time without the conception of any discrete changes to this state. It is also adequate for dealing with more discrete phenomena pertaining to aggregate levels of behavior; i.e., an aggregate inventory level in a manufacturing environment may be considered a continuous variable even though it has a descrete delayed composition. For example, at any instant in time the level of a variable is a distinct single numeric value.

An information feed-back system is defined as one in which information relating to the state of the system at a given time is what determines the future

228

state of the system. Variables are introduced for the purpose of dealing specifically with the flow of information. Time delays are of major importance because they establish the dynamic performance of such systems and also determine the lag between the time in which a change in one variable occurs and the time at which this change is reflected in some other variable; i.e., an increase in one level of inventory may lead to a reduction in the level of orders for inventory.

A closed-loop system is defined as one in which successive states of the system depend upon variables outside the system. The internal structure of the system and the manner in which the basic variables interact is of primary interest. It is not necessary that the system be completely closed. A limited set of external inputs can be provided, although these are intended to serve only as independent stimuli to the systems being manipulated and analyzed.

Also available are provisions and procedures for modifying the state and controlling the dynamic performance of DYNAMO models. DYNAMO simulation model output is generated in the form of time series for any desired variables; i.e., level, rate, or output. The output variable is determined by the level or the rate variables at each output time. DYNAMO programs operate in five phases: (1) Input; cards are read and internal tables are constructed for each equation. From the PRINT and PLOT cards, output specifications are established. (2) Generation; machine coding is developed from skeleton instructions for each type of equation. (3) Running; the concerned equation types having initialization are solved to provide starting values for all variables requiring them at the beginning of a run. (4) Printing/Plotting; such phases convert the output data into specific output format. (5) Rerun; extra or additional cards modify the values of defined constants or other output requirements are read in. The program then returns to the running phase.

Numerical Control

Numerical control pertains to the control of machine tools, drafting machines, etc., by punched paper or magnetic tapes suitably encoded with directive information. Numerically controlled devices rely on their input tapes for detailed and explicit guidance because they have very limited logical or arithmetic capability to keep costs low. This may mean 8 bits for every .001 of motion or a great amount of data on the tape. Using information presented in a more manageable and concise form, it is common for a computer to prepare the control tapes. An example is the automatically programmed tools (APT) system developed by aerospace industry combine. Using APT, the designer describes his tool and the desired part in a high-level geometrically-oriented language. A preprocessor program accepts the high-level language and processes it into a simpler, more formalized internal representation. The tool independent central program converts the material, tool, and geometrical information into tool motion commands. A postprocessor program prepares the tool motion information in a format suitable for the particular control mechanism being used. A simultaneous output for a numerical control drafting machine permits preparation of detail blueprints while the robot tool is making the part, if desired.

APT. APT (Automatically Programmed Tools) is a program specifically designed through the cooperation of the computer industry with substantial assistance of the Univac Division of Sperry Rand, for the ease and convenience of computer controlled machine tools. The machine produces the desired part or product by following the numerically-coded instructions written by the programmer. The program must be very precise and intricate, so it is fundamentally a mathematical operation. The computer automatically controls the function of the machine to produce a part or component when the programmer defines the geometric dimensions of the part he wishes to create. To reference the intersections of these various components with instructions to the cutting tool, the statements are of English-language type. Such instructions are produced on punched paper tape for input to the controlled machine.

Even though APT cut only straight lines, their use is not restricted. These straight lines may be as short as 1/1000 of an inch, so that any conceivable shape can be cut. Because the machine has to be told by the computer to cut each of the tiny segments, this demonstrates the tediousness of programming the operation of the tool. After this is accomplished, with no added instructions, there can be endless repetition of the procedure, and the tape can be stored for later use. APT has made the great step forward by performing many tasks better than can be done with a human operator.

APT III is a UNIVAC system used in computer-assisted programming of machine tools, numerically controlled flame cutters, drafting machines, and other similar equipment. It was written to be production-oriented by simplifying the effort, time, and money needed, taking full advantage of numerically controlled techniques in engineering and manufacturing. Besides being able to provide machine-tool programming capabilities, which are virtually impossible by manual methods, APT system enhances most of the usual advantages found in numerical control: reduced lead time; greater design flexibility and freedom; greater accuracy; lower direct costs; lower tooling costs; improved production forecasting; better engineering control of the manufacturing process; and simplified introduction of changes. The APT III program represents over a century of development and testing man-hours.

STRESS. STRESS is an acronym for STRuctural Engineering System Solver. By using a problem-oriented input language it is designed to solve structural engineering problems. After a minimum study of the manual and without any prior programming experience a structural engineer could use STRESS. STRESS can be used to analyze structures with prismatic members in two or three dimensions, with either rigid or pinned joints, and subjected to distributed or concentrated loads, support motions, or temperature effects. A STRESS user will describe his problem by writing a series of statements specifying size and type of structure, physical dimensions, the loads, and the desired solution. The solution then supplies such information needed as member forces at the member ends, joint displacements, reactions, and support displacements. Employed by STRESS are the recently developed techniques in structural analysis, such as matrix and network formulations. In order to describe all the members and joints of a three-dimensional structure it is necessary to have a common reference system. STRESS employs a right-handed orthogonal cartesian coordinate system. The location of the system's origin can be found at any arbitrary point in the structure; e.g., one of the support joints. Described in terms of joint coordinates with respect to the origin of the coordinate system, are all joint data; and all computed joint reactions and displacements are similarly given in the same system.

COGO. First developed by Professor C. L. Miller and his associates at the Massachusetts Institute of Technology in association with the Puerto Rico Department of Public Works, is COGO, a civil engineering oriented language. Based on the technology of civil engineers, the COGO programming language or system is also applied in other areas. Also available is a special time-sharing version called QUIKTRAN/COGO. The engineer quickly and easily can write a problem using the COGO vocabulary and feed it to the computer for automatic computation. No intermediate programming is required.

The system, based on a coordinate table, and the problem, expressed in terms of angles given in degrees, minutes and seconds, are also the intersection (X, Y axes) points. COGO commands are based from such points formed on the coordinate table. Each point is given an identification number and is referenced by that number. The computer may be instructed to compute distances between points 1 and 2, to dump all coordinates, to locate and calculate bearings from known points, develop parallel lines, compute angles, calculate new points, etc., by a single word or short phrase command of COGO. For qualified engineers who require only a short time to learn its techniques and special power, COGO is a very versatile tool.

APPENDIX E

FLOWCHARTING — ABBREVIATIONS, SYMBOLS, AND PROCEDURES

FLOWCHARTING — ABBREVIATIONS, SYMBOLS, AND PROCEDURES

Unfortunately, flowchart symbols are not yet fully standardized. Principally, this is because manufacturers have produced and distributed hundreds of thousands of plastic templates and, most often, they have differed in some slight respects. However, none of the specifications or conventions (rules) differ significantly. In the literature and in practice three types of charts predominate: Flowcharts, Block Diagrams, and Process Charts. Because of the importance of communications in large systems, another chart, called a Systems Chart, has been frequently used. Most of the symbols and many of the procedures of all of these charts are described in this appendix.

There are very distinct and important advantages concerning diagramming and charting. Most importantly, an individual's thoughts are graphically, and thus more clearly and concisely, conveyed to others. The flow charting process aids and is a tool for organizing problem and program analysis. The logic of the problem is isolated and is more easily understood and handled. The chart or diagram itself helps to recall, explain, or amend various program instructions and the distinct process, program, or system designed. The conventions followed help to standardize the symbols and utility of, for example, input-output media, input-output devices, mass storage, auxiliary operations, manual control, etc.

Generally, there are ten types of symbols used to represent the following: Operations, Decisions, Direction, Connection, Annotation, Variation, Status, Communication, Termination, and Offline Designation. Certain very specific methods and rules should be followed to develop accurate and understandable charts and diagrams. Program steps should be numbered on the right top of the symbols. Connectors should be used extensively between symbols, blocks, pages, and for off-page information. Predefined processes have their own symbol as do program modifications. The gratification of producing a complete picture is achieved when the chart or diagram is modular, so that any part or portion of the "picture" may be "blown-up" into greater detail. Whenever text relating to a symbol or segment cannot be placed within a symbol, it should be

placed alongside the symbol or referenced to the narrative located elsewhere on or with the flowchart.

Chart 1. Program Flowcharting Symbols

Symbol	Represents
▭ *	**PROCESS** A group of program instructions that perform a processing function of the program.
▱ *	**INPUT/OUTPUT** Any function of an input/output device (making information available for processing, recording processing information, tape positioning, etc.)
◇ *	**DECISION** The decision function is used to document points in the program where a branch to alternate paths is possible based upon variable conditions.
⬠	**PROGRAM MODIFICATION** An instruction or group of instructions which changes the program sequence.
▯ *	**PREDEFINED PROCESS** A named process consisting of one or more operations or program steps that are specified elsewhere, e.g., subroutine or logical unit.
⬭ *	**TERMINAL** The beginning, end, or a point of interruption in a program.
◯ *	**CONNECTOR** An entry from, or an exit to, another part of the program flowchart.
⬠	**OFFPAGE CONNECTOR** A connector used to designate entry to or exit from a page.
→ ↑ ↓ * ←	**FLOW DIRECTION** The direction of processing or data flow.
⊐ * ----	**ANNOTATION** The addition of descriptive comments or explanatory notes as clarification.

*This material is reproduced from the American Standard *Flowchart Symbols for Information Processing* X3.5-1966 copyright 1965 by ASA, copies of which may be purchased from the American Standards Association at 10 East 40th Street, New York, N. Y. 10016.

SYMBOL STANDARDS

Almost all computer manufacturers and software developers use flowcharting symbols (Charts 1 and 2) published by the American Stand-ards Association (ASA) and additional ones which remain consistent with the standards as shown on the following pages. An important exception, however, which should be noted, is the use of both the dia-mond and the oval to represent decisions. Lines coming out of either represent the different program paths which result from the decision. An example of this duplication of conventions is shown in Figure 1.

A system flowchart (Chart 2) specifies the flow of data through all parts of a system. In addition to three basic symbols and the supplementary annotation symbol, fourteen system flowchart symbols may be used to depict this flow and the relationships among data (and its medium), equipment, equipment operations, and manual operations. In a system flowchart an entire program run or phase is always represented by a single processing symbol, together with the input/output symbols.

Chart 2. System Flowcharting Symbols

PUNCHED CARD * All varieties of punched cards including stubs.	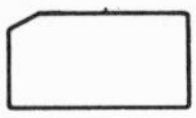 **PUNCHED TAPE** * Paper or plastic, chad or chadless. 
DOCUMENT * Paper documents and reports of all varieties.	 **TRANSMITTAL TAPE** A proof or adding machine tape or similar batch-control information. 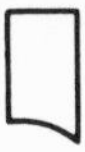
MAGNETIC TAPE *	 **ONLINE STORAGE** * 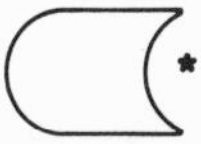
OFFLINE STORAGE * Offline storage of either paper, cards, magnetic or perforated tape.	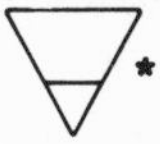 **DISPLAY** * Information displayed by plotters or video devices. 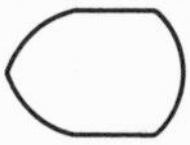
MANUAL INPUT * Information supplied to or by a computer utilizing an online device.	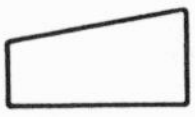 **SORTING, COLLATING** An operation on sorting or collating equipment. 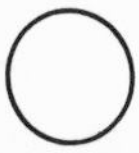
CLERICAL OR MANUAL OPERATION * A manual offline operation not requiring mechanical aid.	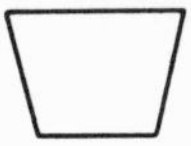 **AUXILIARY OPERATION** * A machine operation supplementing the main processing function. 
KEYING OPERATION An operation utilizing a key-driven device.	 **COMMUNICATION LINK** * The automatic transmission of information from one location to another via communication lines. 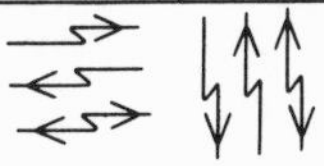

*This material is reproduced from the American Standard *Flowchart Symbols for Information Processing* X3.5-1966 copyright 1965 by ASA, copies of which may be purchased from the American Standards Association at 10 East 40th Street, New York, N. Y. 10016.

Figure 1. Oval or diamond can represent decisions.

Certain conventions are usually followed in the use of the flowcharting symbols:

1. The procedure to be performed is described by the charting symbol and by a notation in words or symbols inside the charting symbol. For example, the diamond indicates a decision stemming from a comparison or test (Fig. 2). The notation inside the decision symbol indicates the type of test.

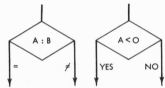

Figure 2. Diamond indicates decision stemming from a comparison or test.

2. The information inside the processing symbol uses standard arithmetic notation (Fig. 3). One symbol with a special computer meaning is $\rightarrow$. This means "to move to." Thus $A \rightarrow B$ means to move the contents of memory location A to memory location B. $A+B \rightarrow C$ means to add the contents of the locations identified as A and B and store the sum in location C. Parentheses are sometimes used to differentiate the "contents of" a memory location from the location itself. $(A) \rightarrow B$ means to move contents of location A to location B and is equivalent to $A \rightarrow B$.

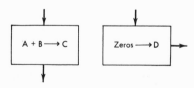

Figure 3. Standard arithmetic notations are used inside the processing symbol.

238

3. A name (label) may be used to identify a block of instructions. It is written above and to the left of the symbol (Fig. 4). The label can be used later in the program or in the computer coding to refer to the block of instructions. A reference is also frequently put in the symbol and separated from the instructions by a line.

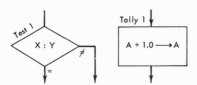

Figure 4. A name may be used to identify a block of instructions.

4. The normal direction of flow in charting is from left to right and from top to bottom.
5. There are no set rules for distinguishing between the alphabetic O and the zero, but programming practice tends to slash the alphabetic O and leave the zero alone. The Z and 2 are similarly differentiated.

Alphabetic	*Numeric*
$\emptyset$ or *O*	0
Z̶	2

Before giving a few examples of basic diagramming or charting (both terms are casually used interchangeably), some further characteristics should be noted. Flowcharts or diagrams of various sorts usually develop from very rough sketches of interviews in the cases relating to systems analysis (i.e., procedure, forms analysis, or forms distributions, etc.) or "blueprints" for calculating solutions of problems. Notes are usually initially entered right on the chart to depict the procedure. Include all pertinent information and the segments describing activities and flows. The charts prove most useful when discussing systems, forms, and mathematical techniques—especially in communication with others. The chart-picture is a distinct aid to management to show variations of procedures and, especially, comparisons with the old, the new, and the projected. The procedure not only portrays exceptional clarity, logical sequence, and stepped procedures, but will usually result in the elimination of unnecessary program steps; the set of charts and diagrams will also usually suggest computational shortcuts and additional useful results.

The direction of flow simply shows the relationship of one symbol to another. Fig. 5 shows that A is executed and then B is executed.

The input/output symbol is used to refer to any operation that involves an input/output device (Fig. 6).

Figure 5. Direction of flow shows relationship of symbols.

Figure 6. Input/output symbol used for input/output operations.

The program symbol is used to represent any steps in the program which are not represented by special symbols (Fig. 7).

The decision symbol represents any logical decision that is contained in the program (Fig. 8).

The stop symbol is used to indicate the end of the program (Fig. 9). If there are several ways to end the program, there may be several stop symbols.

FLOWCHARTING WITH WORDS

When the comparisons are represented in flowchart form, the line of reasoning and four possible paths to solution become clearer. The word

Figure 7. Program symbol used to represent steps not represented by special symbols.

Figure 8. Decision symbols represent logical decisions in a program.

Figure 9. Stop symbol indicates an end of program.

240

picture in Fig. 10 shows the stages of a whole comparison process joined in logical sequence. If the computer could think through the process as can a human being, it might ask the questions illustrated in the diagram.

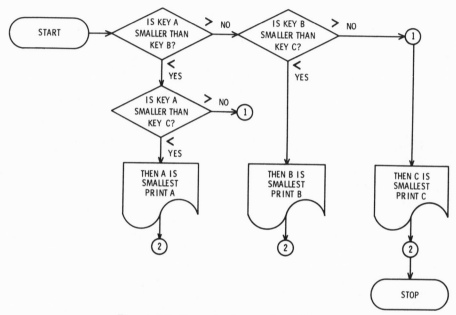

Figure 10. A work-picture flowchart.

A word picture is a realistic description of the problem. However, a large flowchart would become cluttered with too many words. Therefore, symbols are substituted. The same operations are shown in the flowchart in Fig. 11.

Once the instructions for solving a certain problem are worked out, they can be recorded on tape or punched cards and used again and again, whenever the need arises. These "canned programs" (software) enable computer users to take advantage of programming work that has already been done on problems that may be similar throughout an industry, or throughout business generally.

Many longer programs (> 100 FORTRAN statements) should be segmented, i.e., designed, written and compiled as a main program and several subroutines. Although this technique requires careful attention to communication between parts, the net advantage compensates for the additional work. These advantages are twofold:

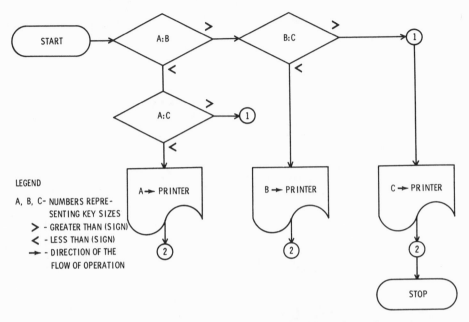

Figure 11. Flowchart using symbols in place of words.

1. Writing, debugging, and changing smaller programs (i.e., subroutines) is usually easier because it is possible to concentrate on and to attend to a smaller, more reasonable number of program details.

2. The time required for handling and processing of jobs is, in in the long run, considerably reduced. This reduction occurs because initial compilation of segmented jobs takes no longer than nonsegmented jobs. However, because 99% of the jobs to be processed require debugging and recompilation, it is necessary in segmented jobs to recompile only those parts (subroutines) that contain errors. This saving in (re)compilation time can be as high as 30% of all the machine time used for compilations.

To generalize programs is to incorporate flexible features that allow the program to operate in a variety of ways, depending on the value of parameters (i.e., new variables or constants) read in during execution, or on the nature of the regular input data. The intent of generalization is to avoid the necessity of reprogramming (and recompiling) for minor changes in data or in output requirements.

FLOWCHART ABBREVIATIONS

ABS—Absolute
ACC—Accumulator
ACCT—Account
ACT—Actual
ADDR—Address
ADJ—Adjust
ADV—Advance
ALG—Algebraic
ALPHA—Alphabetic
ALT—Altermant, alteration
APPROX—Approximate
ARITH—Arithmetic
ASDNG—Ascending
ASMBL—Assemble
ASGN—Assign
AUX—Auxiliary
AVAIL—Availability
BFR—Buffer
BKSP—Backspace
BLK—Block
BLKCNT—Block count
BLNK—Blank
BR—Branch
BM—Buffer mark
CALC—Calculate, calculator
CARR—Carriage
CC—Card column
CD—Card
CHAN—Channel
CHAR—Character
CHK—Check
CHG—Change
CHKPT—Checkpoint
CLR—Clear
CLS—Close
CMP—Compare
CMPL—Complement

CNSL—Console
CNT—Count
COL—Column
CON—Constant
COND—Condition
CONT—Continue
CPLD—Coupled
CTR—Counter
CTRL—Control
CURR—Current
DCMT—Document
DEC—Decision
DECR—Decrement
DEL—Delete
DESGG—Descending
DIM—Dimension
DR—Drive
ELIM—Eliminate
ENT—Entry
EOF—End of file
EOJ—End of job
EOR—End of reel
EQ—Equal
ERR—Error
ES—Electronic switch
EXEC—Execute
FLD—Field
FLDL—Field length
FIG—Figure
FLT—Floating
FMT—Format
FR—From
FREQ—Frequency
FUNC—Function
FWD—Forward
FXD—Fixed
GEN—Generator

GENL—General
GM—Groupmark
HDR—Header
HI—High
HLT—Halt
HSK—Housekeeping
HYPER—Hypertape
IC—Instruction counter
INCR—Increment
IND—Indicate
INDN—Indication
INDR—Indicator
INFO—Information
INQ—Inquire
INT—Initial
INTRPT—Interrupt
I/O—Input/output
INST—Instruction
INVAL—Invalid
IW—Index word
LBL—Label
LD—Load
LIT—Literal
LNG—Length
LOC—Location
LTR—Letter
MACH—Machine
MAX—Maximum
MIN—Minimum
MISC—Miscellaneous
MOD—Modification
MPXR—Multiplexor
MPY—Multiply
MSG—Message
NEG—Negative
NO.—Number
NUM—Numeric
OP—operation
OPN—Open
OPND—Operand
OVFLO—Overflow
OVL—Overlap
OVLY—Overlay
PG—Page

PGLIN—Page and line
PH—Phase
PKD—Packed
PNCH—Punch
PNDG—Pending
POS—Position
PR—Print
PREC—Precision
PREV—Previous
PRI—Priority
PROC—Process
PROG—Program
PT—Point
PRT—Printer
R+S—Reset + Start
R/W—Read/Write
RCD—Record
RCV—Receive
RD—Read
RDY—Ready
REF—Reference
REG—Register
REL—Release
REQ—Request, require
RET—Return
RI—Read in
RLS—Reels
RM—Record mark
RO—Read out
RPT—Report
RSLT—Result
RST—Reset
RSTRT—Restart
RTE—Route
RTN—Routine
RWD—Rewind
SCHED—Schedule, scheduler
SCN—Scan
SCTR—Sector
SECT—Section
SEL—Select
SEN—Sense
SEQ—Sequence
SER—Serial

244

SEG—Segment
SIG—Signal
SIM—Simulator
SM—Storage mark
SNGL—Single
SP—Space
SRCH—Search
SPEC—Specification, specify
ST—Store
STG—Storage
STMNT—Statement
SUB—Subtract
SUMM—Summarize
SUP—Suppress
SYNC—Synchronize, synchronizer
SYST—System
SW—Switch
TBL—Table
TEMP—Temporary
TM—Tapemark
TMN—Transmission

TMT—Transmit
TOT—Total
TP—Tape
TR—Transfer
TRK—Track
TRLR—Trailer
TST—Test
TU—Tape unit
TW/Typewriter
UNC—Unconditional
UNLD—Unload
UNPKD—Unpacked
VAR—Variable
WD—Word
WM—Wordmark
WR—Write
WRK—Work
XPL—Explain, Explanation
XTR—Extra
Z—Zero
ZN—Zone

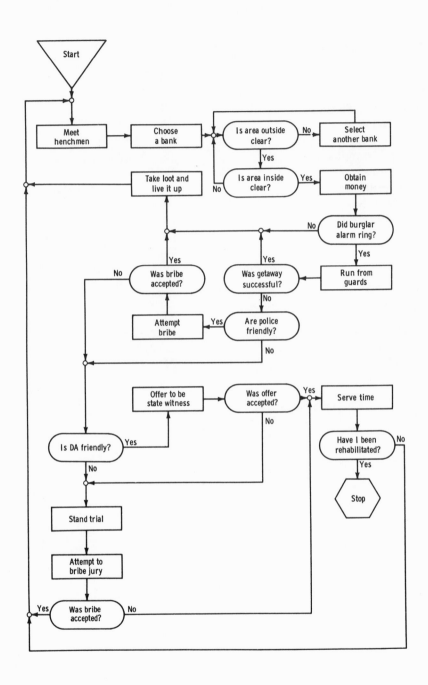

A sample flowchart.